Activate

Question • Progress • Succeed

2

Teacher Handbook

Simon Broadley
Mark Matthews
Victoria Stutt
Nicky Thomas

Assessment Editor
Dr Andrew Chandler-Grevatt

OXFORD

UNIVERSITY PRESS

Contents

Introduction

About the series

Activate is designed to match the 2014 Key Stage 3 Programme of Study and to help prepare your students for success in the new GCSEs and equivalent Key Stage 4 qualifications. Across the Student Books, Teacher Handbooks, and Kerboodle courses *Activate* allows you to track your students' progress through Key Stage 3 using innovative and reliable assessment and learning resources.

Activate is also flexible to suit your preferred route through Key Stage 3. The Programme of Study is covered in *Activate 1* and *Activate 2*, making it a perfect match for a two-year course. If you're continuing Key Stage 3 into Year 9, *Activate 3* offers consolidation and extension of core concepts through engaging contexts, with plenty of practice in the skills needed for success at Key Stage 4.

All of the content in the *Activate* series has been written and reviewed by our expert author and editor teams, all of whom have significant teaching experience, and our Assessment Editor is a school-assessment expert. You can be confident that *Activate* provides the best support for the new curriculum.

Your Teacher Handbook

This Teacher Handbook aims to save you time and effort by offering lesson plans, differentiation suggestions, and assessment guidance on a page-by-page basis that is a direct match to the Student Book.

You can use the Unit Openers to see the knowledge required of students from Key Stage 2 for each topic at a glance. You can also use the Checkpoint Lessons at the end of each chapter to support students who have yet to grasp a secure knowledge of the outcomes covered in each chapter. Lesson plans are written for 55-minute lessons but are flexible and fully adaptable so you can choose the activities that suit your classes best.

Unit Opener

Overview
The Unit Opener provides an overview of the unit (Biology, Chemistry, or Physics) and how it links to Key Stage 2 and Key Stage 4.

Curriculum links
An overview of the chapters in this unit, and the Key Stage 3 topics they link to.

Preparing for Key Stage 4 success
This table provides an overview of the Key Stage 4 skills and underpinning knowledge that are covered in the unit. It also provides details of where Key Stage 4 style assessment questions can be found throughout the unit.

Key Stage 2 catch-up
This table outlines the Key Stage 2 knowledge that is a pre-requisite for this unit. This can be assessed using the automarked Unit Pre-test on Kerboodle.

For each Key Stage 2 statement, a suggestion for how you can help students to catch up is provided, as well as an index of which topic each statement links to.

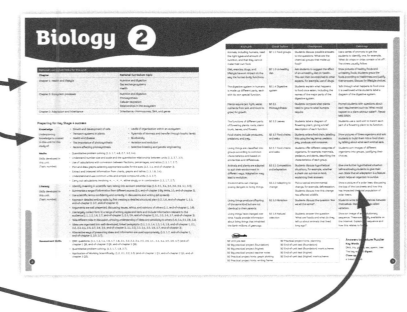

Lesson

Curriculum links
This indicates the area of the 2014 Programme of Study this lesson covers. A Working Scientifically link is also given for most lessons. This indicates the main Working Scientifically focus of the lesson.

Differentiated outcomes
This table summarises the possible lesson outcomes. They are ramped and divided into three ability bands. Levels for each outcome are given in brackets. The three ability bands are explained on the following page.

An indication of where each outcome is covered is given in the checkpoint table, helping you to monitor progress through the lesson.

Maths and Literacy
These boxes provide suggestions of how Maths and Literacy skills can be developed in the lesson. They also indicate when a Maths or Literacy activity is given in the Student Book.

Maths and Literacy skills are ramped through *Activate*. A Progression Grid and Progress Tasks are supplied on Kerboodle.

Assessing Pupil Progress (APP)
Opportunities for integration of APP (based on the 2009 APP framework) are included in the APP box.

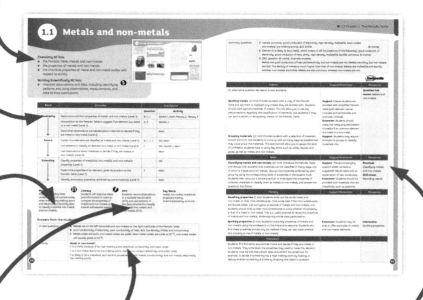

Answers
Answers to the Student Book activities and questions can be found here. For Quality of Written Communication (QWC) questions, only the correct scientific points for marking are given. When marking these questions, attention needs to be given to the quality of the writing in the answer.

Suggested lesson plan
A suggested route through the lesson is provided, including ideas for support, extension, and homework. The right-hand column indicates where Kerboodle resources are available.

Each lesson plan is supported by an editable Lesson Plan and Presentation on Kerboodle.

Checkpoint Lesson

Overview
The Checkpoint Lesson is a suggested follow-up lesson after students have completed the automarked Checkpoint Assessment on Kerboodle. There are two routes through the lesson, with the route for each student being determined by their mark in the assessment. Route A helps students to consolidate what they have learnt through the chapter, whilst Route B offers extension for students who have already grasped the key concepts.

Checkpoint routes
A summary of the two suggested routes through the lesson.

Progression table
This table summarises the outcomes covered in the Revision Lesson, and provides guidance for how students can make progress to achieve each outcome.

The tasks outlined in the table, resources for the Extension Lesson, and detailed Teacher Notes are all available on Kerboodle.

Answers
Answers to the End-of-Chapter questions in the Student Book.

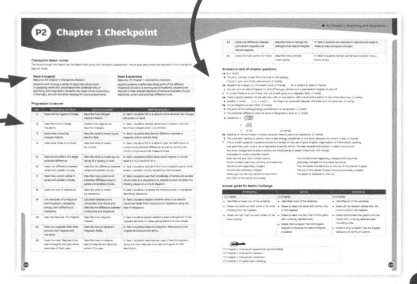

Assessment and progress

About the Assessment Editor

Dr Andrew Chandler-Grevatt has a doctorate in school assessment, and has a real passion for science teaching and learning. Having worked as a science teacher for ten years, of which five was spent as an AST, Andy has a real understanding of the pressures and joys of teaching in the classroom. This stays at the forefront of his mind during all of his work in education.

Alongside his national and international research in school assessment, Andy is a teaching fellow on the PGCE course at the University of Sussex, and is a successful published assessment author.

Welcome

from the Assessment Editor

Welcome to your *Activate 2* Teacher Handbook. The Teacher Handbooks, together with Kerboodle, and the Student Books, provide comprehensive assessment support for the new curriculum.

The new Key Stage 3 curriculum has no prescribed assessment framework. Our assessment model will help your school monitor progress and attainment against the new curriculum, whether you want to continue using levels, or adopt a new model based on curriculum statements. Throughout *Activate*, formative assessment has been made easy, and we have followed a set of guiding assessment principles.

Activate assessment principles

Assessment in *Activate* aims to:

- inform teaching and/or learning directly (have a formative function)
- assess agreed and shared objectives
- provide opportunities for peer- and self-assessment
- provide opportunities for specific feedback to be given to and acted upon by individual students
- provide usable data or information that informs teachers of progress of classes and individuals.

I have been working closely with our expert author teams across all components of *Activate* to ensure consistency in the assessment material, meaning you can be confident when using *Activate* to monitor your students' progress.

Assessing the new curriculum

The current system of levels will be removed from the National Curriculum. Schools are expected to set their own methods of tracking progress, whilst ensuring students gain a secure level of understanding of each block of content.

The *Activate* assessment model is based on bands; the middle band indicates that students have a *secure* grasp of the content or skills specified in the Programme of Study.

The band working towards *secure* is *developing*, and the band moving past *secure* is *extending*. The bands have been matched to levels and grades, meaning you can adopt a system that works for your school.

Activate bands	Developing		Secure		Extending	
Level equivalent	3	4	5	6	7	8
Grade indicator	To ensure grade indicators are up-to-date with KS4 qualifications, this information is stored on Kerboodle.					
Bloom's Taxonomy links	Remembering & Understanding		Application & Analysing		Evaluation & Creating	

Flexible assessment that works for you

Assessment in *Activate* is designed to be flexible, formative, and summative, allowing you to choose what best suits your students and school. All paper assessments are fully editable for you to adapt to your chosen approach.

All automarked assessments have the option of providing either formative feedback (where students receive feedback on each question and additional attempts) or summative feedback (with one attempt at each question and feedback at the end).

Bands	Levels	Grades	Comment only
All outcomes are banded throughout this book and in progress tasks. Use this model to assess students on their grasp of curriculum statements and set improvement targets, with a focus on ensuring students are always aiming for a *secure* band or higher.	All outcomes are matched to levels in this book and in progress tasks. This means you can continue using levels with *Activate* content, as well as integrating content you already have with *Activate*. This enables progress to be monitored and targets to be set.	Grade indicators are provided in Kerboodle. This enables progress to be monitored with reference to KS4 qualifications.	Some schools have adopted the 'no grades or marks' approach to assessment, opting for comment-only feedback. Interactive assessments provide comments and feedback to facilitate progression, and all paper assessments are fully editable, so banding and levelling can be removed.

The Checkpoint system

At the end of each chapter, there is an automarked online assessment. It will help you to determine if your students have a *secure* understanding of the chapter.

Activities for a follow-up Checkpoint Lesson are provided on Kerboodle. There are two recommended routes through the lesson for students, depending on the percentage they achieve in the assessment. Revision and Extension routes can be followed in the same lesson, allowing students to either consolidate their understanding or attempt an extension task.

Each lesson also includes informal checkpoints to track progress through a lesson.

Follow assessment with learning

Activate includes a Checkpoint assessment system.

1. Use the automarked Checkpoint Assessment at the end of each chapter to determine next steps.

2. Use the Checkpoint Lesson and resources to support and extend your students as needed.

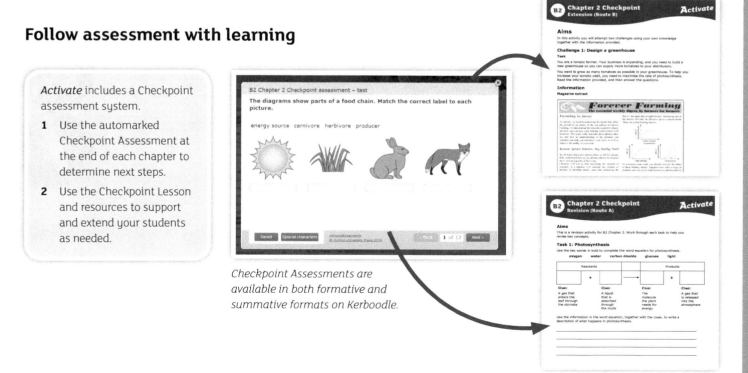

Checkpoint Assessments are available in both formative and summative formats on Kerboodle.

Differentiation and skills

Maths skills

Maths skills have always been important for science but with the introduction of the new GCSEs competence in maths in scientific contexts will be vital for success.

Key Maths skills for science include quantitative problem solving, use of scientific formulae, and the calculation of arithmetic means. Each skill has been integrated across components in *Activate*, with progress in each skill mapped out. You can view the Progression Grid for Maths in Kerboodle.

The **Student Books** contain maths activities and hints to support and develop Maths skills as students work from their books. There are also Maths challenges at the end of some chapters, focussing on quantitative problem solving skills.

In **Kerboodle**, you will find maths Skills Interactives that are automarked and provide formative feedback. Maths questions are also incorporated into other assessments where appropriate, and designated Progress Tasks for Maths will help you track progress.

In this **Teacher Handbook**, you will find maths suggestions for most lessons, linking to the Student Book where relevant. By using *Activate* resources, students will gain plenty of experience in a range of Maths skills that have been identified as vital for success at Key Stage 4.

Literacy skills

Literacy skills enable students to effectively communicate their ideas about science, and access the information they need. Since the introduction of extended writing and QWC at GCSE.

Literacy skills are vital for success in any subject but key Literacy skills for science include understanding meaning of scientific texts and identifying supporting ideas and evidence, adapting writing styles to suit audience and purpose, and the organisation of ideas and information.

The **Student books** contain literacy activities and hints to support and develop Literacy skills as students work from their books. There are also Big Writes at the end of some chapters, focussing on extended writing skills. QWC questions are provided on most spreads, and Key Words and a Glossary help students get to grips with scientific terms.

In **Kerboodle** you will find Skills Interactives and Progress Quizzes that will help assess Literacy skills, including spelling of key words. Question-led Lessons offer an alternative approach to one lesson in each chapter, focussing on the Literacy skills needed to answer a Big Question, and Progress Tasks for Literacy will help you track progress in key skill areas throughout the key stage. You can view the Progression Grid for Literacy in Kerboodle.

In this **Teacher Handbook**, you will find Literacy suggestions for most lessons, linking to the Student Book where relevant. By using *Activate* resources, students will gain plenty of experience in a range of Literacy skills that have been identified as vital for success at Key Stage 4.

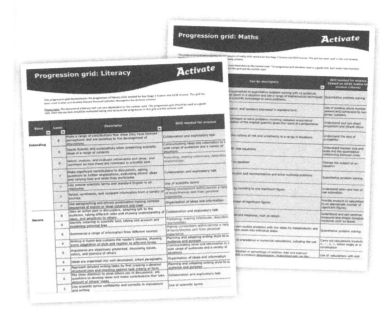

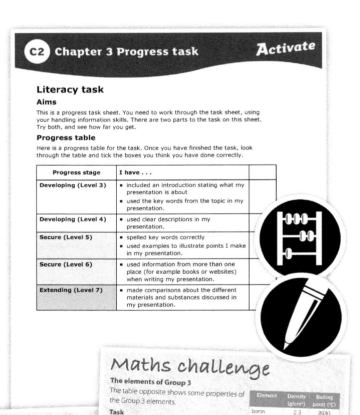

Working Scientifically

Working Scientifically is new to the 2014 Key Stage 3 Programme of Study and the new GCSE criteria. It is divided into four areas, and is integrated into the teaching and learning of Biology, Chemistry, and Physics. The four areas are:

Scientific attitudes, in which students need to be aware of accuracy, precision, repeatability, and reproducibility, and demonstrate understanding of scientific methods and the scientific process.

Experimental skills and investigations, in which students ask scientific questions based on observations, make predictions using scientific knowledge and understanding, carry out investigations to test predictions, make and record measurements, and evaluate methods.

Analysis and evaluation, in which students apply mathematical concepts and calculate results, present and interpret data using tables and graphs, draw conclusions, and evaluate data.

Measurement, in which students calculate results using scientific formulae, using basic data analysis, SI units, and IUPAC chemical nomenclature where appropriate.

Working Scientifically is integrated throughout the **Student Book** , and it also contains activities and hints to help students build their investigative skills and understand the process of working scientifically. A dedicated Working Scientifically chapter is also provided in *Activate 1*.

In **Kerboodle** you will find Practicals and Activities, each with their own Working Scientifically objectives, as well as Interactive investigations, Skills Interactives, Skill Sheets and Progress Tasks.

The **Teacher Handbook** lessons often have one Working Scientifically focus in mind for the activities of that lesson. Working Scientifically outcomes are ramped and included as part of the lesson outcomes.

Differentiation

Activate will help you to support students of every ability through Key Stage 3. A variety of support is available, combining opt-in differentiation, ramped questions and tasks, and differentiation by task, as appropriate for each type of activity.

Differentiation using the Checkpoint system
*   The end-of-chapter Checkpoint lessons will help you to progress students of every ability.
*   The revision tasks are designed to be used with students in need of support. Teacher input will help them grasp important concepts from the chapter.
*   The extension tasks provide an opportunity to stretch students who require an extra challenge. Students can work independently.

Teacher Handbook
Lesson outcomes are differentiated, including Working Scientifically. Suggestions for activities throughout lesson plans are also accompanied by support and extension opportunities.

Student Book
The Summary Questions and End-of-Chapter Questions in the Student Book are ramped. The level of demand of each question is indicated by the number of conical flasks depicted at the beginning of the question.

Practicals and Activities
Each Practical or Activity includes an extension task. Support Sheets or Access Sheets are available as an extra resource for most Practicals and Activities. Support Sheets offer opt-in differentiation, providing additional support with a difficult area of the task. Access Sheets offer alternative lesson activities where the main Practical or Activity is not accessible by some students.

Skill Sheets may also be used in tandem with Practicals and Activities to provide extra support. These can be found in Additional support in Kerboodle.

Interactive Assessments
Interactive Assessments are ramped in difficulty and support is provided in the feedback.

Written assessments
*   End-of-Unit Tests and Big Practical Projects have Foundation and Higher versions.
*   Progress Tasks each contain two tasks and a progress ladder to cater for all abilities.

Kerboodle

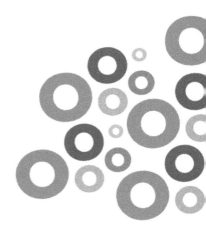

Activate **Kerboodle** is packed full of guided support and ideas for running and creating effective Key Stage 3 Science lessons, and assessing and facilitating students' progress. It's intuitive to use, customizable, and can be accessed online.

Activate **Kerboodle consists of**:

- *Activate* Lessons, Resources, and Assessment (includes teacher access to the accompanying Kerboodle Book)
- *Activate* Kerboodle Books.

Lessons, Resources, and Assessment

Activate **Kerboodle** – **Lessons**, **Resources**, and **Assessment** provides hundreds of engaging lesson resources as well as a comprehensive assessment package. Kerboodle offers flexibility and comprehensive support for both the *Activate* course and your own scheme of work.

You can **adapt** many of the resources to suit your students' needs, with all non-interactive activities available as editable Word documents. You can also **upload** your existing resources so that everything can be accessed from one location.

Kerboodle is online, allowing you and your students to access the course anytime, anywhere. Set homework and assessments through the Assessment system, and **track** progress using the Markbook.

Lessons, Resources, and Assessment provide:

- Lessons
- Resources
- Assessment and Markbook
- Teacher access to the Kerboodle Book.

The resource section contains:

Click on the **Lesson tab** to access the *Activate* lesson presentations and notes.

Ready-to-play Lesson Presentations complement every spread in the Teacher Handbook and Student Book. Each lesson presentation is easy to launch and features lesson objectives, settlers, starters, activity guidance, key diagrams, plenaries, and homework suggestions. You can further **personalise** the lessons by adding in your own resources and notes. This means that the Lesson Presentations and accompanying notes sections are 100% customizable. Your lessons and notes can be accessed by your whole department and they are ideal for use in cover lessons.

> Every lesson is accompanied by teacher notes that provide additional support and extension opportunities, to fully support lesson delivery.

> Resources are built into each lesson presentation so that associated interactive content, practical, or activity worksheets are ready to launch.

> **Nutrients (40 min)**
>
> Students compare nutritional labels for different brands of cereals, using their knowledge to decide which is the healthiest option.
>
> A support sheet is available with an observations table for students to fill in.
>
> Fully-editable resources and Teacher and Technician Notes (offering further guidance on this activity and answers to the questions on the activity sheet) are available from the resources tab on Kerboodle, under Activate 2 > Biology 2 > B2, 1 Health and lifestyle.

Resources

Click on the **Resources tab** at the bottom of the screen to access the full list of *Activate* lesson resources.

Fully customizable content to cater all your classes. Resources can be created using the create button.

Existing resources can be uploaded onto the platform using the upload button.

Navigation panel and search bar allow for easy navigation between resources by book, unit, and chapter.

Page navigator shows resources matching to particular pages in the Student Book and Kerboodle Book.

Resources matching every lesson in the Activate series are shown here.

The resource section contains:

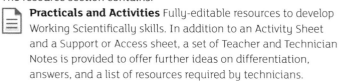 **Practicals and Activities** Fully-editable resources to develop Working Scientifically skills. In addition to an Activity Sheet and a Support or Access sheet, a set of Teacher and Technician Notes is provided to offer further ideas on differentiation, answers, and a list of resources required by technicians.

 **Interactive Screens** Starters and plenaries to accompany each lesson, as an interactive alternative to maximise student participation.

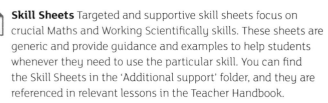 **Skill Sheets** Targeted and supportive skill sheets focus on crucial Maths and Working Scientifically skills. These sheets are generic and provide guidance and examples to help students whenever they need to use the particular skill. You can find the Skill Sheets in the 'Additional support' folder, and they are referenced in relevant lessons in the Teacher Handbook.

 **Animations** Animations focus on explaining difficult concepts using real-life contexts, engaging visuals, and narration. They are structured to clearly support a set of learning objectives and are followed by an Interactive Screen to help consolidate key points.

 **Videos** Videos help students to visualise difficult concepts using engaging visuals and narration. They are structured to clearly address a set of learning objectives.

Skills Interactives Automarked interactive activities with formative feedback focus on key Maths, Literacy, and Working Scientifically skills. You can use these activities in class to help consolidate key skills relevant to the lesson. They can also be set as homework by accessing them through the Assessment tab.

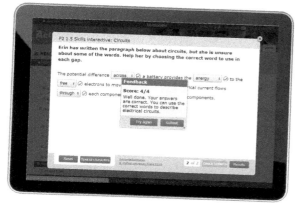

Kerboodle

Assessment and Markbook

All of the Assessment material in Kerboodle has been quality assured by our expert Assessment Editor. Click on the **Assessment tab** to find a wide range of assessment materials to help you deliver a varied, motivating, and effective assessment programme.

It's easy to import class registers and create user accounts for your students. Once your classes are set up, you can assign them assessments to do at home, individually, or as a group.

A **Markbook** with reporting function helps you to keep track of your students' results. This includes both automarked assessments and work that needs to be marked by you.

A Markbook and reporting function help you track your students' progress.

Assign assessments with 'practice' in the title if you want your students to get formative feedback on each answer before having another go.

Assign assessments with 'test' in the title if you want your students to have summative feedback, with only one attempt at each question.

Practice or test?

Each automarked assessment in *Activate* is available in formative or summative versions.

Practice versions of the assessment provide screen-by-screen feedback, focussing on misconceptions, and provide hints for the students to help them revise their answer. Students are given the opportunity to try again. Marks are reported to the Markbook.

Test versions of the assessment provide feedback on performance at the end of the test. Students are only given one attempt at each screen but can review them and see which answers they got wrong after completing the activity. Marks are reported to the Markbook.

The Assessment section provides ample opportunity for student assessment before, during, and after studying a unit.

Before each unit

 Unit Pre-tests These automarked tests revise and assess students' knowledge of Key Stage 2 content. Students are given feedback on their answers to help them correct gaps and misconceptions.

After each unit

 End-of-Unit Revision Quizzes These automarked assessments are ramped and focus on revising content from the unit. They can be assigned to students as homework revision ahead of formal end-of-unit testing.

 End-of-Unit Tests These written assessments mimic examination-style questions. They include QWC, Working Scientifically, and quantitative problem-solving questions and are available in two tiers. The Foundation paper contains developing and secure questions. The Higher paper has a full range of questions, stretching to extending. You can use the Raw Score Converter to convert scores to levels, bands, or grades.

 Big Practical Projects These written assessments focus on Working Scientifically and Literacy skills. Students plan and complete an investigation based on a given scenario. The Foundation paper contains developing and secure questions. The Higher paper has a full range of questions, stretching to extending.

Through each chapter

 Progress Quizzes These automarked assessments focus on content midway through a chapter to help you keep track of students as they move through the course.

 Skills Interactives These automarked interactives focus specifically on Maths, Literacy, and Working Scientifically skills.

 Interactive Investigations These automarked assessments are set in the context of an investigation. Each screen assesses a different Working Scientifically skill.

 Progress Tasks These written task-based assessments focus on progress in Maths, Literacy, and Working Scientifically skills. Each task uses a real-life scenario and comes with a progress ladder for students to self- or peer-assess their work.

 Checkpoint Assessments These automarked assessments determine whether students have a secure grasp of concepts from the chapter. These assessments are ramped in difficulty and can be followed up by the Checkpoint Lesson revision and extension activities.

Kerboodle Book

The *Activate* Kerboodle Book provides a digital version of the Student Book for you to use on your students at the front of the classroom.

Teacher access to the Kerboodle Book is automatically available as part of the Lessons, Resources, and Assessment package. You can also purchase additional access for your students.

A set of tools is available with the Kerboodle Book so you can personalise your book and make notes.

Like all other resources offered on Kerboodle, the Kerboodle Book can also be accessed using a range of devices.

Zoom in and spotlight any part of the text

Use different tools such as sticky notes, bookmarks, and pen features to personalise each page

Every teacher and student has their own digital notebook for use within their Kerboodle Book. You can even choose to share some of your notes with your students, or hide the from view – all student notes are accessible to themselves only

Navigate around the book quickly with the contents menu, key word search, or page number search

Biology (2)

Preparing for Key Stage 4 success

Knowledge

Underpinning knowledge is covered in this unit for KS4 study of:

- Growth and development of cells
- Transport systems in plants
- Health and disease
- The importance of photosynthesis
- Factors affecting photosynthesis
- Levels of organisation within an ecosystem
- Pyramids of biomass and transfer through trophic levels
- Biodiversity
- Variation and evolution
- Selective breeding and genetic engineering

Maths

Skills developed in this unit.
(Topic number)

- Quantitative problem solving (1.3, 1.7, 4.8, 2.7, 3.2, 3.4).
- Understand number size and scale and the quantitative relationship between units (1.3, 2.7, 3.5).
- Use of calculations with conversion between fractions, percentages, and ratios (1.3, 1.7, 2.7).
- Plot and draw graphs selecting appropriate scales for the axes (3.2, 3.4, end-of-chapter 3).
- Extract and interpret information from charts, graphs and tables (1.3, 1.8, 3.4).
- Understand and use common units and simple compound units (1.3, 2.7).
- Carry out calculations involving +, −, ×, ÷, either singly or in combination (1.3, 1.7, 2.7).

Literacy

Skills developed in this unit.
(Topic number)

- Identify meaning in scientific text, taking into account potential bias (1.5, 2.1, 2.4, 2.5, 2.6, 2.9, 3.1, 3.5).
- Summarise a range of information from different sources (2.4, end-of-chapter 2 Big Write, 3.5, end-of-chapter 3).
- Use scientific terms confidently and correctly in discussions and writing (all spreads).
- Approach detailed writing tasks by first creating a detailed structural plan (1.5, 1.6, end-of-chapter 1, 2.3, end-of-chapter 2, 3.7, end-of-chapter 3).
- Arguments are well presented, discussing issues, ethics, and opinions of others (1.1, end-of-chapter 1, 3.6).
- Use largely correct form in a range of writing styles and texts and include information relevant to the audience (1.1, 1.2, 1.6, 1.7, end-of-chapter 1, 2.3, 2.6, end-of-chapter 2, 3.1, 3.5, 3.6, 3.7, end-of-chapter 3).
- Take different roles in discussion, showing understanding of ideas and sensitivity to others (1.6, 2.4, 2.5, 2.8, 3.3).
- Ideas are organised into well-developed, linked paragraphs (1.1, 1.3, 1.4, 1.5, 1.6, 1.8, end-of-chapter 1, 2.1, 2.2, 2.3, 2.4, 2.5, 2.7, 2.8, 2.9, end-of-chapter 2, 3.1, 3.2, 3.3, 3.4, 3.5, 3.6, 3.7, end-of-chapter 3).
- Alternative ways of presenting ideas and information are used appropriately (1.5, 1.7, end-of-chapter 1, end-of-chapter 2, 3.5, 3.7).

Assessment Skills

- QWC questions: (1.1, 1.3, 1.4, 1.6, 1.7. 1.8, 2.1, 2.2, 2.3, 2.4, 2.5, 2.9, 3.1., 3.3, 3.4, 3.5, 3.6, 3.7) (end-of-chapter 1 Q6, end-of-chapter 2 Q6, end-of-chapter 3 Q6).
- Quantitative problem solving: (1.3, 1.7, 1.8, 2.7).
- Application of Working Scientifically: (1.2, 2.1, 2.2, 3.5) (end-of-chapter 1 Q3, end-of-chapter 2 Q3, end-of-chapter 3 Q5).

KS2 Link	Check before	Checkpoint	Catch-up
Animals, including humans, need the right types and amount of nutrition, and that they cannot make their own food.	B2 1.1 Food groups	Students discuss possible answers to the questions 'What are the chemical groups that make up food?'	Use a series of prompts to get the students to identify one, for example, 'What do crisps or chips contain a lot of?'. The others usually follow.
Diet, exercise, drugs, and lifestyle have an impact on the way the human body functions.	B2 1.3 Unhealthy diet	Ask students to suggest the effect of an unhealthy diet on health. This can then be stretched to other aspects, for example, use of drugs.	Show pictures of healthy foods and unhealthy foods. Students group the foods according to healthiness and justify their answers. Discuss for lifestyle choices.
The digestive system in humans is made up different parts, each with its own special function.	B2.1.4 Digestive system	Students explain what happens to food once eaten, including the names of the major parts of the digestive system.	Talk through what happens to food once it is swallowed while students label a diagram of the digestive system.
Plants require (air, light, water, nutrients from soil, and room to grow) for growth.	B2 2.1 Photosynthesis	Students compare what plants need to grow to what humans require.	Prompt students with questions about each requirement such as 'What would happen to a plant without water?'. Recap MRS GREN.
The functions of different parts of flowering plants: roots, stem/trunk, leaves, and flowers.	B2 2.2 Leaves	Students label a diagram of flowering plant, giving a brief description of each function.	Students use a card sort to match each part of a flowering plant to its function.
Food chains include producers, predators, and prey.	B2 2.7 Food chains and webs	Students write a food chain, labelling this using the key terms: predator, prey, producer, and consumer.	Show pictures of three organisms and ask students to build them into a food chain by talking about what each animal eats.
Living things are classified into groups according to common characteristics and based on similarities and differences.	B2 2.7 Food chains and webs	Students offer different categories of organisms, for example, mammals, predators, and plants, describing the characteristics of each group.	Students sort images of different organisms into groups, justifying their choices.
Animals and plants are adapted to suit their environment in different ways. Adaptation may lead to evolution.	B2 3.1 Competition and adaptation	Students discuss hypothetical situations, for example, whether a shark can survive on land, explaining their answers.	Give one further hypothetical situation before allowing students to give their own. State that an adaptation is a feature which helps an organism to survive.
Environments can change, posing dangers to living things.	B2.3.2 Adapting to change	Pick a topical environmental change, for example, deforestation. Students discuss how this change has affected wildlife.	Show a picture of a polar bear, discussing the loss of the ice sheets and how this has impacted the total population of polar bears.
Living things produce offspring of the same kind but are not identical to their parents.	B2 3.3 Variation	Students discuss the question 'Are we all the same?'.	Students write down differences between themselves. State that this is called variation.
Living things have changed over time. Fossils provide information about living things that inhabited the Earth millions of years ago.	B2 3.6 Natural selection	Students answer the question 'What are fossils and what do they tell us about animals that lived long ago?'.	Show an image of an evolutionary sequence. These are readily available on the Internet. Explain the sequence and how this relates to fossils.

kerboodle

B2 Unit pre-test
B2 Big practical project (foundation)
B2 Big practical project (higher)
B2 Big practical project teacher notes
B2 Practical project hints: graph plotting
B2 Practical project hints: writing frame

B2 Practical project hints: planning
B2 End-of-unit test (foundation)
B2 End-of-unit test (foundation) mark scheme
B2 End-of-unit test (higher)
B2 End-of-unit test (higher) mark scheme

Answers to Picture Puzzler
Key Words
DNA, iris, giraffe, ear, sperm, tree
The key word is **digest**.
Close up
a bread crumb

1.1 Nutrients

Biology NC link:
- content of a healthy human diet: carbohydrates, lipids (fats and oils), proteins, vitamins, minerals, dietary fibre, and water, and why each is needed.

Working Scientifically NC link:
- interpret observations and data, including identifying patterns and using observations, measurements, and data to draw conclusions.

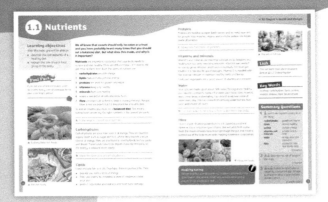

Band	Outcome	Checkpoint	
		Question	Activity
Developing	Name some nutrients in a given diet (Level 3).	3	Starter 2, Plenary 2
	Name the nutrients required by the human body (Level 3).	3	Lit, Starter 2, Plenary 1, Plenary 2
	Extract nutritional information from food packaging (Level 4).		Main
Secure	Describe the components of a healthy diet (Level 5).	3	Lit, Main, Plenary 1, Plenary 2
	Explain the role of each nutrient in the body (Level 6).	B, C, 1–3	Lit, Starter 1, Main, Plenary 1, Plenary 2
	Interpret nutritional information on food packaging to identify a healthy food (Level 6).		Main
Extending	Explain what makes a food a healthy option (Level 7).	3	Main, Plenary 1, Plenary 2
	Explain how each nutrient contributes to a healthy, balanced diet (Level 7).	1–3	Lit, Starter 1, Main, Plenary 1, Plenary 2
	Interpret nutritional information to make health comparisons between foods (Level 7).		Main

Maths
Students interpret numerical data on food packaging, displaying this data in a suitable table to compare the nutritional information of three different cereals.

Literacy
In the student-book activity students organise information about the different nutrients and their importance, and adapt this information for a TV advert aimed at a young audience to encourage them to eat a balanced diet.

Students are also required to use scientific terminology correctly when explaining the importance of food labels, and the food traffic-light system.

APP
Students present data from food packaging from three cereal boxes in a table (AF3), and use this data to draw conclusions (AF5).

Key Words
nutrient, carbohydrate, lipid, protein, vitamin, mineral, fibre, balanced diet

Answers from the student book

In-text questions	**A** An essential substance the body needs to survive. **B** provide energy **C** For growth (new cells) and to repair body tissues. **D** Any four from: sweat, tears, urine, feces, breathing out.
Activity	**Healthy eating** Advert should include all seven nutrients, emphasise their function in a healthy diet, and be engaging to young people to encourage them to eat a balanced diet.

Summary Questions	1 carbohydrates – provide energy vitamins and minerals – remain healthy lipids – energy store and insulation water – needed in cells and bodily fluids protein – growth and repair fibre – provide bulk to food **(6 marks)** 2 Any two from: provides you with a store of energy/keeps you warm by providing a layer of insulation under your skin/protects your organs from damage. 3 QWC question (6 marks). Example answers: A balanced diet is eating food containing the right nutrients in the correct amounts. Nutrients are essential substances that your body needs to survive. A balanced diet should contain: carbohydrates to provide energy lipids to provide an energy store and insulation proteins for growth and repair vitamins and minerals to keep you healthy water, which is needed in all cells and body fluids fibre, which provides bulk to food to keep it moving through the gut. (Only award a maximum of 5 marks if a definition of a balanced diet is not given.)

kerboodle

Starter	Support/Extension	Resources
Food functions (5 min) Interactive resource where students connect nutrients to their function in the body. Can be used to gauge prior knowledge of students.		**Interactive**: Food functions
What's on the menu? (10 min) Students discuss the names of the seven different nutrients before a short class discussion. Project a number of images of different foods or meals on the board (or use flash cards) for students to give the nutrients shown.	**Support**: Give students access to the names of the seven nutrients. **Extension**: Students suggest functions of the seven nutrients.	

Main	Support/Extension	Resources
Nutrients (40 min) Introduce the seven types of nutrients, their functions, and the importance of nutrients in food. Ask students how they know if they eat healthily or not. How would students know which cereal is the healthiest given a choice of three? Provide the students with nutritional information tables from at least three breakfast cereal packets. One should be healthy (whole wheat cereal), one should be highly processed (chocolate-coated rice cereal), and one in between (malted cereal). Students use the food labels to investigate the health value in cereals, and complete questions on the activity sheet.	**Support**: The support sheet has a table to use when collecting data from cereal packaging.	**Activity**: Nutrients

Plenary	Support/Extension	Resources
The importance of labels (10 min) Give students two minutes to discuss in groups how they decided the healthiness of the cereals in the activity. Open the discussion to the class. Students should discuss the importance of food labels, justifying their views using evidence where possible. This activity can be used to summarise the different nutrients and their functions.	**Support**: Group students and give prompts to lead the discussion. **Extension:** Discuss the importance of evidence in scientific investigation.	
The importance of a balanced diet (5 min) Revisit the images of different foods shown at the start of the lesson. Students give the main nutrient for each food shown, and describe the function of the nutrient.	**Extension:** Students suggest which given food is the healthiest.	

Homework		
Students research the traffic-light system of nutritional information on food packaging. Students research what information it provides, why it may be useful, and give at least two examples of it. Further information on the traffic-light system can be found on the 'Live Well' section of the NHS website.		

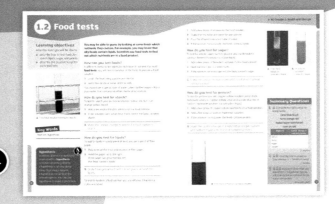

Biology NC link:

- simple food tests for starch, simple (reducing) sugars, protein, and lipids.

Working Scientifically NC link:

- use appropriate techniques, apparatus, and materials during fieldwork and laboratory work, paying attention to health and safety.

Band	Outcome	Checkpoint	
		Question	Activity
Developing	State that food can be tested for starch, lipids, sugar, and protein (Level 4).	B	Starter 2, Main, Plenary 2, Homework
	State that food tests show colour changes (Level 4).	A, C, D, 1	Main, Plenary 2, Homework
	Use appropriate techniques to carry out a food test safely (Level 4).		Main
Secure	Describe how to test foods for starch, lipids, sugar, and protein (Level 6).	B, 2, 3	Main, Plenary 2, Homework
	Describe the positive result for each food test (Level 6).	A, C, D, 1, 2	Main, Plenary 2, Homework
	Use appropriate techniques to carry out a range of food tests safely (Level 6).		Main
Extending	Explain why testing food for starch, lipids, sugar, and protein is important (Level 7).		Main, Plenary 2, Homework
	Explain the meaning of positive or negative results in terms of the food tests (Level 7).		Main, Homework
	Use appropriate techniques to carry out a full range of food tests safely, interpreting the findings, and relating them to everyday situations (Level 7).		Main

Maths

Students measure out required amounts of different solutions in their experiment, showing an understanding of the number scale.

Literacy

Students use scientific terminology when describing observations in their experiment to draw conclusions.

APP

Students record data (AF4) and present this appropriately in a results table (AF3). Students then use their observations to draw conclusions (AF5).

Key Words

food test, hypothesis

Answers from the student book

In-text questions	A orange-yellow to blue-black
	B Rub some food onto a piece of filter paper, if the paper becomes translucent then the food contains lipids.
	C blue to orange-red
	D pale blue to purple

Summary Questions	1 starch – turns blue-black sugar – turns orange-red lipids – makes paper translucent protein – turns purple (4 marks)

1 starch – turns blue-black   sugar – turns orange-red

lipids – makes paper translucent   protein – turns purple   (4 marks)

2 Crush cereal with a pestle and mortar, add a few drops of water, mix well. (3 marks)

3 QWC question (6 marks). Example answers:

Take three samples of the gingerbread-biscuit solution. To test for starch add iodine to one sample. If solution turns blue-black then starch is present.

To test for sugar add Benedict's solution to another sample and heat in a water bath. If solution turns orange-red then sugar is present

To test for protein add copper sulfate and sodium hydroxide to the third sample. If solution turns purple then protein is present.

Starter	Support/Extension	Resources
An alternative question-led lesson is also available. **Food and nutrients** (5 min) Display pictures of different foods on the board and ask students to write the main nutrients shown on their mini-whiteboards. Include foods that will be less obvious for students to guess as a way of introducing the importance of food tests. **Testing not tasting** (5 min) We like food that tastes nice, but we need to know what each food contains. Ask students how they think scientists can learn what chemicals are present in food. Lead the discussion to the idea of doing chemical tests, and how scientists need clear results to tell us whether a food contains a chemical or not.	**Extension**: Students should compare the health value of the foods shown, justifying their answer using knowledge from the previous lesson.	**Question-led lesson**: Food tests

Main	Support/Extension	Resources
Food tests (40 min) Introduce the tests for starch, lipids, sugar, and protein, and observations for positive results in each experiment. Students work in small groups to carry out a circus activity where they will test for themselves, during their allocated time at each station, the presence of starch, lipids, sugar, and protein in the foods provided. Students should be given the opportunity to test for all four chemicals during this practical. Students then work through the questions that follow on the practical sheet.	**Support:** A suggested results table is provided in the accompanying support sheet for students to use when recording observations.	**Practical**: Food tests **Skill sheet**: Recording results

Plenary	Support/Extension	Resources
Discussing anomalies (10 min) Students compare their results before a class discussion of the conclusions. Were there any anomalous results? Allow students to discuss in small groups why these might have occurred (e.g., poor technique or lack of accuracy in observation) before reconvening as a class to discuss potential issues. **Food tests and results** (10 min) Ask students why it is important for scientists to find out the contents of food. Lead the discussion towards specific types of people who may require this information, and why they need to do so. Students then link chemicals in food to the food test and positive result, using the interactive resource provided. This can also be done using mini-whiteboards to increase class participation.	**Extension**: Encourage students to use as many scientific terms as possible when discussing accuracy, precision, and validity of data. **Support**: Allow students to concentrate on either the chemicals used for each test, or on the observations for positive results.	**Interactive**: Food tests and results

Homework	Support/Extension	
Students write a report to describe how food scientists in a drinks company can provide evidence that a new improved drink is nutritionally better than the existing drink. In this report students must describe the methods needed when obtaining this evidence, and the types of results expected.	**Extension**: Students should make links between this lesson on food tests and the concept of a balanced diet from the previous lesson.	

1.3 Unhealthy diet

Biology NC link:
- calculations of energy requirements in a healthy daily diet
- the consequences of imbalances in the diet, including obesity, starvation, and deficiency diseases.

Working Scientifically NC link:
- interpret observations and data, including identifying patterns and using observations, measurements, and data to draw conclusions.

Band	Outcome	Checkpoint	
		Question	**Activity**
Developing	State one potential problem for someone with an unhealthy diet (Level 3).	B–D, 1, 3	Starter 1, Starter 2, Plenary 2
	State that different people require different amounts of energy (Level 4).	2	Main, Plenary 1
	Collect experimental data and record observations (Level 4).		Main
Secure	Describe some health issues caused by an unhealthy diet (Level 5).	B–D, 1, 3	Starter 1, Starter 2, Plenary 2
	Calculate the energy requirements of different people (Level 6).	2	Main, Plenary 1
	Collect experimental data and draw conclusions from results obtained (Level 6).		Main
Extending	Explain how an unhealthy diet causes health issues (Level 7).	3	Starter 1, Starter 2, Plenary 2
	Explain that different people require different amounts of energy, using energy calculations and data to support explanations. (Level 7).	2	Maths, Main, Plenary 1
	Interpret experimental data and suggest ways to improve the experiment (Level 8).		Main

Maths

In the student-book activity students interpret a graph showing typical energy requirements for different types of people. Students extract information from this graph to answer the question posed.

In the practical students carry out simple calculations of temperature changes and energy transferred from the food to the water, using appropriate equations and units.

Literacy

Students use scientific terminology when discussing and explaining experimental results and conclusions, forming links between a healthy diet and energy consumption.

APP

Students carry out an experiment on food energy (AF4), record results in a table (AF3), and draw conclusions from experimental data (AF5).

Some students also suggest improvements to the experimental procedure (AF5).

Key Words

malnourishment, starvation, obese, deficiency

Answers from the student book

In-text questions	A joules/kilojoules
	B The person will often suffer health problems (poor immune system), lack energy, and is likely to suffer from a lack of vitamins or minerals.
	C Any three from: heart disease, stroke, diabetes, some cancers D night blindness

Activity	**Energy requirements** Approximately 9000 kJ, equivalent to a female office worker.
Summary Questions	**1** energy, joules/kilojoules, gain, obese, heart, tired (6 marks) **2a** 11 000 kJ − 9000 kJ = 2000 kJ (2 marks) **b** Difference in energy requirement = 15 000 kJ − 10 000 kJ = 5000 kJ Percentage increase from original job = 5000 kJ ÷ 10 000 kJ × 100 = 50% (4 marks) **3** QWC question (6 marks). Example answers: Underweight people often suffer from health problems, such as a poor immune system, often lack energy to do things, and are likely to suffer from a lack of vitamins or minerals. Overweight people have an increased risk of heart disease, strokes, diabetes, and some cancers.

Starter	Support/Extension	Resources
Unhealthy diets (5 min) Write these four words on the board: scurvy, rickets, obesity, and starvation. Ask students how these words are linked to each other and to this lesson. This is a good opportunity to gauge existing knowledge. Ask students to describe these conditions, possible causes and effects, and treatments of these conditions before offering the answer. **Mass effect** (5 min) Introduce some of the health issues for people who are underweight or overweight. Ask students to discuss the importance of vitamins and minerals before introducing issues caused by deficiencies.		

Main	Support/Extension	Resources
Investigating the energy content of food (45 min) Introduce the idea that all the energy we require for life comes from food. Allow students to discuss in pairs for a few minutes potential ways of comparing energy content in different foods. Demonstrate the energy provided in food by sprinkling fine custard powder into a Bunsen flame. This is a dramatic demonstration that creates a huge roaring flame. Keep students at a reasonable distance away from the experiment. Although this is a good demonstration, students should be able to notice that quantitative data cannot be obtained this way. Students follow instructions on the practical sheet to burn different types of food to heat water in a test tube. They then answer the questions that follow. If time, ask students to discuss whether consuming enough energy for a typical day is the same as eating a balanced diet. This is often a source of confusion for students, so this is a good opportunity to dispel any remaining misconceptions.	**Support**: The accompanying support sheet includes a suggested table of results. **Extension**: If there is time, you may wish to introduce the concept of specific heat capacity. This is the origin of the equation in Extension Question 1.	**Practical**: Investigating the energy content of food **Skill sheet**: Recording results

Plenary	Support/Extension	Resources
Energy consumption (5 min) Interactive resource where students link amounts of energy used per day to types of people who require them. **Consequences of an unhealthy diet** (5 min) Revisit the four key words scurvy, rickets, obesity, and starvation. Get students to explain how these four words are linked, giving further consequences of an unhealthy diet.	**Extension**: Students suggest foods to eat using data from their practical. **Support**: Allow students to work in small groups.	**Interactive**: Energy consumption

Homework	Support/Extension	
Students keep a log of their energy intake for one day. They must record the foods consumed, food types, quantity, energy provided in 100 g of food, and energy intake. Students then calculate their total energy intake for that day and compare this against the energy requirements for a typical teenager of their age. For fresh food, students will need to use the Internet for energy values.	**Support**: Students may require prompts on how to calculate energy from food. **Extension:** Students evaluate the healthiness of their diet.	

1.4 Digestive system

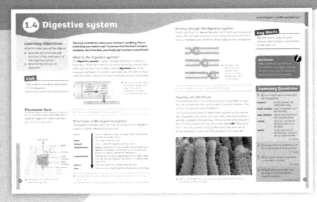

Biology NC link:
- the tissues and organs of the human digestive system, including adaptations to function and how the digestive system digests food (enzymes simply as biological catalysts).

Band	Outcome	Checkpoint	
		Question	Activity
Developing	Name the main parts of the digestive system (Level 4).	B	Starter 1, Starter 2, Main, Homework
	State what is meant by digestion (Level 3).	A	Main, Plenary 1, Homework
	Label a diagram of the digestive system by identifying correct information in text (Level 4).		Main
Secure	Describe the structure and function of the main parts of the digestive system (Level 6).	C, 1, 2	Main, Homework
	Describe the process of digestion (Level 6).	4	Main, Homework
	Give a structured account of digestion using information gathered by research (Level 6).		Main, Plenary 2
Extending	Explain how each part of the digestive system works in sequence, including adaptations of the small intestine for its function (Level 8).	2, 4	Main, Plenary 1, Homework
	Explain why food needs to be digested (Level 7).		Main, Plenary 1,
	Give a detailed explanation of digestion in sequence using information gathered by research (Level 7).		Main, Plenary 2

Literacy
Students retrieve and collate information from a range of different sources to write their own extended account of the digestion of food in the human body.

They organise ideas into well developed and linked paragraphs, explaining scientific terms and processes in a logical and coherent manner.

APP
Students interpret secondary sources and present them in a piece of extended writing to describe the process of digestion in humans (AF3).

Key Words
digestive system, digestion, gullet, stomach, small intestine, large intestine, rectum, anus, villi

Answers from the student book

In-text questions	**A** Large molecules are broken down into smaller molecules. **B** gullet
	C Muscles in the wall of the gut squeeze food along it.
Activity	**Wordbank**
	Wordbanks should include all the key words on the student book spread. Credit sensible additions to this list.

| Summary Questions | 1 stomach – food is mixed with acid and digestive juices
small intestine – small molecules of nutrients are absorbed into the bloodstream
large intestine – water is absorbed back into the body
rectum – feces are stored here until they pass out of the body
mouth – food is chewed and mixed with saliva   (5 marks)
2 The small intestine has a thin wall, large surface area due to villi, and blood capillaries to carry away any nutrients absorbed. (3 marks)
3 Fibre is not digested. It adds bulk to the food, allowing muscles to push against this as food is squeezed along the gut. This prevents constipation. (3 marks)
4 QWC question (6 marks). Example answers:
Food is chewed and mixed with saliva in the mouth. Teeth help to break the food into smaller chunks. Food passes down the gullet into the stomach. Food is churned with digestive juices and acid in the stomach. Small molecules pass through the villi of the intestine wall into the bloodstream in the small intestine. Water passes back into the body in the large intestine. This leaves a solid waste of undigested food called feces. Feces are stored in the rectum. They are passed out of the body through the anus. |

Starter	Support/Extension	Resources
Parts of the digestive system (5 min) Students label the parts of the digestive system using the diagram provided on the interactive resource. This should be used as a recap of organ systems met in Biology 1. **Where in the body?** (10 min) Use an anatomical model of the human torso to show students the location of major digestive organs. Students name these parts. Ask them to suggest differences to the digestive system in other animals based on general knowledge, for example, cows and giraffes have four parts to their stomach.	**Extension**: Students suggest a feasible route for the digestion of food in the human body. **Extension**: Students suggest reasons why different animals have different digestive systems.	**Interactive**: Parts of the digestive system
Main	**Support/Extension**	**Resources**
The digestive system (40 min) The activity sheet contains an unlabelled diagram of the human digestive system. Students are given access to a range of textbooks, including the student book, for 20 minutes. They label the diagram and add notes to describe the digestive process. After 20 minutes remove the textbooks and students use their notes to create a piece of extended writing, describing the journey of food through the human body. Encourage them to plan their accounts before writing. Differentiation can also be provided in this activity by targeting the research materials available to different groups of students, for example, by giving students in need of extension the more advanced text books.	**Support**: The access sheet provides students with a structured framework for their research. Students also get an extra 10 minutes reading time. **Extension**: Students spend time researching enzymes and include this in their account.	**Activity**: The digestive system
Plenary	**Support/Extension**	**Resources**
Why digest? (10 min) Ask students the question 'Why do we digest food?'. Allow students thinking time before opening up as a class discussion. This activity recaps the definition of digestion, and the idea that small molecules are needed for absorption in the small intestine. **Developing skills** (5 min) Ask the students what skills they developed in the research and planning activity. Students discuss their research process from the naming of the skill to how they improved that skill during the lesson.	**Support**: Students work in small groups for the discussion. **Extension**: Students explain adaptations of the small intestine for efficient absorption. **Extension**: Students suggest other ways they can improve the skill further in the future.	
Homework		
Students draw a comic strip showing the journey of Sandy the Sandwich. The comic strip must describe the digestion process accurately, using at least 10 scientific words from this topic.		

1.5 Bacteria and enzymes in digestion

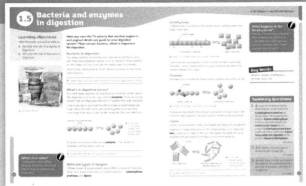

Biology NC link:
- enzymes simply as biological catalysts
- the importance of bacteria in the human digestive system.

Working Scientifically NC link:
- make and record observations and measurements using a range of methods for different investigations; and evaluate the reliability of methods and suggest possible improvements.

Band	Outcome	Checkpoint	
		Question	Activity
Developing	Name some enzymes used in digestion (Level 4).	1, 3	Lit, Main, Plenary 1, Plenary 2
	State where bacteria are found in the digestive system (Level 4).	2, 3	Lit, Plenary 1
	Record measurements from an experiment (Level 4).		Main
Secure	Describe the role of enzymes in digestion (Level 5).	B, 1, 3	Lit, Main, Plenary 1, Plenary 2
	Describe the role of bacteria in digestion (Level 6).	A, 2, 3	Lit, Plenary 1
	Record experimental data using a suitable results table (Level 6).		Main
Extending	Explain how enzymes affect the rate of digestion (Level 8).	3	Lit, Main, Plenary 1
	Explain how some bacteria improve health (Level 7).	A, 2, 3	Lit, Plenary 1
	Record experimental data using a suitable results table, and evaluate the quality of the data obtained (Level 7).		Main

Literacy
Students interpret a set of complex experimental procedures to carry out an experiment using enzymes, and use scientific terminology when explaining observations from their experiment.

APP
Students present experimental observations in a suitable table (AF3), and use the data obtained to draw a valid conclusion (AF5).

Key Words
enzyme, catalyst, carbohydrase, protease, lipase, bile

Answers from the student book

In-text questions	**A** Bacteria in the digestive system make vitamins. **B** They speed up the reaction where large molecules are broken down, without being used up. **C** To break lipids down into small droplets.
Activity	**What happens to the bread you eat?** The flow diagram should start from the breaking down of starch using carbohydrase in saliva, include absorption in the small intestine, and finally the excretion of feces through the anus. There should also be a mention of the importance of bacteria in digestion.

Summary Questions	
	1 carbohydrates, carbohydrase, amino acids, protease, fatty acids and glycerol, lipase (6 marks)
	2 Live yoghurt contains useful bacteria that remain in your gut. These help to break down fibre and produce important vitamins. (3 marks)
	3 Visual summary example answers (6 marks):
	Enzymes are proteins/catalysts.
	Bacteria are organisms that aid the digestion process.
	They speed up digestion by beaking down large molecules into small molecules.
	Three different enzymes exist.
	Carbohydrase break down carbohydrates into sugar molecules.
	Lipase break down lipids into fatty acids and glycerol.
	Proteases break down proteins into amino acids.

kerboodle

Starter	Support/Extension	Resources
Getting a reaction (5 min) Demonstrate the decomposition of hydrogen peroxide, first without a catalyst (where nothing seems to happen), then with a piece of potato added (there should be fizzing). This demonstration serves as a good introduction to enzymes as biological catalysts that speed up reactions, without being used up.	**Extension**: Students can be introduced to inhibitors as the opposite of catalysts.	
Breaking down (5 min) Introduce the definition of an enzyme by holding up a chain of plastic beads and breaking the beads off the chain one by one as a model of enzymatic digestion. Explain how enzymes are biological catalysts that help to break down large 'unusable' molecules in our foods to small molecules that can be absorbed through the walls of our small intestines, all without being used up.	**Extension**: This activity can be extended by introducing the idea of rates of reactions.	

Main	Support/Extension	Resources
Investigating enzyme action (40 min) Formally introduce the idea of catalysts, biological catalysts, and enzymes. Give the definition of an enzyme, examples of enzymes, and their function in the human body. Students then carry out a practical to observe the action of carbohydrase on the breakdown of starch, and answer the questions that follow. You may wish to demonstrate the importance of timing in this practical, and explain what results students are looking for. Encourage students to read the method thoroughly before starting the practical.	**Support:** The support sheet contains a suggested table of results.	**Practical:** Investigating enzyme action **Skill sheet**: Recording results

Plenary	Support/Extension	Resources
Human digestion (10 min) Students use the clues provided on the interactive resource to complete a crossword that contains key words from this lesson.	**Extension:** Students should link all the key words together in explaining the action of bacteria and enzymes in human digestion.	**Interactive**: Human digestion
Enzyme jigsaw (10 min) Create sets of sort cards (one per group) with the following words: carbohydrates, carbohydrase, sugar, proteins, proteases, amino acids, lipids, lipase, fatty acids, and glycerol, and three arrow cards. Give each group of students a set of cards for them to explain enzymatic digestion. Students should then write the resulting word equations in their books.	**Support:** Have special sets of cards where different coloured cards are used to distinguish between substrates, enzymes, and products.	

Homework		
Students draw a cartoon diagram to show how an enzyme works. They should add as many labels to the cartoon as possible. Encourage students to research the lock and key mechanism for enzymes and include this in their cartoons.		

1.6 Drugs

Biology NC link:
- the effects of recreational drugs (including substance misuse) on behaviour, health, and life processes.

Working Scientifically NC link:
- interpret observations and data, including identifying patterns and using observations, measurements, and data to draw conclusions.

Band	Outcome	Checkpoint	
		Question	**Activity**
Developing	Name some recreational and medicinal drugs (Level 4).	D, 2	Main, Plenary 1, Plenary 2, Homework
	State one effect of a drug on health or behaviour (Level 4).	E, 1, 3	Lit, Starter 2, Main, Plenary 1, Plenary 2, Homework
↓	Make observations during an experiment (Level 3).		Main
Secure	Describe the difference between recreational and medicinal drugs (Level 5).	B, C, 1, 2	Starter 2, Homework
	Describe the effects of drugs on health and behaviour (Level 6).	E, 1, 3	Lit, Starter 2, Main, Plenary 1, Plenary 2, Homework
↓	Interpret experimental observations to draw simple conclusions (Level 6).		Main
Extending	Explain why people take different medicinal and recreational drugs (Level 7).		Lit, Starter 2, Main, Plenary 2, Homework
	Explain how recreational drugs can have a negative effect on people's lifestyles (Level 7).	3	Lit, Main, Plenary 1, Homework
↓	Record accurate and detailed observations from an experiment to draw detailed conclusions, and evaluate methods (Level 8).		Main

Literacy
Students use scientific terminology, organise information, and target information to different audiences in extended writing.

Students are asked to write a drug fact sheet on illegal recreational drugs for the student-book activity, and an information leaflet about the issues with drug abuse for Year 7 students for homework.

APP
Students present observations in a suitable table (AF3), and draw conclusions from experimental data obtained (AF5).

Key Words
drug, medicinal drug, recreational drug, addiction, withdrawal symptom

Answers from the student book

In-text questions	**A** A chemical substance that affects the way the body works. **B** A drug taken for a medical purpose. **C** A drug taken for enjoyment. **D** Any three from: heroin, cocaine, cannabis, and ecstasy. **E** Dependency on a drug.
Activity	**Drug factsheet** Factsheet should include information on one of cannabis, cocaine, ecstasy, or heroine. Factsheet should be suitable for a teenage audience, but include scientific information about the effects of taking this drug.

Summary Questions	1 chemicals, recreational, medicinal, addiction, withdrawal symptoms (5 marks) 2 Any three from: Medicinal drugs are used in medicine, benefit health, treat symptoms, or cure an illness. Examples include paracetamol and antibiotics. Recreational drugs are used for enjoyment, may help a person relax or give them more energy, have no health benefit, are harmful in some cases, and many are illegal. Examples include heroin, cocaine, cannabis, and ecstasy. 3 QWC question (6 marks). Example answers: Drugs are chemicals that affect the ways the body works. They alter chemical reactions inside the body. Medicinal drugs are beneficial to health/not taken for enjoyment. For example, paracetamol reduces pain. Recreational drugs are often harmful to health. These are taken for enjoyment/not beneficial to health. For example, caffeine speeds up the nervous system. You can become dependent on a drug/become addicted. If you try to give up you may suffer withdrawal symptoms.

Starter	Support/Extension	Resources
Medicinal or not? (5 min) Students sort a number of drugs into medicinal, legal recreational, or illegal recreational drugs on the interactive resource. This is an opportunity to gauge students's knowledge from Personal, Social, and Health Education (PSHE) or Citizenship sessions. **Doing drugs?** (10 min) Write on the board the names of some legal and illegal drugs. Students discuss what they know about them in small groups. Students then share what they know about each drug and categorise them into medicinal, legal recreational, and illegal recreational drugs.	**Extension**: Students suggest reasons why people use drugs, even if they are illegal. Include drugs such as steroids that can be legal or illegal.	**Interactive:** Medicinal or not?

Main	Support/Extension	Resources
Identifying unknown substances (40 min) Students are presented with four chemicals (sample from a suspect, two known drugs, and sugar) on which they carry out three simple tests. Students use the results from these tests to decide whether the sample obtained from the suspect is an illegal recreational drug or not, and answer questions that follow. Students may need prompting that the way they will identify the unknown sample is by looking for similarities between the unknown sample and known samples' results.	**Support**: The support sheet includes a suggested table of results. **Extension**: Students discuss in groups the importance of drug testing and the need to do several chemical tests, rather than relying on results from one test alone.	**Practical:** Identifying unknown substances **Skill sheet:** Drawing graphs **Skill sheet:** Recording results

Plenary	Support/Extension	Resources
Why are some drugs illegal? (10 min) Split students into groups of three and give each group a mini-whiteboard. Ask each group to discuss as many reasons as they can think of why governments should make certain recreational drugs illegal, noting down the three most important factors. Open up as a class discussion. Students should be able to justify their answers. **Prescribing drugs** (5 min) Split students into groups of three and ask them to make a list of as many medicinal drugs as they can think of, along with their uses. This can be done on mini-whiteboards. After two minutes ask students to sort the drugs into two categories: those that relieve symptoms and those that cure illnesses, justifying their answers.	**Support**: Possible reasons may be offered to students to sort out as a 'diamond nine' activity. **Extension**: Introduce the idea of the different classes of drugs. **Extension**: Students should offer other ways of grouping drugs other than the ones mentioned in the lesson.	

Homework		
Students produce a leaflet to be given to Year 7 students about the dangers of drug abuse. An alternative Webquest homework activity is also available on Kerboodle where students produce a presentation on illegal drugs.		**WebQuest:** Drugs

1.7 Alcohol

Biology NC link:
- the effects of 'recreational' drugs (including substance misuse) on behaviour, health, and life processes
- the effect of maternal lifestyle on the fetus through the placenta.

Working Scientifically NC link:
- present observations and data using appropriate methods, including tables and graphs.

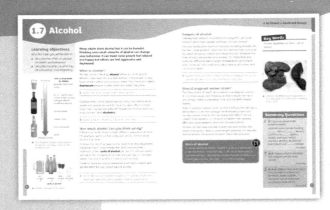

Band	Outcome	Checkpoint	
		Question	Activity
Developing	Name one effect of alcohol on health or behaviour (Level 3).	D, 1, 3	Starter 1, Starter 2, Main, Plenary 1, Plenary 2
	State whether alcohol affects conception and pregnancy (Level 3).	2, 3	Starter 1, Starter 2, Plenary 2, Homework
	Record results in a given table and plot a graph of results obtained (Level 4).		Main
Secure	Describe the effect of alcohol on health and behaviour (Level 5).	D, 1, 3	Starter 1, Starter 2, Main, Plenary 1, Plenary 2
	Describe the effect alcohol has on conception and pregnancy (Level 6).	2, 3	Starter 2, Plenary 2, Homework
	Design a results table and plot subsequent experimental data on an appropriate graph (Level 6).		Main
Extending	Explain in detail how alcohol affects health and behaviour, detailing its effect on life processes (Level 8).	1, 3	Starter 1, Starter 2, Main, Plenary 1, Plenary 2
	Explain the importance of providing information about drinking to the general public, not just pregnant women (Level 7).	1–3	Starter 1, Starter 2, Main, Plenary 2, Homework
	Record data in a well-organised table (with headings and units) and plot an appropriate graph to present results (Level 7).		Main

Maths
In the student-book activity students calculate the units of alcohol in 200 ml of 10 % wine.

Students calculate arithmetic means from experimental data, plot their results along with secondary data on a suitable graph grid, and interpret their graph to draw a conclusion.

Literacy
Students use scientific terms when describing and explaining experimental observations, and in extended writing.

For homework, students take into account the views of others when designing a poster or advert to persuade pregnant women not to drink alcohol. They must ensure that their arguments are well-organised and well-presented, changing their language to suit their audience.

APP
Students present data in tables and graphs (AF3), distinguish between primary and secondary data (AF3), and use these to draw conclusions (AF5).

Key Words
ethanol, depressant, alcoholic, unit of alcohol

Answers from the student book

In-text questions	**A** ethanol **B** A person who is addicted to alcohol. **C** 14 units for adult women, 21 units for adult men **D** Any three from: stomach ulcers, heart disease, brain damage, liver damage (cirrhosis).
Activity	**Units of alcohol** One unit of alcohol = 10 ml pure alcohol. So, 200 ml of 10 % wine = 0.1 × 200 ml = 20 ml of pure alcohol. Units of alcohol in 200 ml of wine = 20 ÷ 10 = 2 units
Summary Questions	**1** ethanol, depressant, nervous, liver (4 marks) **2** Alcohol passes through to baby's bloodstream. It affects development of organs/brain/nervous system. This increases the risk of miscarriage, Fetal Alcohol Syndrome (FAS), stillbirth, premature birth, or low-weight babies. (4 marks) **3** Visual summary example answers (6 marks): Alcohol is a depressant. It affects the nervous system. Some people feel relaxed and happy, while others get aggressive and depressed. Alcohol slows reaction times. People under the influence are more likely to have an accident. Large amounts of alcohol can cause stomach ulcers, heart disease, brain damage, and liver damage. Drinking alcohol whilst pregnant affects the development of the fetus's organs. This increases the risk of miscarriage, FAS, stillbirth, premature birth, or low-weight babies.

Starter	Support/Extension	Resources
The effects of alcohol (5 min) Interactive resource where students describe the effects of alcohol by choosing words to fill in the gaps.	**Extension**: Students add to the list of effects provided.	**Interactive**: The effects of alcohol
Don't drink and drive! (10 min) Show students a video clip of an anti-drinking advert, or project an anti-drinking poster on the board. Ask students to discuss in groups why these adverts are necessary. Students then discuss possible effects of alcohol on the body.	**Extension**: Students discuss if the effects of alcohol vary for different types of people, especially pregnant women.	

Main	Support/Extension	Resources
Investigating the effects of alcohol on reaction times (40 min) Students carry out a short practical to find out their reaction times and compare the data obtained with others in the class and with secondary data about the reaction times of people who have consumed alcohol. Students then answer the questions that follow.	**Support**: The support sheet provides students with a partially filled results table and a graph grid, to help in presenting experimental data.	**Practical:** Investigating the effects of alcohol on reaction times **Skill sheet:** Calculating means

Plenary	Support/Extension	Resources
Checking reaction times (10 min) Use an online reaction-time test at the front of the class. (These are easily found through search engines on the Internet). Invite a group of students to try these out in front of the class. Reaction times can then be discussed with the class, including the conclusion from the practical of how alcohol affects reaction times. Discuss sources of error in the experiment, and how the online test improves the accuracy of results obtained. Students suggest differences in reaction times between different students in the class despite zero alcohol consumption.	**Extension:** Students should be encouraged to differentiate between random and systematic error, and offer ways to improve the method.	
Legal limits (5 min) After the experiment, take a class vote about the legal limit for alcohol and driving. Should it stay the same, be lowered, or be raised? The current legal limit is two to three units (depending on gender, body mass, and metabolism of ethanol). Students justify answers using their graphs.		

Homework		
Students design a poster or advert to persuade pregnant women not to drink alcohol. Scientific information about the effects of alcohol on the mother and fetus should be included.		

1.8 Smoking

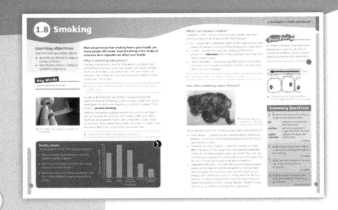

Biology NC link:

- the effects of 'recreational' drugs (including substance misuse) on behaviour, health, and life processes
- the effect of maternal lifestyle on the fetus through the placenta.

Working Scientifically NC link:

- interpret observations and data, including identifying patterns and using observations, measurements, and data to draw conclusions.

Band	Outcome	Checkpoint	
		Question	**Activity**
Developing	Name an effect of tobacco smoke on health (Level 4).	A, 1, 2	Maths, Starter 1, Main, Plenary 1, Plenary 2
	State whether or not tobacco smoke affects the development of a fetus (Level 3).	3	Starter 2, Main, Plenary 2, Homework
	Interpret secondary data and present this data on a bar chart (Level 4).		Main
Secure	Describe the effects of tobacco smoke on health (Level 5).	A, 1, 2, 4	Maths, Starter 1, Main, Plenary 1, Plenary 2
	Describe the effects of tobacco smoke on pregnancy (Level 5).	3	Starter 2, Main, Plenary 2, Homework
	Present secondary data using an appropriate method, interpreting this data to draw conclusions (Level 5).		Main
Extending	Explain how smoking causes disease (Level 7).	1, 2, 4	Starter 1, Main, Plenary 1, Plenary 2
	Explain which chemicals in tobacco smoke affect the development of a fetus (Level 7).	3	Starter 2, Main, Plenary 2, Homework
	Interpret and present secondary data in an appropriate manner, drawing conclusions, and extrapolating data from trends shown (Level 8).		Main

Maths

In both the student-book and main activities students interpret numerical data presented as charts, graphs, and tables to describe the links between smoking and illness.

Literacy

Students target their language and scientific knowledge for the public when making a leaflet on smoking for homework.

APP

Students use secondary data given (AF3) to explain how the evidence provided has contributed to the scientific understanding of smoking (AF1), and use this evidence to contribute towards a conclusion (AF5).

Key Words

passive smoking, stimulant

Answers from the student book

In-text questions	**A** Any three from: breathing conditions, cancer, strokes, heart attacks
	B Breathing in other people's smoke. **C** nicotine
Activity	**Deadly smoke**
	1 lung diseases **2** 1 200 000 − 900 000 = 300 000 **3** 1 000 000 ÷ 500 000 = 2; twice as likely

Summary Questions	
	1 Tar – contains chemicals which cause cancer.
	Nicotine – addictive and makes the heart beat faster.
	Carbon monoxide – reduces the amount of oxygen the blood can carry. (3 marks)
	2 To remove mucus, as cilia that would normally do this are paralysed by smoking. (2 marks)
	3 Two from:
	Increased risk of a miscarriage, cause low-birth-weight babies, affects fetal development. Carbon monoxide in cigarette smoke stops oxygen binding to haemoglobin, so less oxygen reaches baby.
	4 QWC question (6 marks). Example answers:
	Heart disease – arteries blocked, prevents blood flowing properly, causes heart attacks or strokes.
	Emphysema – weakens walls in alveoli/burst, reduces amount of oxygen supplied to blood, person becomes breathless.
	Respiratory infections – cilia paralysed, mucus flows into lungs, makes breathing hard, mucus in lungs cause infections.

Starter	Support/Extension	Resources
Deadly smoke (5 min) Interactive resource where students complete a gap fill on smoking. This is a good opportunity to gauge students' knowledge from PSHE or Citizenship sessions.	**Extension**: Students suggest other effects of smoking from prior knowledge.	**Interactive:** Deadly smoke
Effects on an unborn baby (10 min) Recap the effects of alcohol on a fetus. Allow students to work in small groups to discuss possible effects of smoking on a fetus. Walk around the room to ensure students consider the paths chemicals take, not just the effects. As a class, decide on the sequence of events between the mother smoking and the effect on the unborn baby.	**Support**: Give students sort cards with correct/incorrect statements on smoking during pregnancy. Students choose the correct statements and order them.	

Main	Support/Extension	Resources
Smoking statistics (40 min) Introduce the risks of smoking to health, including risks associated with the development of a fetus during pregnancy.	**Support**: An access sheet is available with reduced data for students to plot. Students are also told to draw a bar chart to display the data given, and are provided with hints to help them get started with the drawing and labelling of axes.	**Activity**: Smoking statistics
Show students photographs of smokers taken in the last 50 years, and ask students if they can spot the change in attitude towards smoking. Ask students to suggest why this may be the case. (Photographs are readily available on the Internet.)		**Skill sheet**: Drawing graphs
		Skill sheet: Choosing scales
Students then work through the activity sheet, presenting smoking statistics on a graph. They learn about several events from 1960 onwards that may have impacted on the decline of smokers in the UK, and answer the questions that follow.		

Plenary	Support/Extension	Resources
Smoking while pregnant (10 min) Students discuss the effects of smoking, and the consequences of smoking whilst pregnant. Students should work in pairs, then fours, before opening up as a class discussion.	**Extension**: Students hold a similar discussion for drinking, comparing effects of using both drugs, and relative severity of each effect.	
Key word pop-up (5 min) Give the definition of key words used in this lesson for students to write the correct key word on their mini-white board, holding it up as quickly as they can.	**Extension**: This activity can be extended to cover both smoking and drinking alcohol.	

Homework		
Students produce an information leaflet on the dangers of smoking. A section for pregnant women should be included.		

Checkpoint lesson routes

The route through this lesson can be determined using the Checkpoint assessment. Percentage pass marks are supplied in the Checkpoint teacher notes.

Route A (support)
Resource: B2 Chapter 1 Checkpoint: Revision

Students can work through the revision activity, supported by the rest of the group, and the teacher. There are a number of tasks relating to groups of outcomes outlined below.

Route B (extension)
Resource: B2 Chapter 1 Checkpoint: Extension

Students play the role of a nutritional advisor. They are given a nutritional diary to analyse, along with nutritional information and information on BMI. Students apply their existing knowledge and information provided to report on the health of the person's diary.

Progression to *secure*

No.	Developing outcome	Secure outcome	Making progress
1	Name some nutrients in a given diet.	Describe the components of a healthy diet.	Students may confuse nutrients and types of food. Stress that nutrients are the substances our bodies need to survive. Nutrients are present in different amounts in different foods.
2	Name the nutrients needed by the human body.	Explain the role of each nutrient in the body.	In Task 1, students use the explanations writing frame to meet this outcome.
3	State one potential problem for someone with an unhealthy diet.	Describe some health issues caused by an unhealthy diet.	Students will usually recognise obesity as a health issue, but may not fully describe the complications this could lead to. Students may also struggle with the less familiar situation of people being underweight. In Task 2, students match the risks with the cause.
4	State that different people require different amounts of energy.	Calculate the energy requirements of different people.	In Task 3, students consider the activity of two different people. They are given information on the energy they need each day for their activities, and then pick the correct diet for each person.
5	State what is meant by digestion.	Describe the process of digestion.	Provide students with four key words (breakdown, large, small, gut) and ask them to use these words to define digestion. Then supplement with additional words (enzymes, soluble, insoluble, mouth, stomach, etc.) and ask them where these words fit in. Additional support is provided in Task 4.
6	Name the main parts of the digestive system.	Describe the structure and function of the main parts of the digestive system.	Key diagrams are provided in Task 4 to help students consider the structure of parts of the digestive system, and how they are related to function. Remind students that they have met structures to increase surface area before (root hair cells in B1).
7	Name some enzymes used in digestion.	Describe the role of enzymes in digestion.	In Task 5, students are provided with diagrams to annotate with descriptions and key words.
8	State where bacteria are found in the digestive system.	Describe the role of bacteria in digestion.	Remind students of product marketing campaigns about 'friendly bacteria'. Can they describe the role of bacteria in digestion? Students may struggle describing exactly what bacteria do, and support is provided in Task 5.
9	State one effect of a drug on health or behaviour.	Describe the effects of drugs on health and behaviour.	In Task 6, students need to write responses to a number of letters sent into a magazine problem page. In their responses they need to describe the effects of drugs, alcohol, and tobacco on different groups of people. A checklist is provided to help students with their responses.
10	Name an effect of alcohol on health or behaviour.	Describe the effect of alcohol on health and behaviour.	Students may need reminding that alcoholic drinks contain a drug. Students can then complete Task 6.
11	State that alcohol affects conception and pregnancy.	Describe the effect that alcohol has on conception and pregnancy.	Remind students that substances pass from the mother to the fetus through the placenta (covered in B1). Students can then complete Task 6.

| 12 | Name an effect of tobacco smoke on health. | Describe the effect of tobacco smoke on health. | Students can complete Task 6. |
| 13 | State whether or not tobacco smoke affects the development of a fetus. | Describe the effect of tobacco smoke on pregnancy. | Students can complete Task 6. |

Answers to end-of-chapter questions

1 carbohydrates – provide energy proteins – used for growth and repair lipids – provide a store of energy and are used to insulate the body vitamins and minerals – needed in small amounts to keep you healthy (4 marks)

2a gullet (1 mark)   **b** Nutrients are absorbed into the blood. (1 mark)   **c** U (1 mark)

d Any two from: churns/mixes the food, contains acid, contains enzymes, breaks down/digests food. (2 marks)

3a pestle and mortar (1 mark)   **b** Any two from: wear eye protection, wash hands immediately if chemicals come into contact with skin, wear gloves, keep alcohol away from naked flame. (2 marks)

c Add copper sulfate solution and sodium hydroxide solution to the food solution. If the solution turns purple, protein is present. (3 marks)

4a Medicinal drugs have a medical benefit to health, recreational drugs are taken for enjoyment. (2 marks)

b Drugs alter chemical reactions in the body. (1 mark)

c Stimulants speed up the nervous system, for example, caffeine, nicotine, ecstasy, cocaine. Depressants slow down the nervous system, for example, alcohol, cannabis, heroin. (2 marks)

5a Enzymes break large molecules down into smaller molecules. (1 mark)

b Enzymes speed up reactions without being used up. (2 marks)

c Example answers (4 marks)
Both are broken down from large molecules into smaller ones. Both are broken down by enzymes. Both are broken down in the stomach and small intestine.
Carbohydrate is broken down by carbohydrase whereas protein is broken down by protease. Carbohydrates are broken down into sugar molecules whereas protein is broken down into amino acids. Carbohydrates are also broken down/digested in the mouth.

d Bile breaks fat into small droplets. Lipase digests fat into fatty acids and glycerol. (3 marks) Do not accept bile digests fat.

6 This is a QWC question. Students should be marked on the use of good English, organisation of information, spelling and grammar, and correct use of specialist scientific terms. The best answers will provide a full explanation of issues with conception and fetal development (maximum of 6 marks).
Examples of correct scientific points:
Alcohol can reduce fertility in men and women.
Alcohol can reduce the number of sperm a man produces, reducing the chances of the egg being fertilised.
When people drink alcoholic drinks, ethanol is absorbed into the blood stream.
The ethanol can have damaging effects on the development of the organs and nervous system of the fetus.
This is because substances are passed from the bloodstream of the mother to the fetus through the placenta.
This can cause Fetal Alcohol Syndrome (FAS), which affects the way the brain develops.
Other complications can include miscarriage, still birth, and low baby weights/premature birth.

Answer guide for Big Write

Developing	Secure	Extending
1–2 marks	3–4 marks	5–6 marks
The article is not presented very logically. However, the student has stated at least one harmful effect of smoking, drinking, and taking drugs.	The article is clearly presented. The student has explained at least one harmful effect of smoking, drinking, and taking drugs. Some arguments are clearly backed up with scientific fact.	The article is clearly presented and engaging. The student has explained a number of harmful effects of smoking, drinking, and taking drugs. Arguments are backed up with scientific fact, and explanations are clear and relevant.

kerboodle

| B2 Chapter 1 Checkpoint assessment (automarked) |
| B2 Chapter 1 Checkpoint: Revision |
| B2 Chapter 1 Checkpoint: Extension |
| B2 Chapter 1 Progress task (Literacy) |

2.1 Photosynthesis

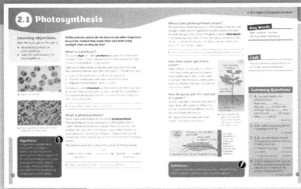

Biology NC link:

- the reactants in, and products of, photosynthesis, and a word summary for photosynthesis
- the dependence of almost all life on Earth on the ability of photosynthetic organisms, such as plants and algae, to use sunlight in photosynthesis to build organic molecules that are an essential energy store and to maintain levels of oxygen and carbon dioxide in the atmosphere.

Working Scientifically NC link:

- use appropriate techniques, apparatus, and materials during fieldwork and laboratory work, paying attention to health and safety.

Band	Outcome	Checkpoint	
		Question	Activity
Developing	State where photosynthesis occurs in a plant (Level 3).	C	Starter 2, Plenary 1, Homework
	State the products of photosynthesis (Level 4).	B, 1	Main, Plenary 1, Homework
	Carry out an experiment to test for the presence of starch in a leaf (Level 4).		Main
Secure	Describe the process of photosynthesis (Level 6).	B, C, 1, 4	Starter 1, Plenary 1, Homework
	State the word equation for photosynthesis (Level 6).	B	Plenary 1, Homework
	Carry out and record observations for an experiment to test for the presence of starch in a leaf (Level 5).		Main
Extending	Explain the importance of photosynthesis in the food chain (Level 7).	A, 2	Plenary 2
	Explain how the plant obtains the reactants for photosynthesis (Level 7).	4	Plenary 1, Homework
	Carry out and record observations for an experiment to test for the presence of starch in a leaf, explaining results obtained (Level 7).		Main

Literacy

Students use scientific terminology when explaining the process of photosynthesis, its links to food chains and food webs, and when describing and explaining their observations in the experiment to test for the presence of starch in leaves.

APP

Students present experimental observations appropriately (AF3), use data to support a conclusion (AF5), while reducing risks in their experiment by writing a risk assessment (AF4).

Key Words

algae, producer, consumer, photosynthesis, chlorophyll

Answers from the student book

In-text questions	**A** An organism that makes its own food. **B** carbon dioxide + water $\xrightarrow{\text{light}}$ glucose + oxygen **C** chloroplasts
Activity	**Hypothesis** Credit hypotheses along the lines of: If a plant is placed in the dark for a week, photosynthesis will decrease/ glucose and oxygen will not be produced. Students should include a suitable plan for testing this hypothesis. **Definitions** Producer – organism that makes its own food. Consumer – organism that has to eat other organisms to gain energy. Photosynthesis – process where plants make their own food.

Summary Questions	1 algae, producers, photosynthesis, carbon dioxide, glucose, light (6 marks) 2 Photosynthesis provides energy for plants to grow. Animals cannot make their own food. Animals have to eat plants to gain energy. (3 marks) 3a Yes because sunlight is available. (1 mark) b No because no sunlight is available. (1 mark) c No because there is no sunlight. There are no chloroplasts in the root hair cells. (2 marks) 4 QWC question (6 marks). Example answers: Carbon dioxide and water are the reactants. Carbon dioxide enters through the stomata in the leaves. Water enters through root/root hair cells by diffusion/osmosis. Water travels up the xylem to leaves (transpiration). Light is also required for photosynthesis to occur. Light is trapped in chlorophyll/chloroplasts in leaf cells. Oxygen and glucose are the products. Oxygen comes out through stomata. Glucose is taken to all cells in the plant (via the phloem). The plant cells use glucose to provide energy.

Starter	Support/Extension	Resources
What I already know (10 min) Students work in pairs to think up key words they know about photosynthesis. They write a sentence for each key word. Open up as a class discussion. Using the most commonly identified key words and definitions, can students produce a brief description of photosynthesis? This is a good opportunity to gauge students knowledge as some schools may have covered photosynthesis in KS2.	**Support**: Provide students with prompt questions to aid discussion.	
Testing for starch (5 min) Introduce that plants make starch as their food source. Recap the chemical test for starch and ask students why a leaf cannot be dipped in iodine to test for starch. This will revise food tests and the structure of plant cells.	**Support**: Show students a plant cell to label as a hint.	

Main	Support/Extension	Resources
Testing a leaf for starch (40 min) Introduce the process of photosynthesis, the word equation, and the importance of photosynthesis in the food chain. Students follow instructions on the practical sheet to carry out an experiment to test a leaf for starch. They write a risk assessment for the experiment and answer the questions that follow. Students can compare observations from different types of leaves (variegated or coloured) if time.	**Support**: The support sheet provides a table to help with the risk assessment. **Extension**: Students use variegated leaves or coloured leaves from a coleus, so observations are harder to interpret.	**Practical**: Testing a leaf for starch

Plenary	Support/Extension	Resources
Photosynthesis reaction (5 min) Students complete the word equation using the words provided on the interactive resource. They must also complete facts about the different substances involved in this word equation.	**Extension**: Students can suggest other facts to add to the interactive resource.	**Interactive**: Photosynthesis reaction
Photosynthesis and life (10 min) Provide the class with the statement 'Photosynthesis is vital for all life'. Divide the class into pairs or small groups and give them five minutes to decide on as many ideas as possible to support this claim. Discuss their suggestions as a class.	**Support**: Prompt students to think about food chains and food webs. **Extension**: Encourage students to use as many scientific words as possible.	

Homework	Support/Extension	
Students research the anatomy of a plant, drawing a labelled diagram of the major organs. They add annotations to explain where the raw materials for photosynthesis enter, where the reaction occurs, and where the products may go. Students include the word equation for photosynthesis.	**Extension**: As a challenge, ask students to find and balance the formula equation for photosynthesis.	

2.2 Leaves

Biology NC link:
- the adaptations of leaves for photosynthesis
- the role of leaf stomata in gas exchange in plants.

Working Scientifically NC link:
- make and record observations and measurements using a range of methods for different investigations; and evaluate the reliability of methods and suggest possible improvements.

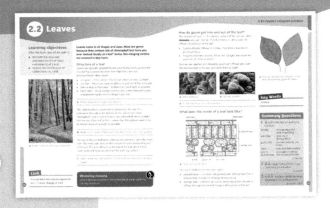

Band	Outcome	Checkpoint	
		Question	**Activity**
Developing	Name the main structures of a leaf (Level 4).	1	WS, Starter 1, Starter 2, Main, Plenary 2, Homework
	State the function of the chloroplasts in a leaf (Level 4).	1	Starter 1, Plenary 1, Homework
	Use observations from the underside of a leaf to label a diagram (Level 4).		Main
Secure	Describe the structure and function of the main components of a leaf (Level 6).	C, D, 1, 2	WS, Starter 1, Starter 2, Main, Plenary 1, Plenary 2, Homework
	Explain the distribution of the chloroplasts in a leaf (Level 6).	B, 3	Starter 1, Plenary 1, Homework
	Make observations of stomata from the underside of the leaf, and record observations as a labelled diagram (Level 5).		Main
Extending	Explain how the structures of the leaf make it well adapted for photosynthesis (Level 7).	B, C, 2, 3	Starter 1, Starter 2, Main, Plenary 1, Plenary 2, Homework
	Explain the role of chloroplasts in photosynthesis (Level 7).	3	Starter 1, Plenary 1, Homework
	Make observations of stomata from the underside of the leaf, and record as a labelled diagram with annotations (Level 7).		Main

Literacy
Students use scientific terms in context when describing the adaptations of a leaf for photosynthesis, and when describing observations in their experiment to explain the role of stomata in photosynthesis.

APP
Students record observations appropriately (AF3), and draw conclusions from data obtained (AF5).

Key Words
stomata

Answers from the student book

In-text questions	**A** They contain chlorophyll.
	B top of the leaf
	C To reduce evaporation of water.
	D They allow gases to diffuse into and out of the leaf. They close to prevent water loss.
Activity	**Observing stomata**
	For the labelled diagram of the underside of a leaf, labels should include: stomata, guard cells, veins, and, possibly, the waxy cuticle

Summary Questions	1 stomata – allow gases to diffuse into and out of the leaf
	waxy layer – reduces amount of water evaporating
	guard cells – open and close stomata
	veins – bring water to cells in leaf
	cells in palisade layer – main site of photosynthesis (5 marks)
	2 To prevent water evaporating. (1 mark)
	3 QWC question (6 marks). Example answers:
	Leaves contain chlorophyll, which traps light. Leaves are thin, which allows gases to diffuse in and out of the leaf easily. Leaves have a large surface area to absorb as much light as possible. Leaves have veins/xylem to transport water to cells. Leaves have a palisade layer/cells with more chloroplasts near the top of the leaf, to maximise the absorption of sunlight. Leaves have stomata to allow carbon dioxide into (and oxygen out of) the leaf.

kerboodle

Starter	Support/Extension	Resources
Leafy cross-section (10 min) Provide students with a diagram of a cross-section of a leaf. Students use corresponding student-book spread to add labels to the major parts of the leaf. Labels include names and descriptions of the functions.	**Support**: Provide students with label lines already added to the diagram.	
External features of a leaf (10 min) Students work in pairs. Provide each pair with a leaf and a hand lens. Students carefully observe the external features of the leaf, producing a labelled diagram. Teacher input will be required for the labelling stage.	**Extension**: Students suggest functions of the external parts before teacher input is given.	

Main	Support/Extension	Resources
Observing the stomata of a leaf (35 min) Briefly recap on the process of photosynthesis and give adaptations of the leaf for this process. Students should explain why each adaptation aids photosynthesis. Then show students a diagram of the cross-section of a leaf and explain the functions of each part. Although it is important to focus on the stomata and guard cells, the two layers of the leaf should also be mentioned. Students then carry out a short practical using a microscope to observe stomata, and answer the questions that follow.	**Support**: Project a microscope image of stomata onto the board to show students what they are looking for. The support sheet also contains a diagram of stomata for students to label and annotate. **Extension**: Encourage students to calculate magnification used, adding this to their diagrams.	**Practical**: Observing the stomata of a leaf

Plenary	Support/Extension	Resources
Leafy adaptations (10 min) Students link adaptations of a leaf to its function in photosynthesis using the interactive resource. Additional questions can be added to test for further knowledge and understanding.	**Extension**: Students answer additional questions on each of the main adaptations. Questions relate to diffusion, transpiration, names of the two veins, and so on.	**Interactive**: Leafy adaptations
Gas exchange role play (10 min) Divide the class into groups of at least five. In each group, two students represent guard cells. The rest of the students play out the different gases exchanged through the stoma. Students explain the roles of each person in terms of gas exchange. This activity works best in mixed-ability groups.	**Support**: Give students the roles of guard cells and carbon dioxide. These are the easiest to explain.	

Homework		
Students write a detailed account of photosynthesis, summarising key points they have learnt so far. It should include the sections of leaves where photosynthesis occurs, where reactants and products come from and go to, and adaptations of leaves to maximise efficiency. They may include labelled diagrams.		

2.3 Plant minerals

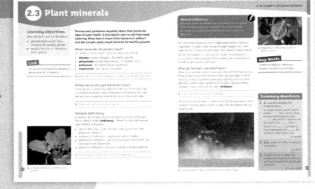

Biology NC link:
- plants making carbohydrates in their leaves by photosynthesis and gaining minerals, nutrients, and water from the soil via their roots.

Working Scientifically NC link:
- undertake basic data analysis including simple statistical techniques.

Band	Outcome	Checkpoint	
		Question	**Activity**
Developing	Name the minerals required by plants (Level 4).	A, 1	Lit, Main, Plenary 1, Plenary 2, Homework
	State that nitrates are essential for plant growth (Level 4).	A, 1, 2	Lit, Main, Plenary 1, Plenary 2, Homework
	Record measurements of plant growth (Level 4).		Main
Secure	Describe how a plant uses minerals for healthy growth (Level 6).	1, 2, 3	Lit, Main, Plenary 1, Plenary 2, Homework
	Explain the role of nitrates in plant growth (Level 6).	1, 2, 3	Lit, Main, Plenary 1, Plenary 2, Homework
	Record measurements in a table, and calculate arithmetic means of results (Level 6).		Main
Extending	Explain deficiency symptoms in plants (Level 7).	3	Lit, Main, Plenary 1, Plenary 2, Homework
	Explain how proteins are made for plant growth (Level 8).	2, 3	Lit, Main, Plenary 1, Plenary 2, Homework
	Record measurements in a table, and calculate arithmetic means of results, giving answers to the correct number of significant figures (Level 7).		Main

Maths
Students use their understanding of number scales to measure the heights of seedlings during their practical. They then calculate arithmetic means using data obtained, and plot a suitable graph to display their results.

Literacy
Students use scientific terms when explaining plant deficiencies in the student-book activity. They also target their scientific knowledge to the general public when writing an advert for a fictional fertiliser.

APP
Students display experimental data appropriately in tables and as graphs (AF3), before using data obtained to draw conclusions about the importance of fertilisers in plant growth (AF5).

Key Words
nitrates, phosphates, potassium, magnesium, deficiency, fertiliser

Answers from the student book

In-text questions	**A** nitrates, phosphates, potassium, and magnesium **B** Dissolved in soil water, absorbed through root hair cells. **C** A plant is not receiving enough of a particular mineral. **D** Chemical product containing plant minerals.
Activity	**Mineral deficiency** Leaflet should include prompts for farmers in their diagnosis of plants using a labelled diagram of a healthy plant. Prompts include nitrate deficiency (plant will have poor growth and older leaves are yellowed), magnesium deficiency (plant leaves will turn yellow), phosphorus deficiency (plant will have poor root growth, and younger leaves look purple), and potassium deficiency (plant has yellow leaves with dead patches).

Summary Questions	1 minerals, hair, xylem, magnesium, nitrates (5 marks)
	2 Nitrates make amino acids, amino acids join together to make proteins, proteins needed for growth. (3 marks)
	3 QWC question (6 marks). Example answers:
	Plants take minerals from the soil. Minerals are absorbed into the plant through root hairs. Plants use minerals for growth. Plants normally return minerals back to the soil when they die/leaves are shed. If crops are removed, the minerals are not returned to the soil. Fertilisers contain minerals. Examples are nitrates, phosphates, and potassium. A supply of minerals is needed for healthy plant growth. Nitrates are used to make amino acids, and subsequently proteins. Magnesium is needed to make chlorophyll.

kerboodle

Starter	Support/Extension	Resources
An alternative question-led lesson is also available.		**Question-led lesson**: Plant minerals
Introducing plant minerals (5 min) Write the chemical formulae of some nitrates and phosphates on the board, and the chemical symbols for potassium and magnesium. Students work out the elements required by plants using the formulae provided, and suggest what each element helps the plant to do.	**Support**: Students use the Periodic Table in the student book to help them identify the names of elements involved.	
What's in a fertiliser? (5 min) Show the class a box of garden fertiliser, or project an image of the contents on the board. Ask students to identify what chemicals are found in the fertiliser, why fertilisers are used, and compare what happens to plants in a natural woodland (without fertiliser) with plants on a farm.	**Extension**: Show students different types of fertiliser (with different NPK ratios) to discuss differences between fertilisers.	

Main	Support/Extension	Resources
Investigating the effect of fertilisers on the growth of seedlings (40 min) Introduce the four minerals needed for plant growth and their specific functions using the term mineral deficiency. Discuss why fertilisers are not needed for plants to flourish in natural woodland but are required in large quantities on farmland. Students are then given two trays of seedlings (one treated with fertiliser, the other without) to compare. They choose an appropriate variable for comparison, record results in a suitable table, plot an appropriate graph to display their results, and answer the questions that follow. Allow five minutes at the end of this activity to discuss conclusions and the importance of calculating means in an experiment like this one.	**Support**: A partially filled results table is provided on the accompanying support sheet. Students may require prompting towards measuring the heights of seedlings as their comparison.	**Practical**: Investigating the effect of fertilisers on the growth of seedlings **Skill sheet**: Hypothesis **Skill sheet**: Recording results **Skill sheet**: Calculating means **Skill sheet**: Drawing graphs

Plenary	Support/Extension	Resources
Mineral crossword (10 min) Interactive resource where students complete a crossword on the mineral requirements of plants. Can also be done in reverse, where students are given the words and have to come up with clues.	**Support**: Students to work in small groups.	**Interactive**: Mineral crossword
Gardeners advice line (10 min) Project photographs that show different plant deficiencies on the board. For example, yellow leaves, wilted plant, or purple leaves. Ask students to diagnose what is wrong with the plant, and suggest a remedy accordingly.	**Extension**: If Starter 2 was used this can be coupled with the different types of fertiliser. Students pick the most efficient fertiliser for each diagnosis.	

Homework		
Students write an advert for a commercial fertiliser, naming the minerals involved and explaining how each mineral is important to the plant.		

2.4 Chemosynthesis

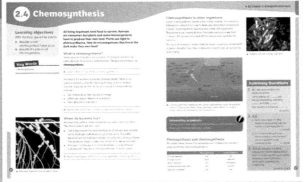

Biology NC link:

- chemosynthesis in bacteria and other organisms.

Working Scientifically NC link:

- understand that scientific methods and theories develop as earlier explanations are modified to take account of new evidence and ideas.

Band	Outcome	Checkpoint	
		Question	Activity
Developing	Name an organism which carries out chemosynthesis (Level 4).	C, 2	Lit, Starter 2, Main, Plenary 1, Homework
	State the energy source for chemosynthesis (Level 4).	A, B, 1, 2	Lit, Starter 2, Main, Plenary 1, Homework
	State how the scientific community view the discovery of chemosynthesis (Level 4).		Main, Plenary 2
Secure	Describe where chemosynthesis takes place (Level 5).	2, 3	Lit, Starter 2, Main, Plenary 2, Homework
	Describe the process of chemosynthesis (Level 6).	A, B, 1	Lit, Starter 2, Main, Homework
	Describe how the view of chemosynthesis by the scientific community changed with time (Level 6).		Main, Plenary 2
Extending	Explain how some chemosynthetic organisms form symbiotic relationships (Level 8).	3	Lit, Main, Homework
	Compare similarities and differences between photosynthesis and chemosynthesis (Level 7).	3	Starter 2, Main, Plenary 1
	Explain why the view of chemosynthesis by the scientific community changed with time (Level 7).		Main, Plenary 2

Literacy

In the student-book activity students research an organism that carries out chemosynthesis and present this to a partner.

Students are also required to read and extract information from text provided, organise ideas independently, and use appropriate scientific terms when explaining chemosynthesis in answering questions.

APP

Students draw conclusions about chemosynthesis using a range of sources (AF5).

Key Words

chemosynthesis

Answers from the student book

In-text questions	**A** Using a chemical reaction to produce glucose.
	B carbon dioxide
	C sulfur bacteria and nitrogen bacteria
Activity	**Interesting organisms**
	Credit research on a different chemosynthetic organism, to be presented to a partner, for example, iron bacteria or methanobacteria.

Summary Questions	**1** bacteria, reactions, glucose, chemosynthesis (4 marks)
	2a sulfur bacteria or nitrogen bacteria (1 mark)
	b Light is not available on the sea floor/underground, so they do not possess chloroplasts, therefore photosynthesis cannot take place. (1 mark)
	3 QWC question (6 marks). Example answers:
	Seaweed are producers.
	They use photosynthesis to create glucose.
	Photosynthesis is powered by light energy from the Sun.
	carbon dioxide + water → glucose + oxygen
	Tubeworms are consumers.
	This means they must eat other organisms to survive.
	Bacteria within tubeworms produce glucose by chemosynthesis.
	Light is not required for chemosynthesis.
	Energy for chemosynthesis comes from chemical reactions.
	carbon dioxide + water + hydrogen sulfide → glucose + sulfur compounds

kerboodle

Starter	Support/Extension	Resources
What's on the menu for tubeworms? (5 min) Show images of organisms like tubeworms. Explain that they have no stomach and no light source. Ask students to suggest ways they may produce food. Allow students to pair-share before collating suggestions from students and revealing the answer (chemosynthetic bacteria live in their stomach).		
What is chemosynthesis? (10 min) Show a short video from the Internet that defines the process of chemosynthesis, and shows some of the organisms which make use of this process. (The video 'Nautilus Behind the Science – Chemosynthesis' contains good examples and is readily available on YouTube.) Hold a short class discussion about what students have seen, drawing particularly on the similarities and differences between photosynthesis and chemosynthesis.	**Extension**: Students should suggest reasons why scientists have known about photosynthesis for years, whereas the process of chemosynthesis has only recently been discovered.	

Main	Support/Extension	Resources
Dinner in the dark (40 min) Formally introduce the idea of chemosynthesis and give examples of chemosynthetic organisms. Give out the information sheet for this activity for students to read more about this process, before they answer the questions that follow. Students may use the student book to help them answer the questions.	**Support**: A support sheet is available where the information is presented using a simpler text. **Extension**: Students can use more advanced textbooks when giving further examples of chemosynthesis, and when explaining the idea of mutualism.	**Activity**: Dinner in the dark

Plenary	Support/Extension	Resources
What's the difference? (10 min) Students summarise the similarities and differences between chemosynthesis and photosynthesis by sorting statements provided on the interactive resource into the appropriate process. **How views change** (5 min) Discuss the importance of changing views in science as different theories and evidence come to light. Ask students to imagine if chemosynthesis hadn't been discovered, would scientists understand how ecosystems can exist on the ocean floor?	**Extension**: Further questions can be posed to students that recap the adaptations of plants to photosynthesis.	**Interactive**: What's the difference?

Homework	Support/Extension	
Students write a short poem about chemosynthesis. The poem should include: • name of organism • location of chemosynthesis • description of how the organism carries out chemosynthesis • summary of chemosynthesis.	**Extension**: Poems should include a mention of mutualism in organisms.	

Biology NC link:

- aerobic respiration in living organisms, including the breakdown of organic molecules to enable all the other chemical processes necessary for life
- a word summary for aerobic respiration.

Working Scientifically NC link:

- select, plan, and carry out the most appropriate types of scientific enquiries to test predictions, including identifying independent, dependent, and control variables, where appropriate.

Band	Outcome	Checkpoint	
		Question	Activity
Developing	State the requirements for aerobic respiration (Level 4).	B, 1	Lit, Main, Plenary 1, Plenary 2
	Give the name of the process where energy is released in cells (Level 4).	A, 1	Lit, Main, Plenary 1, Plenary 2
	Plan an experiment to measure breathing rates (Level 4).		Main
Secure	State the word equation for aerobic respiration (Level 5).	B	Starter 2, Main, Plenary 2
	Describe the process of respiration (Level 6).	1–3	Lit, Starter 2, Main, Plenary 2, Homework
	Plan an investigation to measure the effect of exercise on breathing rates (Level 6).		Main
Extending	Explain how the reactants for respiration get into the cells (Level 7).	D, 2, 3	Main, Plenary 2, Homework
	Explain the process of aerobic respiration (Level 7).	2, 3	Main, Plenary 2, Homework
	Plan an investigation to explain the effect of exercise on respiration rates (Level 8).		Main

Maths
Students may be required to calculate arithmetic means if they carry out repeats in their experiment.

Literacy
Students use scientific terminology to plan a method for investigating the effect of exercise on breathing rate, and analyse data obtained to draw a valid conclusion.

APP
Students plan an investigation to investigate the effect of exercise on breathing rate (AF4), present experimental data appropriately in tables (AF3), and draw conclusions from results obtained (AF5).

Key Words
aerobic respiration, plasma, haemoglobin

Answers from the student book

In-text questions	**A** (aerobic) respiration
	B glucose + oxygen → carbon dioxide + water (+ energy)
	C in the mitochondria
	D red blood cells or haemoglobin
	E plasma
Activity	**Defining respiration**
	Answers should include a definition and a description of aerobic respiration. Students could include the word equation for aerobic respiration.
	Students should swap answers with a partner, and discuss ways to improve their answers.

Summary Questions	
	1 mitochondria, respiration, glucose, energy, water (5 marks)
	2 Aerobic respiration occurs in the mitochondria. Mitochondria are found in cells. Oxygen reacts with glucose. It releases carbon dioxide and water, together with energy. (4 marks)
	3 QWC question (6 marks). Example answers:
	Inhaling fills alveoli in the lungs with oxygen. Oxygen diffuses into the bloodstream. Oxygen is carried to the cells in the red blood cells/haemoglobin. Glucose is taken in through food. Food is digested and glucose is absorbed through the wall of the small intestine. Glucose is carried to the cells in the blood (plasma). Respiration occurs in the mitochondria of cells, releasing carbon dioxide and water. Waste carbon dioxide is carried to the lungs in the blood plasma. Carbon dioxide is exhaled. Excess water is lost as water vapour in exhaled breath, or in urine.

kerboodle

Starter	Support/Extension	Resources
Releasing energy from fuels (5 min) Demonstrate the burning of food (e.g., sugar or custard powder) by sprinkling this over a Bunsen flame. Students give observations from this reaction in a class discussion, linking their observations to exothermic changes and the transfer of energy from food, and therefore why we eat.	**Extension**: Ask students to suggest if this is the way our cells release energy from food.	
Energy for athletes (10 min) Show a video clip from the Internet of an athlete running a 100-metre sprint. Ask students what the athlete needs to release energy. Their answers should revolve around food/fuel/glucose. Ask students to predict the changes in breathing rate during exercise and why this happens. This discussion should relate to respiration where possible.	**Extension**: Students should be able to construct a simple word equation for (aerobic) respiration based on the information provided in the class discussion.	

Main	Support/Extension	Resources
Investigating the effect of exercise on breathing rates (40 min) Introduce the idea of aerobic respiration in the mitochondria of cells. Discuss where reactants come from and where products go afterwards. Show students the word equation for aerobic respiration, and ask them to compare this to the word equation of photosynthesis. (They should notice that aerobic respiration is the reverse of photosynthesis.) Students then plan an investigation to measure the effect of exercise on breathing rates. If time, hold a class discussion after the experiment for groups to evaluate the success of their experimental procedure and suggest ways to improve their experiments.	**Support**: An access sheet is available with prompts to help students write their hypothesis and method. This sheet also includes a partially filled results table and simpler questions to answer.	**Practical**: Investigating the effect of exercise on breathing rates **Skill sheet:** Planning investigations **Skill sheet:** Recording results

Plenary	Support/Extension	Resources
Aerobic respiration (10 min) Students use clues provided to complete a crossword on the key words of this topic.	**Extension**: Students suggest other key words learnt this lesson, and provide hints for them.	**Interactive**: Aerobic respiration
The respiring athlete (5 min) Students draw a human outline on mini-whiteboards, with arrows in and out of the body. They label the arrows with the reactants and products of respiration. Students give the word equation of respiration.	**Extension**: Students explain the process of respiration, discussing the organs involved	

Homework	Support/Extension	
Design a poster that tracks energy from the Sun, through photosynthesis into sugars, through the diet in consumers, and finally released in respiration to its final use in muscle action. Posters should be fully labelled and annotations should be included to give a brief description of each process.	**Extension**: Students should include detailed descriptions of photosynthesis, digestion, and respiration.	

2.6 Anaerobic respiration

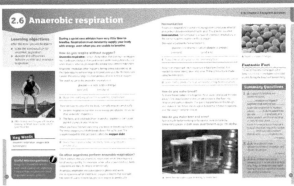

Biology NC link:

- anaerobic respiration in living organisms, including the breakdown of organic molecules to enable all the other chemical processes necessary for life
- the process of anaerobic respiration in humans and micro-organisms, including fermentation, and a word summary for anaerobic respiration
- the differences between aerobic and anaerobic respiration in terms of the reactants, the products formed, and the implications for the organism.

Working Scientifically NC link:

- evaluate data, showing awareness of potential sources of random and systematic error.

Band	Outcome	Checkpoint	
		Question	Activity
Developing	State the products of anaerobic respiration (Level 4).	A, 1	Lit, Main 1, Plenary 1, Plenary 2
	State one difference between aerobic and anaerobic respiration (Level 4).	B, 2	Plenary 1
↓	Identify one source of error in data collected (Level 4).		Main 1
Secure	State the word equation for anaerobic respiration (Level 6).	A, C	Starter 1, Main 1, Plenary 2
	Describe the differences between aerobic and anaerobic respiration (Level 6).	B, 2, 3	Plenary 1
↓	Evaluate data collected, suggesting possible sources of error (Level 6).		Main 1
Extending	Explain the uses of the products from anaerobic respiration (Level 7).		Lit, Main 1, Plenary 1
	Explain the differences between the two types of respiration (Level 7).	B, 2, 3	Plenary 1
↓	Evaluate data collected, showing awareness of potential sources of random and systematic errors (Level 8).		Main 1

Maths
Students obtain numerical data in their practical for which they must calculate arithmetic means. They then present their results on a suitable graph.

Literacy
Students use scientific terminology to describe and explain trends and conclusions from their experiment.

APP
Students carry out an experiment and record numerical data as a table and a graph (AF3). They then draw conclusions from the results obtained (AF5), and discuss possible errors in the experiment (AF4).

Key Words
anaerobic respiration, oxygen debt, fermentation

Answers from the student book

In-text questions	**A** glucose → lactic acid (+ energy)
	B Aerobic respiration releases more energy and doesn't cause muscle cramps (from lactic acid).
	C glucose → ethanol + carbon dioxide (+ energy)
	D bread, beer, wine
Activity	**Useful microorganisms** Credit correct description of how anaerobic respiration is used to make bread, beer, or wine.

Summary Questions	1 anaerobic, oxygen, energy, lactic acid, cramp, fermentation, ethanol (7 marks)
	2 Anaerobic respiration is without oxygen, produces lactic acid, does not produce water, produces less energy per glucose molecule. Aerobic respiration is with oxygen, does not produce lactic acid, does produce water, has more energy per glucose molecule. (3 marks)
	3 Example answers (6 marks):
	A marathon runner requires energy over a long period of time. A sprinter requires a lot of energy in a short period of time. A person can only respire anaerobically for a short period of time but can respire aerobically for a long period of time. A sprinter requires extra energy for a short period of time. A sprinter cannot take in enough oxygen to respire aerobically to produce the required amount of energy. If a runner respires anaerobically for a longer period of time, lactic acid would build up in their muscles. This would cause cramp.

Starter	Support/Extension	Resources
The exhausted sprinter (5 min) Show a video clip of a sprinter who becomes exhausted, pulls up in pain, or show images of footballers who have pulled up with cramp. Students suggest what has happened to the bodies of these sports people. Introduce the idea of anaerobic respiration in short bursts to supply energy without the need for oxygen, making lactic acid as a by-product.	**Extension**: Students should be able to use the description of anaerobic respiration to write a word equation.	
Useful respiration (10 min) Recap briefly on aerobic respiration and why it is useful. Show images of bread, beer, and wine and ask students to suggest links between the three. Then introduce a second type of respiration: anaerobic.	**Support**: Students may be prompted to think about yeast as a living organism.	

Main	Support/Extension	Resources
Investigating the rate of fermentation (30 min) Introduce the word equation for anaerobic respiration for students to interpret. Students give comparisons between aerobic and anaerobic respiration before discussing uses of anaerobic respiration, in particular fermentation. Students carry out an experiment to investigate the effect of changing the concentration of glucose on the rate of fermentation. You may wish to save time by splitting the class into at least five groups, so each group carries out the experiment for one concentration. If this is done, allow time for students to collate results from other groups. This can be done at the front of the class. Students then answer the questions on their practical sheet.	**Support**: The accompanying support sheet includes a suggested results table.	**Practical**: Investigating the rate of fermentation **Skill sheet**: Calculating means **Skill sheet**: Drawing graphs
Types of error (10 min) The difference between systematic and random errors can easily be demonstrated by the following experiment. Issue students with stopwatches and they time how long it takes for a piece of paper to fall to the ground. Hold the piece of paper in a horizontal position for the first test, and repeat with the piece of paper in the vertical position. Errors in this demonstration are the way the paper was held (systematic) and human error in recording the time taken (random).	**Extension**: Encourage students to discuss the effect of making repeat measurements on errors.	

Plenary	Support/Extension	Resources
True or false? (10 min) Students sort statements about respiration in the interactive resource as being true or false. Students correct the false statements.	**Extension**: Students should write statements on mini-whiteboards for the class to categorise (and correct if false).	**Interactive**: True or false?
Respiration equations (5 min) Issue cards with all the words and arrows necessary for the three equations for respiration (aerobic, anaerobic, fermentation). Students make the three equations by arranging the cards.		

Homework		
Complete the questions on the practical sheet, then find a recipe for brewing beer or baking bread. They annotate it with the scientific processes involved.		
An alternative WebQuest homework activity is also available on Kerboodle where students research food products made with microorganisms.		**WebQuest**: Microorganisms in the food industry

2.7 Food chains and webs

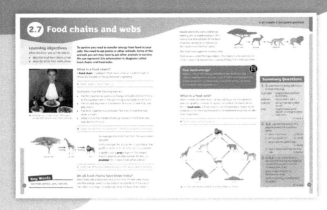

Biology NC link:

- the interdependence of organisms in an ecosystem, including food webs and insect pollinated crops.

Band	Outcome	Checkpoint	
		Question	Activity
Developing ↓	State the definition of a food chain (Level 4).	A, 1	Starter 1, Starter 2, Main, Plenary 2
	State the definition of a food web (Level 4).	D, 1	Main, Plenary 2
Secure ↓	Describe what food chains show (Level 5).	C, 1, 3	Starter 1, Starter 2, Main, Plenary 1, Plenary 2, Homework
	Describe what food webs show (Level 5).	2	Main, Plenary 1, Homework
Extending ↓	Explain the link between food chains and energy (Level 7).	1, 3	Maths, Main
	Explain why a food web gives a more accurate representation of feeding relationships than a food chain (Level 7).		Main, Plenary 1

Maths
Students carry out simple calculations using percentages to calculate the amount of energy that is transferred between different levels of food chains.

Literacy
Students describe and explain food chains and food webs using scientific terminology.

APP
Students use models to explain food chains and food webs (AF1).

Key Words
food chain, predator, prey, food web

Answers from the student book

In-text questions	**A** It is a diagram that shows what an organism eats. It shows the flow of energy between organisms. **B** A herbivore only eats plants, a carnivore only eats other animals. **C** A predator eats other animals, whereas prey are eaten by other animals. **D** A set of linked food chains.
Activity	**How much energy?** First level = 1000 kJ Second level = 0.1 × 1000 kJ = 100 kJ Third level = 0.1 × 100 kJ = 10 kJ 10 kJ would be passed to the top predator.

Summary Questions	**1** food chain – diagram showing the flow of energy through organisms
	 food web – diagram showing linked food chains
	 predator – animal that eats another animal
	 prey – animal that is eaten (4 marks)
	 2a giraffe/impala/zebra (1 mark)
	   b acacia tree/grass (1 mark)
	   c acacia tree (1 mark)
	   d Credit any suitable answer. For example, grass → impala → leopard → lion
	     (1 mark for correct order of organisms, 1 mark for arrows in correct direction)

3 Example answers (6 marks):

Grasshopper eats grass, field mouse eats grasshopper, owl eats field mouse.

The producer is the grass.

The herbivore is the grasshopper.

The carnivores are the field mice and the owls.

The predators are the field mice an the owls.

The prey are the grasshoppers and the field mice.

The top predator is the owl.

500 kJ of energy are transferred to the grasshopper.

50 kJ are transferred to the field mouse.

5 kJ are transferred to the owl.

Starter	Support/Extension	Resources
Who eats who? (10 min) Students share ideas in pairs about some of the key words in this lesson (food chain, carnivore, herbivore, omnivore, predator, and prey), as students will have met simple food chains in KS2. Discuss as a class before using the interactive resource to complete some simple food chains.	**Extension**: Encourage students to use scientific terms throughout the activity.	**Interactive**: Who eats who?
Feeding definitions (5 min) Prepare a set of cards, each with a key word or a definition. Students match the words with their definitions. Cards should include: food chain, carnivore, herbivore, omnivore, producer, consumer, predator, and prey. Students use what they have learnt from the key words to make simple food chains.	**Extension**: Challenge students to make food chains that are three, four, and five levels long.	

Main	Support/Extension	Resources
Food chains and webs (40 min) Introduce the definition of a food web and show an example. Students to discuss in pairs what they see before discussing as a class. You can assess students' understanding of the key terms in this lesson by using mini-whiteboards during questioning, increasing class participation. Students then make their own food webs using the organisms provided on the activity sheet, and answer the questions that follow.	**Support**: The support sheet provides students with a reduced number of organisms to make food webs. Images of organisms are accompanied by short notes explaining what they eat and what they are eaten by.	**Activity**: Food chains and webs

Plenary	Support/Extension	Resources
Chains from webs (5 min) Present students with a food web and ask them to write as many food chains as possible from that web using mini-whiteboards. Alternatively, present students with several food chains, and ask them to construct a food web from the food chains provided.	**Extension**: Students suggest the merits of using food chains and food webs as a scientist.	
Role-playing food chains (10 min) Project a jumbled-up list of organisms on the board. Students work in small groups of three to five to act out a food chain from the organisms provided in three minutes. Watch the role plays, and students evaluate each other's role plays using the definitions of food chains and food webs.	**Extension**: Encourage students to work towards longer food chains and where possible, team up with another group to act out a food web.	

Homework		
Students construct a food web from a different environment of their choice. Students include as many organisms as they can in their food web, before choosing one food chain from their food web to annotate using key words from the lesson.		

2.8 Disruptions to food chains and webs

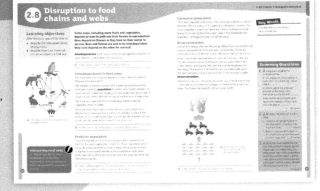

Biology NC link:

● how organisms affect, and are affected by, their environment, including the accumulation of toxic materials.

Working Scientifically NC link:

● present observations and data using appropriate methods, including tables and graphs.

Band	Outcome	Checkpoint	
		Question	Activity
Developing	State that one population of organisms can affect another (Level 4).	A, 1, 2	Lit, Starter 2, Main 1, Plenary 2, Homework
	State that toxic material can get into food chains (Level 4).	D, 1	Main 2, Plenary 2, Homework
	Present population data as a graph, and describe simple patterns shown (Level 4).		Main 1
Secure	Describe the interdependence of organisms (Level 5).	C, 1, 2	Lit, Starter 2, Main 1, Plenary 2, Homework
	Describe how toxic materials can accumulate in a food web (Level 6).	D, 1, 3	Main 2, Plenary 2, Homework
	Present population data as a graph to describe trends and draw conclusions (Level 6).		Main 1
Extending	Explain the interdependence of organisms (Level 7).	1, 2	Lit, Starter 2, Main 1, Plenary 2, Homework
	Explain why toxic materials have greater effect on top predators in a food chain (Level 8).	1, 3	Main 2, Plenary 2, Homework
	Present population data as a graph, explaining trends and drawing detailed conclusions from data provided (Level 8).		Main 1

Maths
Students interpret numerical data given in tables, and plot graphs accordingly.

They also interpret and sketch graphs to demonstrate changes in populations for different organisms.

Literacy
Students use scientific terminology when carrying out discussions on factors affecting populations of organisms, and causes of bioaccumulation.

APP
Students present numerical data on population as graphs (AF3).

Key Words
interdependence, population, bioaccumulation

Answers from the student book

In-text questions	**A** Organisms depending on each other to survive, grow, and reproduce.
	B Number of animals or plants of the same type that live in the same area.
	C Population of consumers will decrease.
	D The build-up of (toxic) chemicals through a food chain.
Activity	**Interpreting food webs** Credit sensible suggestions for what would happen to other organisms in the food web if disease reduced the population of frogs. For example: Fox will consume more rabbits and voles, due to lack of frogs. The population of rabbits and voles would decrease. Hawks will consume more voles and thrushes, due to lack of frogs. The population of voles and thrushes would decrease. Few predators for insects and slugs. The population of insects and slugs may increase.

36

Summary Questions	**1** interdependence, decrease, bioaccumulation (3 marks)
	2a Rabbit population would increase as it has no predators/it will not get eaten. (2 marks)
	b The hawk and fox population may decrease as they have reduced food supplies.
	The insect population may increase as they have fewer predators. (4 marks)
	3 QWC question (6 marks). Example answers:
	plankton → fish → fish-eating birds
	Insecticide runs into river.
	Taken up by plankton.
	DDT accumulates in fish when they eat the plankton.
	One fish eats lots of plankton, but not enough to cause death.
	DDT accumulates in birds when they eat the fish.
	One bird eats many fish.
	DDT level is now so high/concentrated that it causes death in the bird.

kerboodle

Starter	Support/Extension	Resources
Key words and definitions (10 min) Write the key words interdependence, population, and bioaccumulation on the board. Students should discuss possible definitions in pairs, before offering these in a class discussion.		
Up or down? (5 min) Interactive resource where students predict how populations will change for different organisms in different circumstances. This is a good opportunity for students to practise maths skills as the population changes are shown as graphs.	**Extension**: Students should offer explanations to justify their answers.	**Interactive**: Up or down?

Main	Support/Extension	Resources
Changes in population (25 min) Students are given data about the population of gannets on the island of Grassholm over a period of 18 years. Students present the information using a suitable graph, and answer questions that follow.	**Support**: Pre-labelled graph axes are provided on the accompanying support sheet.	**Activity**: Changes in population **Skill sheet:** Drawing graphs
What killed the herons? (15 min) Students play a card game in groups of three using the sort cards provided to work out the mystery of 'What killed the herons?'. The cards give small pieces of information that add together to explain the process of bioaccumulation. Students must then write their own account of bioaccumulation.	**Support**: Prompt students towards the first card in the sequence.	**Activity**: What killed the herons?

Plenary	Support/Extension	Resources
Best and worst (5 min) Students work in pairs to discuss features needed for the best and worst pesticides farmers can use. Follow up with a class discussion of ideas. Students can use mini-whiteboards to hold up the features that they think are most important.	**Support**: Give prompts such as good pesticides would be species-specific, biodegradable, and insoluble.	
Human impact (10 min) Students work in pairs to think up as many ways as possible that humans can affect a population of organisms. Students write this down and swap ideas with another group. Groups must then work out what effect the human activities listed will have on a population (increase or decrease) and explain their answers to each other.		

Homework	Support/Extension	
As an extension to the activity Changes in population, ask students to write a prediction on the population of gannets for each of the following scenarios: • A new competitor for the gannet arrives. • An oil spill has resulted in a temporary fall in fish stocks in the area. • A new colony of fish move to the area. • The local farmer starts to use vast quantities of insecticides toxic to animals. Students must give explanations for their answers.	**Extension**: Students should sketch the corresponding population curve for each scenario given.	

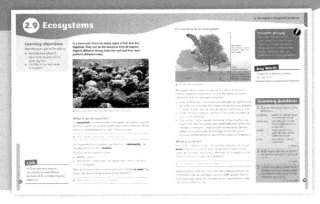

Biology NC link:
- the interdependence of organisms in an ecosystem, including food webs and insect pollinated crops.

Working Scientifically NC link:
- apply sampling techniques.

Band	Outcome	Checkpoint	
		Question	Activity
Developing	State that different organisms can co-exist (Level 3).	A, 1	Lit, Starter 1, Main, Plenary 1
	State the definition of the term niche (Level 4).	C, 1	Lit, Starter 1, Main, Plenary 1
	Record data from sampling an ecosystem (Level 4).		Main
Secure	Describe how different organisms co-exist within an ecosystem (Level 5).	2, 3	Main, Plenary 1, Plenary 2, Homework
	Identify niches within an ecosystem (Level 6).	3	Main, Plenary 1, Plenary 2, Homework
	Use quadrats to take measurements in an ecosystem, describing trends observed (Level 6).		Main
Extending	Explain why different organisms are needed in an ecosystem (Level 7).	2, 3	Main, Plenary 2, Homework
	Explain why different organisms within the same ecosystem have different niches (Level 8).	2, 3	Main, Plenary 2, Homework
	Use quadrats and transects to take unbiased measurements in an ecosystem, describing trends observed in data (Level 8).		Main

Maths
Students must show an understanding of number size and scale when carrying out sampling techniques using quadrats and transects.

Some students will also estimate the number of a named plant in a given area using sampling data provided.

Literacy
Students use scientific terminology, including their definitions, when describing trends shown by their sampling technique, and when discussing the co-existence of organisms in an ecosystem.

APP
Students collect data through appropriate sampling techniques (AF4), present data in a table (AF3), and draw conclusions using data obtained (AF5).

Key Words
ecosystem, community, habitat, co-exist, niche

Answers from the student book

In-text questions	**A** Name given to plants and animals found in a particular location, and the area/habitat in which they live.
	B The area in which an organism lives.
	C A particular place or role occupied by an organism within an ecosystem.
Activity	**Scientific glossary**
	Credit key words from this chapter given with definitions. Each key word should be accompanied by an example or a diagram where possible.

Summary Questions	1 ecosystem – living organisms in a particular area, and the habitat they live in
	community – plants and animals found in a particular habitat
	habitat – place where a plant or animal lives
	niche – particular place or role that an organism has in an ecosystem (4 marks)
	2 Bees and birds have different niches. They eat different things. Bees require nectar from flowers, whereas birds live off insects living on the leaves. (2 marks)
	3 QWC question (6 marks). Example answers:
	A niche is the place or role that an organism has in a habitat. For example, many organisms live in an oak tree (or suitable example). Not every organism lives in the same part of the tree. Microorganisms at the base of the tree break down old leaves. This gives the tree further nutrients to absorb for growth. Insects live in the tree trunk. The insect larvae are food for birds that may live in the canopy. Squirrels and bees also live in the canopy. Bees gather pollen and nectar when the tree is in blossom. Squirrels gather acorns as food. The activities of each organism do not conflict each other, and so different organisms can co-exist.

Starter	Support/Extension	Resources
Ecosystem key words (5 min) Interactive memory matching game where students match key words of this topic to their definitions. The key words included are ecosystem, niche, environment, community, co-existence, habitat, population.	**Extension**: Give the key words and students to suggest definitions before starting the game.	**Interactive**: Ecosystem key words
Sampling techniques (5 min) Show students a quadrat or an image of a quadrat on a grass field. Talk about the sampling techniques used to count the number of plants in a field.	**Extension**: Introduce the idea of using transects when sampling to control bias.	

Main	Support/Extension	Resources
Investigating the distribution of a plant (45 min) Introduce students to the idea of ecosystems, habitats, communities, and niches. Explain to students how different organisms can co-exist in the same environment. Take the class onto the school field and split into small groups. Issue each group with a transect line (30 m long, marked at metre intervals) and a quadrat (1 m² or 0.25 m²). Students measure the abundance of a named plant on the school field (e.g., dandelion), using sampling techniques and recording their observations. Students then return to the classroom to answer the questions on their practical sheets.	**Extension**: Encourage students to estimate the total number of their plant, given the dimensions of their school field, from their results. Students also discuss whether their estimate is accurate, explaining in terms of dependence on light, competition, and other factors on the distribution of plants.	**Practical**: Investigating the distribution of a plant **Skill sheet**: Recording results

Plenary	Support/Extension	Resources
Key word definitions (5 min) Revisit the seven key words from the start of the lesson (ecosystem, habitat, community, niche, population, co-existence, and environment) and ask students to provide the definition for each key word using a mini-whiteboard.	**Extension**: Encourage students to use each key word in a sentence.	
Living together (5 min) Divide class into groups of three. Each student in the group is assigned one of three organisms found in the school field: grass, earthworm, and starling. Students describe how the organisms are able to all live in the habitat and how they interact, identifying the roles of each organism in this habitat.	**Extension**: Add additional organisms at each tropic level to introduce the idea of different niches. For example, dandelions as competitors, or grasshoppers with a different niche to the earthworm.	

Homework	Support/Extension	
Students research an ecosystem of their choice. They produce an image of the ecosystem (as a drawing or print-out), and select a number of different organisms within the ecosystem to write a short explanation on how these organisms can live together.	**Support**: Provide students with a list of terms to use in their explanation, for example, niche.	

Checkpoint lesson routes

The route through this lesson can be determined using the Checkpoint assessment. Percentage pass marks are supplied in the Checkpoint teacher notes.

Route A (support)
Resources: B2 Chapter 2 Checkpoint: Revision

Students can work through the revision activity, supported by the rest of the group, and the teacher. There are a number of tasks relating to groups of outcomes outlined below. Templates are provided to help students get to grips with word equations, reactants, and products.

Route B (extension)
Resources: B2 Chapter 2 Checkpoint: Extension

Students are set several challenges, stretching them to apply what they have learnt from the chapter to complex situations. Challenges include designing a greenhouse using knowledge of photosynthesis, and explaining bioaccumulation to the public following an accumulation of toxic waste in an ecosystem.

Progression to *secure*

No.	Developing outcome	Secure outcome	Making progress
1	State where photosynthesis occurs in the plant.	Describe the process of photosynthesis.	In Task 1 students are given a template to help them describe photosynthesis and state the word equation. They first work through the task using the words to fill the gaps. They can then use the description writing frame and clues to help them compose a description.
2	State the products of photosynthesis.	State the word equation for photosynthesis.	After completing the gaps in Task 1, students will have stated the word equation, and have a better understanding of the reactants and products to help remember it.
3	Name the main structures of the leaf.	Describe the structure and function of the main components of the leaf.	Discuss with students the key external features of a leaf, whilst using a leaf as a model. Focus on green colour, veins, thin, and surface area. Students can suggest reasons for the features. They then move onto the internal structures of the leaf. In Task 2, students need to match the descriptions of function to the correct structures.
4	State the function of chloroplasts in a leaf.	Explain the distribution of the chloroplasts in the leaf.	In Task 2 students need to explain the distribution of chloroplasts, which should follow on naturally from the previous tasks.
5	Name the minerals required by a plant.	Describe how a plant uses minerals for healthy growth.	Students should be reminded that chloroplasts need magnesium, and that nitrates are needed for amino acids (and so proteins for growth). In Task 3 students match descriptions of deficiency symptoms with the correct minerals.
6	State the requirements for aerobic respiration.	State the word equation for aerobic respiration.	In Task 4 students are given a template to help then describe respiration and state the word equation. They first work through the task using the words to fill in the gaps. Ask students to compare their word equation in Task 4 to Task 1.
7	Give the name of the process where energy is transferred into cells.	Describe the process of respiration.	Students can then use the description writing frame and clues to help them write a description in Task 4.
8	State the products on anaerobic respiration.	State the word summary for anaerobic respiration.	Students should now be familiar with the format of word equations, and are given guidance in Task 4 for anaerobic respiration.
9	State one difference between aerobic and anaerobic respiration.	Describe the differences between aerobic and anaerobic respiration.	Students can compare aerobic and anaerobic respiration using the prompts in Task 4. It may benefit some students to discuss the meaning of the words (e.g., 'aero' means 'living with oxygen').
10	State the definition of a food chain.	Describe what food chains show.	In Task 5 students are given the names of three organisms. Students create a food chain and then use the guidance to describe what it shows.
11	State the definition of a food web.	Describe what food webs show.	Ask students to build a few simple food chains based on what they have eaten, for example, cereal grains, wheat, various meats. Then build them into a simple food web. Ask why the web is more helpful than the simple chains.

12	State that one population can affect another.	Describe the interdependence of organisms.	Start with a simple food chain, and ask the students what would happen if all the carnivores die. They will usually be able to answer. They discuss how each population has an impact on the other. Students can complete the cloze activity in Task 6 to describe interdependence.
13	State that toxic materials can get into the food chain.	Describe how toxic materials can accumulate in a food web.	In Task 7 students are given a food chain and information of toxin absorption into a producer. Students should consider how many producers will be eaten by the herbivore in a week. Continuing through the chain, students should recognise the impact of bioaccumulation.
14	State that different organisms can co-exist together.	Describe how different organisms co-exist within an ecosystem.	In Task 7 students are given information and prompts for an ecosystem. They can complete the cloze activity, describing how the organisms co-exist.

Answers to end-of-chapter questions

1a (aerobic) respiration (1 mark)   **b** mitochondria (1 mark)   **c** oxygen, carbon dioxide (2 marks)

2a corn → mouse → owl (1 mark)   **b** corn (1 mark)

c Producers have energy transferred from glucose.
Consumers have energy transferred from the organisms they eat. (2 marks)

d The spider population would increase as less organisms eat them. (2 marks) (Alternatively, spider population stays the same/decreases as shrew and mice population increase due to no predators, so eat the excess spiders.)

3a oxygen (1 mark)   **b** carbon dioxide and water (2 marks)

c Bubbles would stop/decrease, photosynthesis would stop, as there is no light. (3 marks)

d Stomata allow carbon dioxide in to the leaf and allow oxygen out of the leaf. (2 marks)

4a The mice population would increase as there are no predators/nothing would eat them. (2 marks)

b The grasshopper population would decrease as shrews and spiders would need to eat more of them to survive. (2 marks)

c Mice and shrews occupy different niches because they eat different foods. (2 marks)

d Any three from: toxic chemical builds up in the food chain. Owls eat many other organisms so owls receive a higher dose of the toxic chemical. High levels can cause death to an organism. Correct use of term bioaccumulation. (4 marks)

5a Minerals are absorbed into root (hair) cells by diffusion. They travel through the xylem/water vessels to different parts of the plant. (3 marks)

b Magnesium deficiency means less chlorophyll. Chlorophyll absorbs light for photosynthesis. (2 marks)

c large surface area, contains lots of chloroplasts/chlorophyll, chloroplasts concentrated in top of leaf/palisade layer. (3 marks)

6 This is a QWC question. Students should be marked on the use of good English, organisation of information, spelling and grammar, and correct use of specialist scientific terms. The best answers will provide a full explanation of fermentation, with the process explained in a logical order (maximum 6 marks).
Examples of correct scientific points:
Fermentation is a type of anaerobic respiration. It occurs in some microorganisms/yeast.
These microorganisms respire in the absence of oxygen.
Energy is transferred from glucose.
glucose → ethanol + carbon dioxide (+ energy)
The ethanol product can be used in alcoholic drink production.
The carbon dioxide product is used in bread production/to make dough rise.

Answer guide for Big Write

Developing	Secure	Extending
1–2 marks	3–4 marks	5–6 marks
The essay has little structure. However, the student has correctly used at least two scientific terms or one word equation.	The essay contains some structure, with an attempt to use paragraphing. The student has correctly used at least two scientific terms and one word equation.	The essay is well structured, with key ideas clearly presented in separate paragraphs. The student has correctly used more than two scientific terms and two word equations.

kerboodle

B2 Chapter 2 Checkpoint assessment (automarked)	B2 Chapter 2 Checkpoint: Extension
	B2 Chapter 2 Progress task (Working
B2 Chapter 2 Checkpoint: Revision	scientifically)

3.1 Competition and adaptation

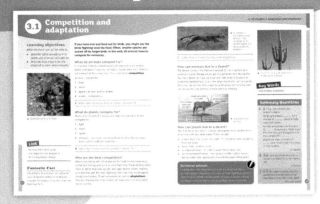

Biology NC link:

- the variation between species and between individuals of the same species means some organisms compete more successfully, which can drive natural selection.

Band	Outcome	Checkpoint	
		Question	Activity
Developing	State some resources that plants and animals compete for (Level 3).	A, B, 1	Starter 1, Main, Plenary 1, Homework
	State what is meant by the term adaptation (Level 4).	C	Lit, Starter 2, Main, Plenary 2, Homework
Secure	Describe some resources that plants and animals compete for (Level 5).	1	Starter 1, Main, Plenary 1, Homework
	Describe how organisms are adapted to their environments (Level 5).	2	Lit, Starter 2, Main, Plenary 2, Homework
Extending	Explain the effect of competition on the individual or the population (Level 7).	1	Main, Plenary 1, Homework
	Explain how adaptations help an organism survive in their environment (Level 7).	2, 3	Lit, Starter 2, Main, Plenary 2, Homework

Literacy
Students present adaptations in a coherent and logical manner, using scientific terminology when explaining the competition of resources and the importance of adaptations to survive.

APP
Students use secondary data provided and present their ideas in an appropriate table (AF3).

Key Words
competition, adaptation

Answers from the student book

In-text questions	**A** food, water, space, and mates
	B light, water, space, and minerals
	C Features that enable an organism to be successful and so survive.
Activity	**Nocturnal animals**
	Credit suitable information poster on a nocturnal animal of the student's choice (e.g., owl), and how the animal is adapted for hunting at night.
	Poster should include features of the animal with special adaptations, explained using as many scientific terms as possible.

Summary Questions	**1** compete, resources, mates, light, adaptations (5 marks)
	2 Any three from: waxy layer, spines instead of leaves, large root system, stems which can store water.
	3 QWC question (6 marks). Example answers:
	Concentrated urine and dry feces so little water is lost through excretion.
	Large body so the surface area is relatively small to reduce risk of overheating.
	Moves at night to feed to avoid extreme daytime temperatures.
	Does not sweat to avoid water loss through this mechanism.
	Stands in breezes at the top of sand dunes to help cool its body.
	Wide feet to avoid the oryx sinking into soft sand.

kerboodle

Starter	Support/Extension	Resources
Competitions galore (10 min) Ask students to think about as many competitions as they can. Most will talk about competitions in sport, music, or the arts. Steer students towards competition for living organisms to survive. Ask students to pair-share ideas and write these on mini-whiteboards, filtering their lists to those applicable to plants, animals, or both.	**Support**: Allow students to work in small groups	
Something fishy! (10 min) Interactive resource where students link adaptations of a fish with the function of the adaptation that helps it survive.	**Extension**: Students give adaptations for another living organism, for example, a camel.	**Interactive**: Something fishy!

Main	Support/Extension	Resources
Competition and adaptation (35 min) Formally introduce the idea of competition for resources, and the importance of adaptations in different organisms. A good video to show at this stage is 'The Adaptation Song' that can be found on YouTube.	**Support**: Students should concentrate on two or three adaptations for the image provided.	**Activity**: Competition and adaptation
Divide the class into small groups of four or five students, and distribute each group with an image of a different organism. Students must use the images to highlight four adaptations of the organism in the table provided on their activity sheet, before answering the questions that follow.		

Plenary	Support/Extension	Resources
The result of competition (10 min) Give students the hypothetical situation where two wolf packs have moved into the same area of forest. Students pair-share ideas on what the two packs will compete for, and what is likely to happen in terms of outcome for this competition. Finish this activity as a class discussion.		
Super predators (10 min) Students have five minutes to work in small groups to design the best-adapted predator. This predator can be real or imaginary, but a drawing of this predator must be accompanied by annotations of its adaptations. Students then compare their predator with one another group has designed.	**Support**: Prompt students to think about a real-life predator, for example, a lion. Students can then transfer adaptations that make a lion successful to a fictional predator.	

Homework		
Students research the adaptations of a squirrel and the population difference between red and grey squirrels. Students should then use what they have learnt this lesson to suggest reasons for their relative population sizes in terms of competition and its effects.		

3.2 Adapting to change

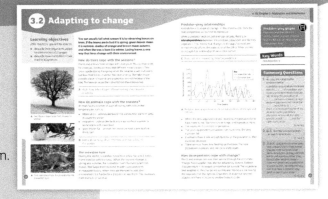

Biology NC link:

- differences between species
- changes in the environment may leave individuals within a species, and some entire species, less well adapted to compete successfully and reproduce, which in turn may lead to extinction.

Working Scientifically NC link:

- interpret observations and data, including identifying patterns and using observations, measurements, and data to draw conclusions.

Band	Outcome	Checkpoint	
		Question	**Activity**
Developing	Name an environmental change (Level 3).		Starter 1, Main 1
	Give a possible reason for adaptation or extinction (Level 4).	3	Starter 2, Main 1, Main 2, Homework
	Interpret secondary data to describe trends in predator–prey relationships (Level 4).		Maths, Main 2
Secure	Describe how organisms adapt to environmental changes (Level 6).	A, B	Starter 1, Main 1, Plenary 1
	Describe how competition can lead to adaptation (Level 6).	2	Starter 2, Homework
	Interpret secondary data to describe trends and draw simple conclusions about predator–prey relationships (Level 6).		Maths, Main 2
Extending	Explain how organisms are adapted to seasonal changes (Level 7).		Starter 1, Plenary 1
	Explain how competition or long-term environmental change can lead to evolutionary adaptation or extinction (Level 7).	2, 3	Starter 2, Main 1, Main 2, Homework
	Interpret secondary data to explain trends and draw detailed conclusions about predator–prey relationships (Level 8).		Maths, Main 2

Maths

Students draw, extract, and interpret information from graphs about predator–prey populations.

Literacy

Students read and extract information from text to answer questions that follow.

Students use scientific terminology when describing adaptations, seasonal changes, and population changes.

APP

Students present numerical data as a graph (AF3), and interpret data to describe trends and draw conclusions (AF5).

Key Words

interdependence

Answers from the student book

In-text questions	**A** Any two from: saves energy, nutrients can be reused, provide a layer of warmth/protection at the base of the tree. **B** hibernation, migration, grow thicker fur
Activity	**Predator–prey graphs** Graph of fox population against rabbit population should resemble that of the snowshoe hare and the Canadian lynx in the student book. When the population of the rabbit is high, the fox population increases. This reduces the number of rabbits, which in turn reduces the number of foxes, and the whole cycle starts again.

Summary Questions	
	1 population, predators, prey, decrease, increase (5 marks)
	2 Changes to a habitat cause an increased competition for survival. Those organisms best adapted to the change will survive and reproduce. This increases the population of that species. Unsuccessful organisms will have to move to another habitat, or die. (3 marks)
	3 Example answers (6 marks):
	Initially, the population of European ladybirds will increase significantly because they can feed on aphids and other ladybird species. Eventually their food supply will decrease, which will lead to starvation for many seven-spotted ladybirds. The population of seven-spotted ladybirds will decrease, which allows the population of aphids to increase. The cycle then starts again. (Students must include a correct predator-prey graph.)

Starter	Support/Extension	Resources
In six months' time (10 min) Students describe possible changes to the organisms in the school grounds in six months' time. If students initially talk about animals grow bigger, steer them towards how deciduous trees change through the season and the presence/absence of hibernating animals. Students should suggest why these changes have occurred as an adaptation to seasonal changes.	**Extension**: Encourage students to give further examples of seasonal changes in organisms.	
Winners and losers (10 min) Show an image or a short film of a cheetah hunting. Students identify the adaptations of the cheetah that make it a successful hunter. Introduce the hyena and that cheetahs have low stamina. They often lose their food to hyenas in the wild. This is a good recap of adaptation and competition, and is a useful introduction to the effects on population when animals fail to adapt to a changing environment.	**Extension**: Encourage students to offer further examples of changes in environment. This can lead the discussion to evolution and extinction.	

Main	Support/Extension	Resources
Introduce the idea of seasonal changes and how this links in with adaptation. Explain how adaptation can also be brought about by competition.		
Climate change and polar bears (20 min) Students read an article about the environmental changes in the Arctic, and the effects of these changes on polar bears and their population before answering questions that follow.	**Support**: Read text as a class or in small groups to ensure students can understand the material given.	**Activity**: Climate change and polar bears
Predator–prey relationships (20 min) Students plot a graph to show the number of Canadian wolves in Quebec 2001–13. This graph is drawn on top of an existing graph showing the number of caribou in the same period. Students must interpret the graphs to answer the questions that follow.	**Support**: An access sheet is provided where the predator–prey graphs are already drawn and the questions are simpler.	**Activity**: Predator–prey relationships

Plenary	Support/Extension	Resources
Competition or environment (5 min) Students use the interactive resource to decide whether the environment or competition is the cause of the changes provided. Students can use mini-whiteboards to answer each statement, as a way of increasing class participation.	**Extension**: Students explain their answers.	**Interactive**: Competition or environment
Competitive graphs (5 min) Students sketch a graph for a predator–prey relationship, with a third line to show the effect of competition on populations. For example, students consider the populations of zebras, cheetahs, and hyenas when cheetahs and hyenas are hunting the same prey.	**Support**: Students should concentrate only on the basic predator–prey sketch graph.	

Homework		
Ask students to carry out research on a pair of organisms similar to the cheetah and the hyena (where one organism has adapted better than the other). Students write a short paragraph about each of their adaptations, and explain how the population of one has been affected by the other.		

3.3 Variation

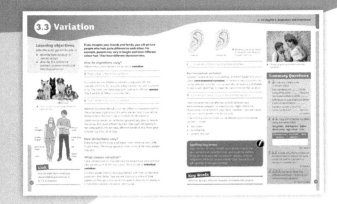

Biology NC link:
- differences between species.

Working Scientifically NC link:
- interpret observations and data, including identifying patterns and using observations, measurements, and data to draw conclusions.

Band	Outcome	Checkpoint	
		Question	**Activity**
Developing	State what is meant by the term variation (Level 4).	A, 1	Main, Plenary 2
	State that variation is caused by the environment or inheritance (Level 4).	C, D, 1	Starter 1, Starter 2, Main, Plenary 1
	Record observations of variations between different species of gull (Level 3).		Main
Secure	Describe how variation in species occurs (Level 5).	1, 3	Starter 1, Starter 2, Main, Plenary 2, Homework
	Describe the difference between environmental and inherited variation (Level 5).	1–4	Starter 1, Starter 2, Main, Plenary 1, Homework
	Record and categorise observations of variations between different species of gull (Level 5).		Main
Extending	Explain how variation gives rise to different species (Level 8).		Main, Plenary 2, Homework
	Explain that some variation is affected by both environmental and inherited factors (Level 7).	2–4	Starter 1, Starter 2, Main, Plenary 1
	Record and categorise observations of variations between different species of gull to suggest species boundaries (Level 7).	1	Main

Literacy
Students test their spelling of key words used in the student-book activity.

They will then use scientific terminology to describe and suggest reasons for the variation in different species of seagulls.

APP
Students make observations to find variation between different types of seagulls (AF4).

Key Words
variation, species, inherited variation, environmental variation

Answers from the student book

In-text questions	**A** Differences in characteristics within a species.
	B A group of organisms which share very similar characteristics (and are able to produce fertile offspring).
	C Variation between organisms in a species due to the characteristics inherited from their parents.
	D Variation caused by a person's surroundings and lifestyle.
Activity	**Spelling key terms** Students should test their spelling of the following words with a partner: species, variation, adaptation, inherited, environmental.

Summary Questions	1 species, characteristics, offspring, variation, environmental, inherited (6 marks)
	2 Environmental: tattoo, scar. Inherited: blood group, eye colour. Both: body mass, intelligence (6 marks)
	3 Identical twins have the same inherited characteristics. Any differences must therefore be caused by environmental factors. (2 marks)
	4 QWC question (6 marks). Example answers: Variation is the difference in characteristics within a species. Inherited variation depends on characteristics inherited from parents. For example, lobed or lobe-less ears, eye colour, and blood type. Environmental variation depends on changes in a person's surroundings and/or lifestyle. For example, dyed hair, tattoos, and scars. Many characteristics are affected by both inherited and environmental variation. For example, height. Some characteristics are not affected by environmental factors at all. For example, eye colour, blood group.

Starter	Support/Extension	Resources
What is variation? (10 min) Students work in pairs to discuss what the word variation means, and give a possible definition with examples. Give an example of inherited variation (e.g., dog breeds), environmental variation (e.g., colours of flamingos), and variation affected by both (e.g., height). Students suggest a reason for the variation of each type.	**Extension**: Students suggest other factors for each category of variation.	
Causes of variation (5 min) Students read a short passage of text provided on the interactive resource about a day at the zoo, and select types of variation dependent on inherited factors, environmental factors, or both.	**Extension**: Students suggest a definition for inherited and environmental variation.	**Interactive**: Causes of variation

Main	Support/Extension	Resources
Variation (40 min) Formally introduce the key words for this lesson: variation, inherited variation, environmental variation, and species. Discuss possible variation in humans due to the three types of factors (inheritance, environmental, or both) before moving on to the activity. In the activity students study images of different species of seagulls and record variations within the different species, then answer the questions. It is important to go through differences within a species (e.g., dog breeds) and differences between species (e.g., kangaroos and wallabies) before issuing this activity.	**Support**: A support sheet is available where students are given a list of possible variations within the gulls to choose from.	**Activity**: Variation

Plenary	Support/Extension	Resources
Variation in humans (10 min) Working in small groups students list human variations, and categorise them as inherited, environmental, or variations affected by both. Discuss their lists as a class.		
Variation definitions (5 min) Students give the definitions of variation, inherited variation, and environmental variation.	**Extension:** Students suggest the point at which variation is significant enough for organisms to become different species, using examples.	

Homework	Support/Extension	
Provide students with a list of four pet animals. For example, two different dogs (e.g., a Labrador and a Yorkshire terrier), a rabbit, and a goldfish. Ask students to list as many variations between the animals as possible, classify the variations, and suggest possible causes.	**Extension**: Students use their list to explain why the dogs are the same species but dogs, rabbits, and goldfish are different species.	

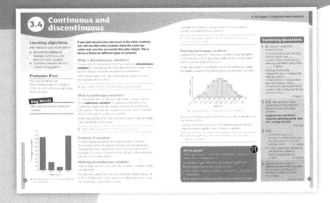

Biology NC link:

- the variation between individuals within a species being continuous or discontinuous, to include measurement and graphical representation of variation.

Working Scientifically NC link:

- present observations and data using appropriate methods, including tables and graphs.

Band	Outcome	Checkpoint	
		Question	Activity
Developing	State that there are two types of variation (Level 3).	1, 2	Starter 2, Main, Plenary 1
	State the two types of graphs that can be drawn when representing the two types of variation (Level 4).	1	Maths, Main, Plenary 2
	Record results in a table and plot a graph on axes provided (Level 4).		Main
Secure	Describe the difference between continuous and discontinuous variation (Level 6).	A, B, 4	Starter 2, Main, Plenary 1
	Represent variation within a species using graphs (Level 6).	C, D, 1	Maths, Main, Plenary 2
	Record results in a table and plot a histogram (Level 6).		Main
Extending	Explain the causes of continuous and discontinuous variation (Level 7).	3, 4	Main, Plenary 1
	Represent variation within a species using the appropriate type of graph (Level 7).	C, D	Maths, Main, Plenary 2
	Record results in a table and identify and plot an appropriate graph (Level 7).		Main

Maths

Students suggest the appropriate type of graph to draw for different continuous and discontinuous variations in the student-book activity.

Students will then display the results of the class experiment on arm span in an appropriate graph, and interpret results to answer questions relating to mode, mean, and range.

Literacy

Students use scientific terminology when describing the differences between continuous and discontinuous data, and when drawing conclusions from results of the class experiment to measure arm span.

APP

Students collect results using appropriate ranges (AF4), display data obtained appropriately in tables and graphs (AF3), and draw conclusions using their data (AF5).

Key Words

discontinuous variation, continuous variation

Answers from the student book

In-text questions	**A** Characteristics that can only result in certain values.
	B Characteristics that can take any value within a range.
	C bar chart
	D histogram, often with a line added
Activity	**Which graph?**
	a bar chart
	b histogram
	c histogram
	d histogram

Summary Questions	
	1 discontinuous, continuous, graph, bar chart, histogram (5 marks)
	2 Continuous: length of arm, maximum sprinting speed, average leaf size. Discontinuous: hair colour, shoe size. (5 marks)
	3a Most people are of an average height, around 150 cm. Few people are very short, below 135 cm. Few people are very tall, above 170 cm. (3 marks)
	b Height is affected by both inherited and environmental factors. If your parents are tall, you are also likely to be tall (inherited). However, growth can be affected by environmental factors, for example, malnourishment. (3 marks)
	4 QWC question (6 marks). Example answers: Continuous variation is variation that can take any value within a range. For example, height, body mass, arm span, hair length, or length of feet. Continuous data should be plotted on a histogram. A line is often added to the histogram to see the shape of the graph. This type of variation usually produces a curve known as a normal distribution. Discontinuous variation is variation that can only result in certain values. For example, gender, blood type, eye colour, or shoe size. Discontinuous variation should be plotted on a bar chart.

kerboodle

Starter	Support/Extension	Resources
Types of variation (10 min) Ask students to look around them. List as many sources of variation as they can just by looking at their classmates. Students should suggest different ways they can categorise the variations listed, justifying their suggestions using examples. Feedback as a class discussion.	**Support**: Students concentrate on listing variations, not grouping them.	
Discontinuous or continuous (10 min) Introduce the difference between discontinuous and continuous variation using examples. Students will then apply their new-found knowledge to group variations given on the interactive resource into the correct category.	**Extension**: Students should offer other variations to add to the existing list.	**Interactive**: Discontinuous or continuous

Main	Support/Extension	Resources
Investigating arm span (40 min) Formally introduce the difference between continuous and discontinuous variation. For students struggling to grasp this idea, parallels can be drawn to continuous and discrete data (which they have met in the Working Scientifically unit in Book 1 as well as in Maths lessons). Demonstrate how to measure arm span before issuing the practical sheet. Split the class into groups of five or six for students to measure the arm spans of students within their own group. Collate results at the front of the class. Students then plot a suitable graph to show the class results for arm span and answer the questions that follow.	**Support**: A labelled graph grid is available for students in the accompanying support sheet.	**Practical**: Investigating arm span **Skill sheet**: Drawing graphs **Skill sheet**: Recording results **Skill sheet**: Calculating range

Plenary	Support/Extension	Resources
Causes of discontinuous or continuous variation (5 min) Ask the class to work in pairs to list eight ways humans vary. Students should categorise these variations into continuous and discontinuous variations, and suggest possible causes for these (inherited, environmental, or both).	**Extension**: Students should spot trends in their results, for example, that most inherited variations are discontinuous.	
Which type of graph? (5 min) Call out different types of continuous (e.g., hair length) and discontinuous variations (e.g., tongue-rolling), for students to decide on the correct type of variation using a mini-whiteboard. Students should also suggest the type of graph needed to display the results.	**Extension**: Students should justify their choice of graph and draw a sketch-graph for one of the variations mentioned.	

Homework	Support/Extension	
During the lesson draw a tally chart on the board with a list for eye colour. Students should add their eye colour to the tally during the course of the lesson, copy the tally at the end of the lesson, and prepare a suitable graph to display results for homework.	**Extension**: Students should state the type of variation this is, and describe possible trends shown by the graph.	

3.5 Inheritance

Biology NC link:

- heredity as the process by which genetic information is transmitted from one generation to the next
- a simple model of chromosomes, genes, and DNA in heredity, including the part played by Watson, Crick, Wilkins, and Franklin in the development of the DNA model.

Working Scientifically NC link:

- understand that scientific methods and theories develop as earlier explanations are modified to take account of new evidence and ideas, together with the importance of publishing results and peer review.

Band	Outcome	Checkpoint	
		Question	Activity
Developing	State what is meant by a gene (Level 4).	C, 1	Starter 2, Plenary 2, Homework
	State that more than one scientist was involved in discovering the structure of DNA (Level 4).	3	Lit, Main
	State that the different teams of scientists produced different pieces of evidence (Level 4).	3	Lit, Main
Secure	Describe how characteristics are inherited (Level 6).	1, 4	Starter 2, Plenary 2, Homework
	Describe how scientists worked together to develop the DNA model (Level 6).	3	Lit, Main
	Describe that one team of scientists built on earlier work of another team in the discovery of DNA structure (Level 6).	3	Lit, Main
Extending	Explain how characteristics are inherited through and coded for by genes (Level 7).	B, C, 1, 4	Starter 2, Plenary 2, Homework
	Explain the contribution of each team of scientists to the development of the model of DNA (Level 7).	3	Lit, Main
	Explain how poor communication between the teams of scientists held back the discovery of the structure of DNA (Level 8).		Main

Maths
Students must understand quantitative size and scale to appreciate how DNA molecules fit in with cells, nuclei, chromosomes, and genes.

Literacy
Students read text on the discovery of the double-helix structure of DNA, extracting relevant information to summarise roles different teams played in discovery.

APP
Students use models to explain the structure of DNA (AF1), and suggest how collaborative approaches to investigations improve the evidence collected (AF3).

Key Words
DNA, chromosome, gene

Answers from the student book

In-text questions	A Genetic material stored in the nucleus, containing all the information needed to make an organism. B A long strand of DNA. C A section of DNA that contains the information to produce a characteristic. D 46
Activity	**DNA timeline** Must show key steps in scientists' understanding of DNA: role of Darwin (evolution), Mendel (selective breeding), discovery of double-helix structure of DNA, DNA fingerprinting, Human Genome Project, Dolly the sheep

Summary Questions	1 nucleus, DNA, chromosomes, characteristic, genes (5 marks)
	2 gene, chromosome, DNA, nucleus, cell (2 marks)
	3 Image produced using X-rays by Franklin and Wilkins. Image shared with Watson and Crick. Watson and Crick deduced double-helix structure. (2 marks)
	4 QWC question (6 marks). Example answers: Genes code for characteristics. Genes are found on chromosomes. A human has 46 chromosomes. Each parent supplies 23 chromosomes. A sex cell/egg/sperm contains 23 chromosomes. During fertilisation the egg and sperm combine. An embryo/fertilised egg has 46 chromosomes. The embryo/fertilised egg contains chromosomes from both parents.

Starter	Support/Extension	Resources
An alternative question-led lesson is also available. **What's the fuss with DNA?** (5 min) Project an image of the double-helix structure of DNA. Ask students what it is. Other questions to ask include: What is DNA? Why is it important? What do you know about it? Where do we get our DNA from? Why did we want to find the structure of it? **What's the DNA?** (10 min) Interactive resource where students decide if statements about DNA are true or false. They then correct the false statements.	**Extension**: Introduce the idea that DNA molecules are made from strands made from the bases A, T, C, and G. **Extension**: Students justify the changes they have made.	**Question-led lesson**: Inheritance **Interactive**: What's the DNA?
Main	**Support/Extension**	**Resources**
The discovery of the structure of DNA (40 min) Introduce the importance of DNA and its role in inheritance and variation. Discuss how DNA links in with the wider picture of cell, nucleus, DNA, chromosome, and gene. This can be shown visually using the 'Scale of the Universe' animation. Students use the information sheets provided and work in groups to determine the relative contribution of the two research teams towards the discovery of the double-helix structure of DNA. They discuss factors given on the information cards that contributed or hindered the progress of research into DNA structure, before summarising their findings on the grids provided.	**Support**: Ask groups of students to concentrate on three contributing factors towards the discovery of the structure of DNA **Extension**: Students rank each factor on their grid according to relative importance. Students write a short paragraph to discuss whether it was fair to leave Rosalind Franklin out of the Nobel Prize for this discovery.	**Activity**: The discovery of the structure of DNA
Plenary	**Support/Extension**	**Resources**
Where now? (10 min) Discuss as a class how our knowledge of DNA has moved scientific understanding forward. You may wish to use the following questions: 　Have scientists carried on with DNA research? 　Have there been any DNA stories in the news recently? 　What is DNA fingerprinting? 　Has our knowledge of DNA helped cure any diseases? **Sugary DNA** (5 min) Show students a ready-made model of DNA using liquorice laces, toothpicks, jelly babies, and/or marshmallows. Ask students to describe different parts of the model, and relate these to facts learnt from this lesson.	**Support**: Allow students to work in small groups when discussing these questions. Give prompts where necessary. **Extension**: If models are made 'accurately', students should be able to distinguish between the different pairs of bases that are constantly repeated.	
Homework	**Support/Extension**	
Students make a poster to explain the role of DNA in inheritance and variation. Students explain how chromosomes determine the different characteristics shown and how traits are inherited by future generations.	**Extension**: Students should include a short paragraph explaining what genetically modified (GM) crops are, and the implications they may have on society.	

3.6 Natural selection

Biology NC link:

- how organisms affect, and are affected by, the environment
- the variation between species and between individuals of the same species, natural selection.

Working Scientifically NC link:

- present reasoned explanations, including explaining data in relation to predictions and hypotheses.

Band	Outcome	Checkpoint	
		Question	Activity
Developing	State how survival rates differ for successful adaptation (Level 3).	C, 2	Lit, Main, Plenary 2
	State organisms have changed over time, giving examples (Level 4).	A, 1	Lit, Main
	Create a simple evolutionary sequence (Level 3).		Lit, Main
Secure	Describe the process of natural selection (Level 6).	C, 2, 3	Lit, Starter 2, Main, Plenary 2
	Describe how organisms evolve over time (Level 6).	1, 3	Lit, Starter 2, Main
	Create an evolutionary family tree, giving justification for the route chosen in the tree (Level 6).		Main
Extending	Explain how natural selection leads to evolution (Level 7).	C, 2, 3	Lit, Main, Plenary 2
	Explain how scientists know that organisms have changed over time (Level 7).	B, 1	Main, Plenary 1
	Create an evolutionary family tree, and present reasoned arguments to justify the structure of the tree (Level 8).		Main

Literacy

Students explain the evolution of a species using scientific terminology and apply these throughout the lesson.

Students also prepare a short presentation to justify the path they have chosen for their evolutionary family trees, listening to each other and contributing to discussions throughout the activity.

APP

Students make an evolutionary family tree display from images provided (AF3), using this as a model to explain evolution and to demonstrate how scientific knowledge has progressed using evidence from fossils (AF1).

Key Words

evolution, fossil, natural selection

Answers from the student book

In-text questions	**A** The process of species gradually developing/changing over time.
	B The remains of plants or animals that lived a long time ago, which have changed to stone.
	C Organisms with the characteristics that are most suited to the environment survive and reproduce. Less well adapted organisms die.
Activity	**Evolution cartoon**
	Credit sensible cartoon strip demonstrating variations in a species, 'survival of the fittest', and evolution of the species. Species concerned can be real or imaginary as long as the scientific concepts shown are sound.
	For example, peppered moths are pale coloured at first because tree bark was pale. Dark coloured ones were readily predated on as they were less camouflaged. The Industrial Revolution turned tree barks dark so the trend reversed. Pale coloured moths now less well camouflaged and dark coloured moths better camouflaged. The population of dark coloured moths now outweighs that of the pale coloured moths.

Summary Questions	
	1 evolved, millions, fossils, remains, stone (5 marks)
	2 Organisms which have adaptations suited to their habitat survive for longer. This means they produce more offspring. Offspring are likely to inherit their parents' advantageous characteristics. Therefore more offspring with the advantageous characteristics survive, continuing the process. (3 marks)
	3 QWC question (6 marks). Example answers: Prior to the Industrial Revolution, pale moths were more successful because the pale moths were camouflaged from predators on pale tree bark. Therefore most of the peppered moth population was pale. The Industrial Revolution caused trees to become blackened. Pale moths became less camouflaged/ successful. Dark moths became more camouflaged/successful. Therefore dark moths reproduced more than pale moths. The population of dark moths increased rapidly. The population of pale moths decreased rapidly. Therefore a greater proportion of peppered moths were dark in colour.

Starter	Support/Extension	Resources
Evolutionary terms (5 min) Interactive resource where students complete a crossword based on the key words of this topic.		**Interactive**: Evolutionary terms
Change over time (5 min) Select an everyday object such as a piece of technology (e.g., the mobile phone). Display images from the Internet to show how the device has changed over time. Discuss as a class, leading on to the fact that modern phones are more suited to our lifestyle. This analogy can then be used when talking about the gradual change in a named plant or animal.		

Main	Support/Extension	Resources
Evolutionary family tree (40 min) Introduce the idea of evolution, including the key concepts of adaptations and natural selection. Discuss the idea of an evolutionary family tree. Introduce an example as an image from the Internet, and discuss what the branches show. Students then work in small groups to construct their own family tree using the images provided on their activity sheet, and discuss with you how they have arranged their tree. Students prepare a short presentation of their family tree to the rest of class, where a justification for their design is required. Students should be prepared to answer questions on this topic from other students and from you. This activity does not necessary require students to reach the 'correct' sequence in the family tree. The skill of applying their understanding of adaptation and evolution is more important here.	**Support**: Students should be given a starting organism to work from on their family tree. If necessary, provide prompts for students to group organisms into similar groups first, before forming an evolutionary chain.	**Activity**: Evolutionary family tree

Plenary	Support/Extension	Resources
Fossils (10 min) Show the class fossils or images of fossils from the Internet. Ask students to state what is being shown to them, explain what fossils are made from, and what scientists can deduce from fossils.	**Support**: Show students images of gradual changes in fossil records. **Extension**: Students suggest how scientists may be able to date fossils, or place fossils in chronological order.	
Survival of the fittest (10 min) Show an image of an insect-eating bird. Students should describe the diet (insects) of this bird, based on its adaptations. Use coloured counters/dots on the board to denote populations of different coloured insects, and ask students to predict the effects on future generations of these insects if the bird prefers one type of insect over another, or if one insect is better adapted for survival than the others.		

Homework		
Students choose an animal of their choice. They carry out research to write an explanation of how this animal has evolved over time.		

3.7 Extinction

Biology NC link:

- changes in the environment may leave individuals within a species, and some entire species, less well adapted to compete successfully and reproduce, which in turn may lead to extinction
- the importance of maintaining biodiversity and the use of gene banks to preserve hereditary material.

Working Scientifically NC link:

- understand that scientific methods and theories develop as earlier explanations are modified to take account of new evidence and ideas, together with the importance of publishing results and peer review.

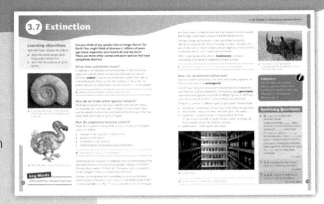

Band	Outcome	Checkpoint	
		Question	Activity
Developing	State what is meant by the term extinct (Level 3).	A, 1, 3	Lit, Starter 2, Main
	State how scientists try to prevent extinction (Level 3).	1, 2	Starter 1, Starter 2, Main, Plenary 1, Homework
	Extract information from scientific text about a possible theory for dinosaur extinction (Level 4).		Main
Secure	Describe some factors that may lead to extinction (Level 5).	B, 1, 3	Lit, Starter 1, Starter 2, Main
	Describe the purpose of gene banks (Level 6).	D, 1, 2	Starter 1, Starter 2, Main, Plenary 1, Homework
	Interpret evidence provided in scientific texts to explain the most likely theory for dinosaur extinction (Level 6).		Main
Extending	Explain some factors that may have led to extinction (Level 7).	3	Lit, Starter 2, Main
	Explain the different types of gene bank (Level 7).	2	Starter 1, Main, Plenary 1, Homework
	Interpret evidence provided in a range of scientific texts to explain the most likely theory for dinosaur extinction (Level 7).		Main

Literacy

Students read scientific information, interpret evidence provided for one possible theory for dinosaur extinction, and listen to the viewpoints of others when discussing other possible theories to draw conclusions.

APP

Students use secondary information to explain different pieces of evidence that science cannot fully answer (AF1).

Key Words

extinct, gene bank

Answers from the student book

In-text questions	**A** An extinct species is one that has completely died out; no new organism can be created.
	B Any three from: changes to the organism's environment, destruction of habitat, outbreak of a new disease, introduction of new predators and competitors
	C dinosaur, dodo
	D The storage of genetic samples of different species.

Activity	**Extinction**
	Newspaper article describes how the organism they have chosen became extinct. Students should use scientific terminology, but also show an awareness of their audience.
Summary Questions	**1** extinct, anywhere, environment, predators, research (5 marks)
	2 Gene banks store genetic samples from many different species. These samples can be used for research. These samples can be used to create new individuals. (3 marks)
	3 QWC question (6 marks). Example answers:
	Species live in habitats where they are successfully adapted. Changes to the habitat (e.g., climate change or introduction of a disease) can cause individuals to die/become less well adapted. This could lead to more competition for food/food sources become more scarce. Disease may also kill organisms. Fewer/no offspring are produced as a result. Population of the species decreases. Extinction occurs when all individuals of a species, throughout the world, have died.

Starter	Support/Extension	Resources
Gene banks (10 min) Introduce the idea of gene banks. Discuss the different types of gene banks and their purpose. Students then apply this knowledge to categorise statements as being true or false.	**Extension**: Students should discuss the ethical implications of gene banks.	**Interactive**: Gene banks
Extinct or endangered? (5 min) Show students images on the board of extinct and endangered animals, for example, Siberian tigers, giant pandas, dinosaurs, and dodos. Ask students to suggest ways to separate these animals into two groups. Students should then offer suggestions to the definition for the words endangered and extinct.	**Extension**: Students should consider what factors contribute to organisms becoming extinct or endangered, and what humans can do to stop this.	

Main	Support/Extension	Resources
Extinction of the dinosaurs (40 min) Introduce possible factors leading to the extinction of certain species, and explain the importance of human intervention (such as gene banks) in reducing the risks of future extinction of endangered species.	**Support**: The information card about climate change contains text that is easily accessible.	**Activity**: Extinction of the dinosaurs
Students then read about three possible theories to explain the extinction of dinosaurs using a home and an expert group format by working in groups of three. They must teach each other about the different theories suggested, decide on the theory that seems most credible, and answer the questions.	**Extension**: The information sheet on the super-volcano theory is most conceptually challenging, and contains a mixture of evidence supporting and refuting the theory for students to evaluate.	
Please note that the three information sheets provided are ramped and should be allocated accordingly.		

Plenary	Support/Extension	Resources
Why bother with gene banks? (10 min) Ask students to explain what the term gene bank means and give examples of the gene banks available. Students should explain why gene banks are necessary, and why humans want to safeguard endangered species.		
Fact or theory? (5 min) Discuss as a class the conclusions from the dinosaur extinction activity. Ask students to explain the differences between fact and theory. Students should suggest reasons why it is difficult to prove which of the three theories is actually true.	**Support**: Different facts and theories can be provided to students for them to categorise. **Extension**: Students should give the types of evidence required by scientists to prove a theory.	

Homework		
Students write a paragraph to explain in detail how scientists could have used gene banks to save the dinosaurs. Students should also research the importance of biodiversity in organisms in order to prevent extinction.		
An alternative WebQuest homework activity is also available on Kerboodle where students research an extinct organism.		**WebQuest**: Extinction

Checkpoint lesson routes

The route through this lesson can be determined using the Checkpoint assessment. Percentage pass marks are supplied in the Checkpoint teacher notes.

Route A (support)

Resources: B2 Chapter 3 Checkpoint: Revision

Students work through tasks in the revision activity, to improve understanding and use of vocabulary, and compose detailed descriptions. They are also supported in producing a histogram.

Route B (extension)

Resources: B2 Chapter 3 Checkpoint: Extension

Students will complete a Twin studies case study task to extend their knowledge of variation.

Progression to *secure*

No.	Developing outcome	Secure outcome	Making progress
1	State some resources that plants and animals compete for.	Describe some resources that plants and animals compete for.	In Task 1 students are first asked to identify the resources, and must then write a paragraph to demonstrate they know why animals and plants compete for each resource.
2	State what is meant by the term adaptation.	Describe how organisms are adapted to their environments.	Task 2 helps students to provide full answers, describing adaptations for given examples and explaining how they help the organism survive.
3	Name an environmental change.	Describe how organisms adapt to environmental changes.	In Task 3 there is a focus on vocabulary. Students are given key words (e.g., hibernation) and are asked to write definitions and think of examples.
4	Give a possible reason for adaptation or extinction.	Describe how competition can lead to adaptation.	It is important to reinforce that competition might drive adaptation in a population over time, not an individual. Failure of the population to adapt might lead to extinction. An example is given in Task 3 for students to extract information from.
5	State what is meant by the term variation and state that variation is caused by the environment or inheritance.	Describe how variation in species occurs and describe the difference between environmental and inherited variation.	Students need to select the correct definition of variation in Task 4, and can then go on to identify environmental and inherited characteristics in the given example.
6	State that there are two types of variation.	Describe the difference between continuous and discontinuous variation.	Discuss with students variations in blood group and height. In Task 5 students are given prompts to help them recognise the difference.
7	State the two types of graphs that can be drawn when representing the two types of variation.	Represent variation within a species using graphs.	In Task 5 students are given a step-by-step guide to help them plot a histogram. Before plotting their graph they are asked to predict the shape of the graph from given examples.
8	State what is meant by a gene.	Describe how characteristics are inherited.	Students may struggle understanding the relationship between DNA, chromosomes, and characteristics. Students may not realise that chromosomes are made from DNA, and so demonstrating the difference in size may be helpful. Students can complete a cloze activity in Task 6.
9	State how survival rates differ for successful adaptation.	Describe the process of natural selection.	You can use a mnemonic 'Not Very Clear And Simple Problem' where: N = numbers in population large A = adaptations may give V = variation between advantages individuals S = survival of the fittest C = competition to survive P = pass on genes Students can then begin to complete Task 6, in which they are given guidance to write a full description.
10	State that organisms have changed over time.	Describe how organisms evolve over time.	Students are given a template to complete in Task 6, which will help them understand the process of evolution for a given example.

11	State what is meant by the term extinction.	Describe some factors that may lead to extinction.	Use the factors the can cause extinction to pose scenarios to students. Students can consider what could happen in each case. In Task 7 students can identify factors in a given example.
12	State how scientists try to prevent extinction.	Describe the purpose of gene banks.	Start with asking students 'How did they bring the dinosaurs back in Jurassic Park?'. Most will answer that the scientists had the DNA. Then expand the discussion to suggesting if we could store the DNA for any species we could keep the species alive.

Answers to end-of-chapter questions

1a Arctic (1 mark)   **b** white fur– camouflage   large feet– to stop the bear sinking into snow
thick fur– insulation   sharp claws and teeth– to catch and eat prey (4 marks)

2a shelter/food (1 mark)   **b** Different to **a**, for example: food/shelter/mates (1 mark)
  c Plants are producers they make their own food using photosynthesis. (2 marks)   **d** light (1 mark)

3a nucleus (1 mark)   **b** DNA (1 mark)   **c** A chromosome is a long strand of DNA. A gene is a (short) section of DNA. Chromosomes contain many genes and each gene codes for a single characteristic. (2 marks)
  d Half of chromosomes come from the mother and half from the father. Genetic material is transferred from mother via the egg and from father via sperm. Sperm and egg's genetic material combine during fertilisation. Embryo/fertilised egg contain pairs of chromosomes/46 chromosomes. (4 marks)

4a fossils (of dinosaur skeletons) (1 mark)   **b** No organisms of that species are alive anywhere in the world. (1 mark)
  c The introduction of new predators can mean more organisms in a species are eaten than number of offspring produced. Destruction of habitat can mean loss of shelter for organisms, which leads to the death of individuals through exposure. Credit any other sensible suggestions of causes of extinction with a relevant explanation. (4 marks)
  d Gene banks store genetic samples, for example, seeds/eggs/sperm/tissue. Samples from gene bank can be used to create new organisms in the future. Samples can also be used for research. (3 marks)

5a Differences in a characteristic within a species. (1 mark)   **b** balance/(bathroom) scales (1 mark)
  c histogram (1 mark)   **d** x-axis for mass of student, y-axis for number of students (2 marks)
  e Each student's body mass could take any value (between the smallest and largest mass). (1 mark)
  f Some variation is passed on in genes (from parents). This is inherited variation. Diet/exercise/lifestyle also affect body mass. This is environmental variation. Overall body mass is a result of both environmental and inherited variation. (4 marks)

6 This is a QWC question. Students should be marked on the use of good English, organisation of information, spelling and grammar, and correct use of specialist scientific terms. The best answers will provide an full overview of the process of natural selection in a logical order (maximum of 6 marks).
Examples of correct scientific points:
Organisms evolve through natural selection slowly over time.
Organisms in a species show variation – this is caused by differences in their genes.
The organisms with the characteristics that are best adapted to the environment survive and reproduce.
Less well adapted organisms die.
This process is known as 'survival of the fittest'.
Genes from successful organisms are passed to the offspring in the next generation.
This means the offspring are likely to possess the characteristics that made their parents successful.
This process is then repeated many times.
Over a long period of time this can lead to the development of a new species.

Answer guide for Big Write

Developing	Secure	Extending
1–2 marks	3–4 marks	5–6 marks
• The presentation has little or no logical structure. However, the student has correctly used at least one scientific term. • An attempt has been made to explain the process of natural selection, but this may contain some misconceptions.	• The presentation contains some structure. The student has correctly used at least two scientific terms. • The process of natural selection has been explained, but may lack detail.	• The presentation is well structured. The student has correctly used a range of scientific terms. • The student has clearly explained the process of natural selection through the example of the peppered moth.

kerboodle

B2 Chapter 3 Checkpoint assessment (automarked)	B2 Chapter 3 Checkpoint: Extension
B2 Chapter 3 Checkpoint: Revision	B2 Chapter 3 Progress task (Handling information)

Chemistry (2)

Preparing for Key Stage 4 Success

Knowledge Underpinning knowledge is covered in this unit for KS4 study of:	• The principles underpinning the modern Periodic Table • Properties and trends in properties of elements in Groups 1, 7, and 0 • Chemical symbols and formulae • Chemical equations, including state symbols • Reactions of acids • Displacement reactions as redox reactions • The reactivity series of metals • Pure and impure substances • Separation techniques for mixtures of substances • Ceramics, polymers, and composites • The efficacy of recycling • The composition and evolution of the atmosphere since its formation • Carbon dioxide and methane as greenhouse gases
Maths Skills developed in this unit. (Topic number)	• Quantitative problem solving (3.5, 4.7). • Understand and use direct proportion and simple ratios (3.2, 3.3, 3.5, 4.7). • Use of calculations with and conversion between fractions, percentages, and ratios (3.5, 4.5). • Calculate arithmetic means (4.3). • Extract and interpret information from charts, graphs, and tables (1.1, 1.2, 1.3, 1.4, 1.5, 2.1, 2.2, 2.3, 3.6, 4.1, 4.6). • Plot and draw graphs selecting appropriate scales for the axes (1.2, 1.3, 1.4, 1.5, 3.7, 4.7). • Understand number size and scale and the quantitative relationship between units (1.1, 1.2, 1.3, 1.4, 1.5, 3.7, 4.4). • Carry out calculations involving $+$, $-$, $\times$, $\div$, either singly or in combination (2.2, 2.4, 2.6). • Understand and use the symbols $=$, $<$, $>$, $\sim$ (3.4).
Literacy Skills developed in this unit. (Topic number)	• Identify meaning in scientific text, taking into account potential bias (1.2, end-of-chapter 1, 2.6). • Summarise a range of information from different sources (1.2, 1.3, 1.5, 2.2, end-of-chapter 2, 3.1, 3.2, 3.6, 3.8, 4.1, 4.4). • Use scientific terms confidently and correctly in discussions and writing (2.2, 2.4, 2.6, end-of-chapter 2, 3.2, 3.6, 4.2, 4.4). • Collaboration and contribution to group discussions (1.4, 1.5, 2.3, 2.5, 2.6, 3.3, 3.4, 4.1, 4.2, 4.4, 4.6). • Identify main ideas and supporting evidence in text (1.2 ,1.4, 1.5, 2.2, 2.3, 2.5, 3.4, 3.5, 3.7, 3.8, 4.2, 4.3, 4.4, 4.7). • Use largely correct form in a range of writing styles and text, and include information relevant to the audience (1.4, 2.2, 2.3, 3.3, 3.6, 4.4, 4.6). • Ideas are organised into well-developed, linked paragraphs (1.1, 1.3, 1.4, 2.1, 2.6, 3.1, 3.4, 3.6, 3.7, 3.8, 4.1, 4.3, 4.5).

- QWC questions: (1.1, 1.3, 1.4, 2.1, 2.3, 2.5, 3.1, 3.3, 3.5, 3.7, 4.1, 4.3, 4.6, 4.7) (end-of-chapter 1 Q3, end-of-chapter 2 Q 3, end-of-chapter 3 Q6, end-of-chapter 4 Q5).

- Quantitative problem solving: (1.2, 1.3, 1.4, 2.3, 3.5, 3.7, 4.1, 4.3, 4.6, 4.7) (end-of-chapter 1 Q1, end-of-chapter 2 Q2, Q4).

- Application of Working Scientifically: (1.1, 1.5, 2.1, 2.2, 2.4, 2.5, 2.6, 3.1, 3.2, 3.3, 3.4, 3.6, 3.8, 4.2, 4.4, 4.5) (end-of-chapter 1 Case Study, end-of-chapter 2 Q2, end-of-chapter 3 Case Study, Q2, end-of-chapter 4 Case Study, Q4).

KS2 Link	Check before:	Checkpoint	Catch-up
All materials are made up of one or more elements.	C2 2.1 What are mixtures	Students discuss the differences between elements, compounds, and mixtures.	Students use beads, models, or particle diagrams to show the differences between elements, compounds, and mixtures.
Mixtures can be separated through filtering, sieving, and evaporating.	C2 2.4 Filtration	Students explain how they would separate named mixtures.	Use diagrams, animations, and simulations to demonstrate the difference between basic separation techniques.
Some changes result in the formation of new materials, which are not reversible.	C2 3.1 Acids and metals	Demonstrate bicarbonate of soda reacting with vinegar. Students list the signs of reactions observed and explain whether this is a reversible or irreversible change.	Students compare bread being toasted with chocolate being melted and cooled.
Changes that are not reversible include burning, oxidation, and reactions of acid.	C2 3.1 Acids and metals	Ask students if lighting a match is a reaction that can be reversed or what happens when bread is toasted.	Demonstrate a match being lit. Show how it looks before and after the reaction. Discuss the new substances that have been formed.
The properties of everyday materials, for example, hardness and solubility.	C2 3.6 Ceramics	Ask students to write a list of different properties a material can possess.	Students use a card sort activity to match the properties of substances to their definitions.
Properties of materials that make them suitable for particular purposes.	C2 3.6 Ceramics	Students explain why they wouldn't use lead to make a shopping bag.	Compare items with their uses, for example, a strong iron nail compared with silk used in clothing.
Simple descriptions of the three states of matter.	C2 4.1 The Earth and its atmosphere	Students name two materials for each state, giving the characteristics of each state of matter.	Give simple materials to observe and classify, such as chocolate and water.
Rocks can be grouped according to their appearance and properties.	C2 4.2 Sedimentary rocks	Students use hand lenses to group rocks according to their appearance.	Provide students with a list of possible properties to look out for when observing rocks and repeat the exercise.
The effect of temperature on substances such as chocolate, butter, and cream.	C2 4.3 Igneous and metamorphic rocks	Ask students to explain what happens to a chocolate bar in a hot car.	Demonstrate the melting of wax and allow students to observe it cooling back to a solid.
Dissolving, mixing, and changes of state, are reversible changes.	C2 4.3 Igneous and metamorphic rocks	Students explain what happens to melted chocolate if it is put into a fridge.	Observe melted chocolate after being placed in a fridge.

kerboodle

C2 Unit pre-test	C2 Practical project hints: writing frame
C2 Big practical project (foundation)	C2 End-of-unit test (foundation)
C2 Big practical project (higher)	C2 End-of-unit test (foundation) mark scheme
C2 Big practical project teacher notes	C2 End-of-unit test (higher)
C2 Practical project hints: graph plotting	C2 End-of-unit test (higher) mark scheme
C2 Practical project hints: planning	

Answers to Picture Puzzlers
Key Words

mercury, explosion, test tube, acid, lava
The key word is **metal**.

Close Up

Banded iron rock with coloured mineral layers.

1.1 Metals and non-metals

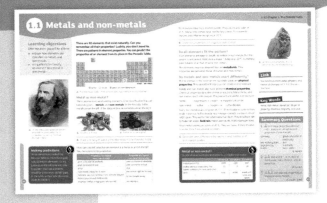

Chemistry NC link:
- the Periodic Table: metals and non-metals
- the properties of metals and non-metals
- the chemical properties of metal and non-metal oxides with respect to acidity.

Working Scientifically NC link:
- interpret observations and data, including identifying patterns and using observations, measurements, and data to draw conclusions.

Band	Outcome	Checkpoint	
		Question	**Activity**
Developing	State some common properties of metals and non-metals (Level 3).	B, C, 1	Starter 1, Main, Plenary 1, Plenary 2
	Use position on the Periodic Table to suggest if an element is a metal or a non-metal (Level 4).	A, 2	Starter 1
	State what observations are needed about materials to decide if they are metal or non-metal (Level 4).		Main
Secure	Explain how elements are classified as metals and non-metals (Level 5).	B, C, 1, 3	WS, Main
	Use patterns to classify an element as a metal or non-metal (Level 6).	C	WS, Starter 1, Main
	Use observations about materials to decide if they are metals or non-metals (Level 5).		Main
Extending	Classify properties of metalloids into metallic and non-metallic properties (Level 7).		WS
	Predict the properties of an element, given its position on the Periodic Table (Level 7).	2	Main
	Identify anomalous properties exhibited by some materials (Level 7).		Main

Maths
Students will show their understanding of number scales when interpreting melting-point and electrical-conductivity data to classify materials into metals and non-metals.

Literacy
Students will organise ideas and information in order to compare the properties of metals and non-metals and answer subsequent questions.

APP
Students record observations in a suitable results table (AF3) and use patterns in the data obtained to classify materials into metals and non-metals (AF5).

Key Words
metal, non-metal, metalloid, physical property, chemical property, acid rain

Answers from the student book

In-text questions	**A** Metals are on the left-hand side and non-metals on the right-hand side of the Periodic Table.
	B poor conductivity of electricity, poor conductivity of heat, dull, low density, brittle, and not sonorous
	C Metal oxides are basic, non-metal oxides are acidic. Most metal oxides are solids at 20 °C, non-metal oxides are usually gases at 20 °C.
Activity	**Metal or non-metal?**
	X is a metal because of its high melting point, electrical conductivity, and basic oxide.
	Y is a non-metal due to its low melting point, inability to conduct electricity, and acidic oxide.
	Z is likely to be a metalloid, as it exhibits properties of both metals (conductivity) and non-metals (reasonably low melting point).

Summary Questions	1 metals: sonorous, good conductors of electricity, high density, malleable, basic oxides
	non-metals: low melting points, dull, brittle (8 marks)
	2 Element A is likely to be a metal, which means it will be (credit six of the following): good conductor of electricity, good conductor of heat, shiny, high density, malleable, ductile, sonorous. (6 marks)
	3 QWC question (6 marks). Example answers:
	Metals are good conductors of heat and electricity, but non-metals are not. Metals are shiny, but non-metals are dull. The density of metals is much higher than that of non-metals. Metals are malleable and ductile, whereas non-metals are brittle. Metals are also sonorous, whereas non-metals are not.

kerboodle

Starter	Support/Extension	Resources
An alternative question-led lesson is also available.		**Question-led lesson**: Metals and non-metals
Spotting metals (10 min) Provide students with a copy of the Periodic Table and ask them to highlight any metals they are familiar with. Students should state typical properties of metals. This will allow you to see any preconceptions regarding the classification of elements. Ask students if they can spot a pattern in recognising metals on the Periodic Table.	**Support**: Ensure students are provided with simplified Periodic Table (with element names included and lanthanides and actinides omitted). **Extension**: Students should apply this newly acquired pattern to predict if an unknown element is a metal or a non-metal.	
Grouping materials (10 min) Provide students with a selection of materials around the room. Ask students to come up with as many ways as possible that they could group the materials. This exercise will allow you to gauge the level of confidence students have in using key terms such as solids, liquids, and gases, as well as metals and non-metals.	**Support**: Students may require prompts on groups to classify materials into.	

Main	Support/Extension	Resources
Classifying metals and non-metals (40 min) Introduce the Periodic Table and discuss with students that materials can be classified in many ways, one of which is metals and non-metals. Discuss the properties exhibited by each group by using the corresponding table of properties in the student book. Students then carry out a simple practical to investigate the properties of unknown materials to classify them as metals or non-metals, and answer the questions that follow.	**Support**: The accompanying support sheet contains a suggested results table and an explanation of new vocabulary. **Extension**: Students should be provided with materials that are metalloids, such as graphite.	**Practical**: Classifying metals and non-metals **Skill sheet**: Recording results

Plenary	Support/Extension	Resources
Recalling properties (5 min) Students write out the words metal and non-metal on their mini-whiteboards. (This works best if the mini-whiteboards are double-sided.) Call out typical properties of metals and non-metals, and students should hold up their mini-whiteboards to show whether the property is that of a metal or non-metal. This is a useful exercise to revise the properties of metals and non-metals, while ensuring whole-class participation.		
Spotting properties (5 min) Students locate key properties of metals and non-metals using the wordsearch on the interactive resource. Students who find these properties should only be credited if they can also state whether this property is one of metals or non-metals.	**Extension**: Students may be able to offer examples of metals and non-metal elements.	**Interactive**: Spotting properties

Homework		
Students find five items around their home and decide if they are metals or non-metals. They write down the properties they used to make this decision. Students must be told that certain tests should NOT be carried out, for example, to decide if something has a high melting point by heating, or testing whether something is brittle by dropping the object in question.		

Chemistry NC link:
- the Periodic Table: periods and groups
- the principles underpinning the Mendeleev Periodic Table.

Working Scientifically NC link:
- apply mathematical concepts and calculate results.

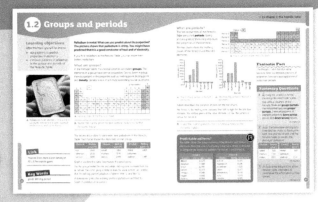

Band	Outcome	Checkpoint	
		Question	Activity
Developing	Identify changes in properties between elements of the same group or period (Level 4).	2	Maths, Main
	Describe in simple terms what pattern is shown in a given property of a group or period (Level 4).	2	Maths, Main
	Describe trends shown by numerical data (Level 4).		Maths, Main
Secure	Use patterns to predict properties of elements (Level 6).	2	Main
	Compare patterns in properties in the groups and periods of the Periodic Table (Level 5).	2	Maths, Main
	Use trends shown by numerical data to predict missing values (Level 6).	2	Main
Extending	Explain how the position of an element can be used to suggest properties of elements (Level 7).		Main
	Apply patterns shown within groups or periods to unknown elements (Level 7).	2	Main
	Explain how missing values can be predicted using numerical trends, and compare similar trends between groups and periods (Level 7).		Maths, Main

Maths
Students interpret numerical data in tables, draw bar charts to represent this data, and predict numerical values of missing data based on trends shown in the student-book questions and activity.

Literacy
Students predict and describe relationships between elements using scientific terminology when answering questions.

APP
Students identify and analyse the development of the Periodic Table through the emergence of new, accepted ideas and evidence (AF1).

Key Words
group, density, period

Answers from the student book

In-text questions	**A** groups
	B periods
Activity	**Predictable patterns?**
	Credit bar charts to show atomic radii of elements in Period 2 and Period 3.
	For both periods, atomic radii are larger at the start of the period (Li and Na) than at the end (F and Cl).
	Atomic radii decrease more rapidly at the start of a period than at the end.
	Atomic radii for Period 3 are larger than those of Period 2.

Summary Questions	
	1 groups, periods, down, across (4 marks)
	2 Credit suitable bar charts for density data (one for cobalt, rhodium, and iridium, and another for nickel and platinum). Credit a predicted palladium density of 9–15 g/cm^3. The actual density of palladium is 10.4 g/cm^3. (3 marks)
	3 Example answers (6 marks):
	Vertical columns are called groups. Horizontal rows are called periods. Numerical data for one element can be predicted given data of surrounding elements. These elements can be neighbouring elements in periods or groups. Melting points increase down a group. Atomic radii decrease across a period. The density of elements increases down a group.

kerboodle

Starter	Support/Extension	Resources
Finding elements (5 min) Call out element names, symbols, or clues about elements such as well-known uses, and ask students to locate them on a Periodic Table. When they find them, students should describe the location in terms of how many rows down and how many columns across.		
Elemental mnemonic (10 min) Ask groups of students to pick a period or group of the Periodic Table and make up a mnemonic or song to see if they can remember the order. Reassure the students that this is just to get them familiar with the Periodic Table – they will not need to remember the actual location of elements in the Periodic Table.		

Main	Support/Extension	Resources
Patterns, groups, and periods in the Periodic Table (40 min) Discuss the layout of the Periodic Table, including an introduction to the terms groups and periods. Explain how scientists have built up a wealth of data on elements, and how similarities in properties, both physical (melting point) and chemical (types of reactions) have led to the current layout of the Periodic Table. Use one example of periodic trends to illustrate this. The student book contains several examples of periodic trends. Students then carry out the task on the activity sheet and answer the questions that follow. Students should also carry out the Maths task and Summary Question 2 on the corresponding student-book spread if time.		**Activity**: Patterns, groups, and periods in the Periodic Table

Plenary	Support/Extension	Resources
Recalling patterns (10 min) In small groups, ask students to list as many chemical and physical properties as possible, and recall as many trends as they can from the discussions this lesson.	**Support**: Prompts for properties to consider can be given for discussion.	
Patterns in the Periodic Table (5 min) Students drag possible missing values in a table of data illustrating trends in the Periodic Table, using the interactive resource. Students should justify the choice of a particular value based on patterns shown in the table, using their scientific knowledge and the Periodic Table to help them.	**Extension**: Students should identify the odd one out in the table (colour) and suggest why this cannot be predicted.	**Interactive**: Patterns in the Periodic Table

Homework	Support/Extension	
Students write a short paragraph about the history of the Periodic Table. You may wish to give students key words and people to include, such as patterns, Newlands, Mendeleev, metals, non-metals, groups, and periods.	**Extension**: Students should include what the future holds for the Periodic Table, including the name of a recently-discovered element and its properties.	

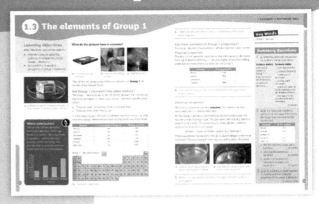

Chemistry NC link:

- the varying physical and chemical properties of different elements
- how patterns in reactions can be predicted with reference to the Periodic Table.

Working Scientifically NC link:

- make and record observations and measurements using a range of methods for different investigations.

Band	Outcome	Checkpoint	
		Question	Activity
Developing	Describe, in simple terms, how one property changes for the elements of Group 1 (Level 4).	B, 2	WS, Main, Plenary 1, Plenary 2
	State the products of the reaction between two Group 1 metals with water (Level 4).	C	Main, Homework
	Make simple observations about the reactivity of Group 1 metals in water (Level 4).		Main
Secure	Interpret data to describe patterns in properties of the Group 1 elements (Level 6).	B, 2	WS
	Use patterns to predict properties of Group 1 elements (Level 6).	2	Main
	Record observations about how Group 1 metals react with water, and the pH of the solution formed (Level 5).		Main
Extending	Describe patterns in the properties of Group 1 elements using data given (Level 7).	B, 2	WS, Main
	Compare predictions with evidence, and from reactions involving Group 1 elements (Level 7).		Main
	Use experimental observations to explain reactivity trends in Group 1, and write balanced equations to explain the reactions observed (Level 8).		Main

Maths

Students interpret and plot bar graphs when answering questions in the student book.

Literacy

Students use scientific terminology to describe the patterns exhibited by the Group 1 metals when explaining observations from the demonstrations of Group 1 metals reacting with water.

APP

Students interpret experimental observations to find patterns and draw conclusions about the reactivity trends of Group 1 metals (AF5).

Key Words

Group 1, reactive

Answers from the student book

In-text questions	**A** Group 1 metals have lower melting points than other metals.
	B decreases
	C hydrogen

Activity	**Which conclusion?**
	Credit reasonable explanations that support either Sam's or Ben's theory.
	A more detailed description of the pattern may be: The density of Group 1 metals increases down the group in a roughly linear fashion. Potassium is an anomaly because it has a smaller density than that of sodium. Densities of caesium and francium are required to understand the trend in Group 1 metal densities better.
Summary Questions	**1** Any five from:
	From top to bottom of Group 1, boiling point decreases.
	From top to bottom of Group 1, the vigour of the reaction with water increases.
	From bottom to top of Group 1, melting point increases.
	All Group 1 elements have low densities.
	All Group 1 elements conduct electricity.
	All Group 1 elements react with water to make hydrogen and an alkaline solution.
	2a Credit appropriate bar chart, with hardness decreasing from Li to Cs. (6 marks)
	b Hardness decreases down Group 1. (2 marks)
	c 0.4, because hardness decreases by 0.1 for each element down Group 1. (2 marks)
	3 QWC question (6 marks). Example answers:
	Physical properties down Group 1: decreasing hardness, decreasing melting point, decreasing boiling point.
	Chemical properties down Group 1: increased reactivity with water.

Starter	Support/Extension	Resources
Group 1 elements (10 min) Ask students to locate Group 1 on the Periodic Table, and find out the names of the elements in it. Pose the question 'Are these metals or non-metals?'. This is a good opportunity to correct any confusion between periods and groups from the previous lesson, and consolidate existing knowledge by asking students to suggest possible similarities and differences between the elements in Group 1.		
Recalling pH values (10 min) Ask students to recall the pH values for acids and alkalis, and to describe the colours seen when universal indicator is added to each. Ask students to suggest reasons pH is being discussed in a lesson about Group 1 elements. (Group 1 elements react with oxygen to form bases.)	**Extension**: Students can be shown a pH probe so the discussion can lead to accuracy and precision.	

Main	Support/Extension	Resources
How do Group 1 elements react with water (40 min) Demonstrate the reactions of lithium, sodium, and potassium with water, whilst students record their observations in their results table. Students should discuss and suggest what they expect the reactions of rubidium, caesium, and francium would be like, based on the reactivity trends they have observed and work through the questions that follow. Students then complete the questions on the activity sheet before being shown video clips from the Internet of the reactions of rubidium and caesium in water.	**Extension**: Students should justify predictions for the reactions between rubidium, caesium, and francium with water, using scientific terminology and periodic trends.	**Activity**: How do Group 1 elements react with water **Skill sheet**: Recording results

Plenary	Support/Extension	Resources
Facts about Group 1 (5 min) Students consolidate what they have learnt from this lesson, and the previous lesson on Group 1 trends using the interactive resource. Students are required to categorise statements according to whether they are true or false, and correct the statements that are false.	**Extension**: Students should explain why they have corrected the statements that are false using their scientific knowledge.	**Interactive**: Facts about Group 1
Pattern paragraphs (5 min) Ask students to write a short paragraph, without using their notes from the lesson, describing the patterns they can recall about the Group 1 elements.		

Homework		
Students write a paragraph on why Group 1 metals would not be suitable metals to make saucepans from. Encourage students to research other reactions of Group 1 metals, other than those with water, to justify their answer.		

1.4 The elements of Group 7

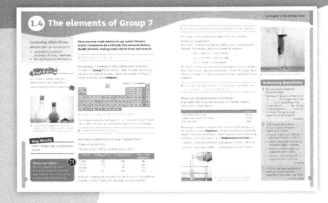

Chemistry NC link:

- the varying physical and chemical properties of different elements
- how patterns in reactions can be predicted with reference to the Periodic Table.

Working Scientifically NC link:

- evaluate risks.

Band	Outcome	Checkpoint	
		Question	Activity
Developing	State a pattern shown by the Group 7 elements (Level 4).	C, D, 1	Main 2
	State simply what happens in a displacement reaction (Level 4).	2	Main 2, Plenary 1
	State what hazards are associated with the Group 7 elements (Level 4).		Main 2, Homework
Secure	Use patterns to predict properties of Group 7 elements (Level 6).	2	Main 2, Plenary 2
	Describe displacement reactions (Level 5).	3	Main 2, Plenary 1
	Identify risks of using Group 7 elements using the hazard symbols associated with them (Level 5).		Main 2, Homework
Extending	Explain any predictions made about the Group 7 elements (Level 7).	2	Main 2, Plenary 2
	Write word equations to represent displacement reactions (Level 7).		Main 2, Plenary 2
	Suggest where to find information about the risks of the Group 7 elements and how to control these (Level 7).		Main 2, Homework

Maths

In the student-book activity students plot bar charts for boiling-point data for Group 7 elements.

Students are required to interpret numerical data in tables to spot trends in physical properties of Group 7 elements.

Literacy

Students use scientific terminology when discussing the risks and uses of Group 7 elements and compounds, and when describing displacement reactions of halides.

APP

Students record observations appropriately in a results table (AF3), interpret patterns in experimental data to draw conclusions relating to the reactivity of Group 7 elements (AF5), and identify risks of Group 7 elements and how to control them (AF4).

Key Words

Group 7, halogen, displace, displacement reaction

Answers from the student book

In-text questions	**A** Destroy bacteria to make water safe to drink or swim in.
	B fluorine, chlorine, bromine, iodine, astatine
	C Boiling points increase down Group 7.
	D Reactions become less vigorous down the group.
Activity	**Better bar charts** Credit correctly drawn bar charts where boiling points increase down Group 7 (from F to At). Students should offer suggestions on how to improve each other's bar charts.

Summary Questions	1 halogens, right, non-metals, increase, less (5 marks)
	2 Reactions a, c, and d will happen. In each case the Group 7 element on its own is more reactive/higher up in Group 7 than the Group 7 element in the compound. A displacement reaction occurs. (6 marks)
	3 QWC question (6 marks). Example answers:
	As non-metals, Group 7 elements do not conduct electricity. They have low melting points that increase down the group. They have low boiling points that increase down the group. Fluorine and chlorine are gases, but bromine is a liquid and; iodine and astatine are solids. Reactivity of Group 7 elements decreases down the group. This means that halogens can displace metal halides in chemical reactions.

Starter	Support/Extension	Resources
Locating the Group 7 elements (10 min) Students locate the Group 7 elements in the Periodic Table and make a list of their names and symbols. Students state whether Group 7 elements are metals or non-metals based on their location, and give possible trends in physical and chemical properties. (Students are likely to get this wrong, since the trends for Group 7 are the opposite to those of Group 1.)		
Group 7 elements and their compounds (10 min) In small groups ask students to locate the elements of Group 7 in the Periodic Table and make a list of substances that they think contain Group 7 elements or compounds. Discuss ideas as a class.	**Extension**: Students link everyday observations to their scientific understanding, for example, swimming pools or bleach with chlorine.	

Main	Support/Extension	Resources
Introducing Group 7 (10 min) Show students samples of chlorine, bromine, and iodine in a fume cupboard. Explain that the Group 7 elements are known as the halogens, and are very reactive and very hazardous. Demonstrate, using simple experiments, that reactivity decreases down Group 7 (unlike Group 1). If demonstrations are difficult to carry out, then use video clips on the Internet. Discuss that as you move down the group, from fluorine to iodine, the elements become less reactive.		
Displacement of halides (30 min) Students watch a teacher-led demonstration or video clips for the displacement of potassium halide solutions using chlorine, bromine, and iodine water. Students fill in their observations in the results table provided and carry out a short task evaluating the hazards of Group 7 elements. Students answer the questions on the activity sheet. This consolidates reactivity trends in Group 7 elements and introduces displacement reactions. (Displacement reactions are covered later for metals and metal salts.)	**Support**: The support sheet includes descriptions of hazard symbols to use in the first task, and example word equations to use as guidance when writing about displacement reactions.	**Activity**: Displacement of halides

Plenary	Support/Extension	Resources
Displacement (5 min) Ask students to state the definition of displacement and then explain what happens in a displacement reaction using a role play.	**Support**: Use analogies when explaining displacement reactions, such as celebrity love triangles.	
Displacement (5 min) Interactive resource where students complete a paragraph on the reactivity of Group 7 elements and displacement reactions.	**Extension**: Students write balanced formula equations for the displacement reactions.	**Interactive**: Displacement

Homework		
Students produce a leaflet for swimming pools, explaining to the general public the merits and risks of adding chlorine to water. This leaflet should include suggestions on how to reduce risks.		

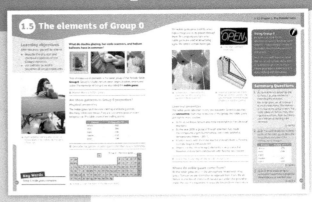

Chemistry NC link:
- the varying physical and chemical properties of different elements
- how patterns in reactions can be predicted with reference to the Periodic Table.

Working Scientifically NC link:
- interpret observations and data, including identifying patterns and using observations, measurements, and data to draw conclusions.

Band	Outcome	Checkpoint	
		Question	Activity
Developing	State a chemical and a physical property of Group 0 elements (Level 4).	1	Lit, Main 1, Main 2, Plenary 1, Plenary 2
	Describe the reactivity of Group 0 elements (Level 4).	1	Lit, Starter 2, Main 2, Plenary 2
	Interpret data to plot a graph of atomic masses for Group 0 elements (Level 4).		Main 2
Secure	Describe the physical and chemical properties of the Group 0 elements (Level 5).	B, 1–3	Lit, Main 1, Main 2, Plenary 1, Plenary 2
	Use patterns to predict properties of Group 0 elements (Level 6).	2	Main 1, Main 2
	Draw conclusions on the properties and trends of Group 0 elements based on experimental and secondary data (Level 6).		Main 2
Extending	Link information about Group 0 elements to their properties (Level 7).		Lit, Main 2, Homework
	Compare the trends in Group 0 with those of Group 1 and Group 7 elements (Level 7).		Plenary 1, Plenary 2
	Explain how missing data can be predicted by using data from other elements (Level 8).		Main 2

Maths
Students interpret numerical data from tables to draw conclusions about trends in physical properties of Group 0 elements.

They draw graphs of Group 0 atomic masses to predict the missing data.

Literacy
Students use scientific terminology when describing trends in physical properties and reactivity of Group 0 elements.

APP
Students record data appropriately in tables and graphs (AF3) and interpret data to describe patterns in the physical properties of Group 0 elements, make predictions, and draw conclusions (AF5).

Key Words
Group 0, noble gases, unreactive

Answers from the student book

In-text questions	**A** helium, neon, argon, krypton, xenon, and radon
	B Boiling points increase down Group 0.
	C Takes part in very few reactions.
Activity	**Using Group 0**
Credit suitable eye-catching and persuasive adverts about the merits of using Group 0 elements or compounds in the correct product.
For example, neon in advertising signs, helium in balloons, argon as insulating gas between the layers in double glazing, or krypton in lasers.

Summary Questions	1 The noble gases are all in Group **0** of the Periodic Table. The element at the top of the group is **helium**. The noble gases are **non-metals**. They have **very few** reactions. From bottom to top of the group, boiling point **decreases**. (5 marks) 2 Melting point increases down Group 0. Credit predictions for the melting point of argon between −180 and −220 °C. (The melting point of argon is −189.4 °C.) 3 Song or rap must include six of the following (6 marks): Melting point increases down Group 0. Boiling point increases down Group 0. They are all colourless gases at room temperature. They glow brightly when high-voltage electricity passes through them. They are all very unreactive. They are found in the atmosphere, mixed with other gases. Helium can be found with natural gas underground or under the sea.

Starter	Support/Extension	Resources
Where are the noblemen? (5 min) Students use the Periodic Table to find the names of Group 0 elements, and complete the wordsearch provided on the interactive resource.		**Interactive**: Where are the noblemen?
Why are Group 0 elements noble? (10 min) Ask students to decide in small groups what noble means. Then ask them why the Group 0 elements may be called noble. Ask students to make up a short role play of how Group 0 elements may behave in the company of other elements, given their title.	**Extension**: Students could be told that Group 0 elements are also called inert gases.	

Main	Support/Extension	Resources
What are the noble gases like? (10 min) Show photographs or video clips from the Internet of the noble gases' various uses. Inform students that the noble gases are the elements found in Group 0 of the Periodic Table and that they are very unreactive, but their reactivity slightly increases down the group. Show students the boiling point and melting point trends for Group 0 elements using the corresponding student-book spread, and discuss the trends in physical properties.		
Trends in the noble gases (30 min) Students consider data on the atomic masses of the noble gases, and use this data to plot a bar graph. Students are also required to make predictions using the data given and answer questions that follow on the activity sheet.	**Support**: A partially labelled graph grid is available to help students when drawing their bar graph.	**Activity**: Trends in the noble gases **Skill sheet**: Drawing graphs

Plenary	Support/Extension	Resources
Noble gas patterns (10 min) Ask students to write down as many patterns as they can recall about the noble gases. Discuss each pattern in turn, in order to correct any outstanding misconceptions.	**Extension**: Students should make comparisons between Group 1 and Group 7 trends.	
Reactivity (5 min) Ask students to define the words reactive and unreactive with respect to the elements in Group 1, Group 7, and Group 0.	**Extension**: Students should give examples that illustrate the difference in reactivity of the elements down the groups.	

Homework		
Students draw a humorous cartoon of the noble gases near other elements, showing and explain why they are considered to be noble.	**Extension**: Encourage students to research reasons for the unreactive nature of Group 0 elements.	
An alternative WebQuest homework activity is also available on Kerboodle where students research the Periodic Table.		**WebQuest**: The value of the Periodic Table

Checkpoint lesson routes

The route through this lesson can be determined using the Checkpoint assessment. Percentage pass marks are supplied in the Checkpoint teacher notes.

Route A (support)
Resource: C2 Chapter 1 Checkpoint: Revision

Students work through a series of tasks that allows them to gradually revisit and consolidate their understanding of the Periodic Table. Students can then use their responses to plan a documentary about the Periodic Table for homework.

Route B (extension)
Resource: C2 Chapter 1 Checkpoint: Extension

Students prepare a documentary describing some of the key features of the Periodic Table. Students plan their script to explain periodic trends of Group 1, Group 7, and Group 0 elements. Students may also plan for extra resources that illustrate patterns in the Periodic Table, for example, videos showing reactions of different elements.

Progression to *secure*

No.	Developing outcome	Secure outcome	Making progress
1	State some common properties of metals and non-metals.	Explain how elements are classified as metals and non-metals.	In Task 1 students work through a list of properties and categorise them according to properties of metals or non-metals.
2	Use position on the Periodic Table to suggest if an element is a metal or a non-metal.	Use patterns to classify an element as a metal or non-metal.	In Task 1 students are given unknown elements to sort into metals or non-metals given a series of properties.
3	Identify changes in properties between elements of the same group or period.	Use patterns to predict properties of elements.	In Task 2 students are given missing entries in a set of phase-change data. They must complete the missing entries based on patterns in the group/period.
4	Describe in simple terms what pattern is shown in a given property of a group or period.	Compare patterns in properties in the groups and periods of the Periodic Table.	In Task 2 students are given sets of data from two periods for comparison.
5	Describe, in simple terms, how one property changes for the elements of Group 1.	Interpret data to describe patterns in properties of the Group 1 elements.	In Task 3 students describe trends in reactivity, density, and melting points given relevant data for Group 1 elements.
6	State the products of the reaction between two Group 1 metals with Water.	Use patterns to predict properties of Group 1 elements.	In Task 3 students fill in missing data in the table provided using the trends shown in Group 1 metals.
7	State a pattern shown by the Group 7 elements.	Use patterns to predict properties of Group 7 elements.	In Task 4 students predict if displacement reactions of Group 7 will occur using reactivity trends in the group.
8	State simply what happens in a displacement reaction.	Describe displacement reactions.	In Task 4 students describe displacement reactions using examples from Group 7.
9	State a chemical and a physical property of Group 0 elements.	Describe the physical and chemical properties of the Group 0 elements.	In Task 5 students categorise a list of properties of Group 0 elements into chemical or physical properties.
10	Describe the reactivity of Group 0 elements.	Use patterns to predict properties of Group 0 elements.	In Task 5 students use trends provided to predict properties of Group 0 elements.

Answers to end-of-chapter questions

1a Going down the group from titanium to hafnium, melting point increases. (2 marks)

b 1850 °C (2 marks)

2a Mendeleev left gaps for elements he predicted should exist, but that had not yet been discovered. (1 mark)

b Mendeleev predicted a low melting point for the missing element, and was correct in this prediction, since 30 °C is a low melting point for a metal. (2 marks)

c So that he could find the mean value. This value is more likely to be accurate than the value obtained from one measurement. (1 mark)

d $(30.14 + 30.16 + 30.14 + 30.15 + 30.16 + 30.16) \div 6 = 30.15$ °C (1 mark)

e Mendeleev predicted a density of 6.0 g/cm^3, and Boisbaudran measured a value of 4.7 g/cm^3. Boisbaudran probably decided to do the experiment again because his value was not close to that predicted by Mendeleev. (2 marks)

3 This is a QWC question. Students should be marked on the use of good English, organisation of information, spelling and grammar, and correct use of specialist scientific terms. The best answers will provide a detailed comparison between patterns in properties of Group 1 and Group 7 elements (maximum of 6 marks).

Examples of correct scientific points:

Going down Group 1, the elements become more reactive.

For example, the reactions with water become more vigorous.

Going down Group 7, the elements become less reaction.

For example, the reactions with iron become less vigorous.

These patterns also apply to the reactions with oxygen and with displacement reactions.

Melting points decrease going down Group 1.

On the other hand, melting points increase going down Group 7.

Answer guide for Maths challenge

Developing	Secure	Extending
1–2 marks	3–4 marks	5–6 marks
• One or both bar charts include element names on the x-axis. • One Y-axis labelled correctly, but units not included. • Uneven scales on y-axes on both bar charts. • Some bars drawn accurately on both bar charts. • Sentence such as Going down Group 3, density increases or Going down Group 3, boiling point decreases.	• One or both bar charts include element names on the x-axis. • Y-axis on one bar chart labelled density, but units missing. • Y-axis on other bar chart labelled boiling point, but units missing. • Even scales on y-axes on both bar charts. • Most bars plotted accurately on both bar charts. • One or two sentences such as Going down Group 3, density increases or Going down Group 3, boiling point decreases.	• Both bar charts include element names on the x-axis. • Y-axis on one bar chart labelled density (g/cm^3). • Y-axis on other bar chart labelled boiling point (°C). • Even scales on y-axes on both bar charts. • Bars plotted accurately on both bar charts. • Sentence such as 'Going down group 3, density increases for the first three elements'. • Several sentences such as Going down Group 3, boiling point decreases. At the top, boron has the highest value of 3930 °C, and at the bottom thallium has the lowest value of 1460 °C.

kerboodle

C2 Chapter 1 Checkpoint assessment (automarked)

C2 Chapter 1 Checkpoint: Revision

C2 Chapter 1 Checkpoint: Extension

C2 Chapter 1 Progress task (Handling information)

2.1 Mixtures

Chemistry NC link:
- the concept of a pure substance
- mixtures, including dissolving
- the identification of pure substances.

Working Scientifically NC link:
- use appropriate techniques, apparatus, and materials during fieldwork and laboratory work.

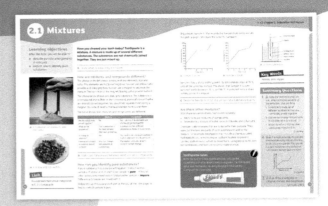

Band	Outcome	Checkpoint	
		Question	**Activity**
Developing	State that parts of mixtures are not joined together (Level 3).	A, B, 1	Plenary 1
	State that different substances in mixtures have their own melting points (Level 4).	C, 2, 3	Plenary 2
	Choose a simple separation technique with help (Level 3).		Main 2
Secure	Describe particle arrangements in mixtures (Level 5).	A, B, 1, 3	Main 2, Plenary 1
	Explain how to identify pure substances (Level 6).	C, 2	Plenary 2
	Select appropriate separation techniques for different mixtures (Level 5).		Main 2
Extending	Use particle models to represent mixtures (Level 7).		Main 2, Plenary 1
	Comment on a substance's purity by interpreting temperature change data (Level 7).	C, 2	Plenary 2
	Explain why separation techniques are suitable, in terms of the properties of constituent substances (Level 7).		Main 2

Maths
Students interpret numerical data in graphs in order to determine whether substances are pure or impure.

Literacy
Students explain the terms mixtures, pure, and impure, using these words when describing and explaining experimental observations.

APP
Students select appropriate separation techniques when separating mixtures (AF4) and interpret melting and boiling point data to draw conclusions on the purity of substances (AF5).

Key Words
mixture, impure, pure

Answers from the student book

In-text questions	**A** Several different substances not chemically joined together.
	B Credit two of the following:
	Substances in mixtures are not chemically joined together whereas in compounds they are.
	Properties of mixtures are the same as the constituent elements, whereas in compounds they are different.
	Mixtures of substances are easy to separate, whereas a chemical reaction is required to separate compounds to their elements.
	Relative amounts of elements can change in a mixture, whereas in compounds they cannot.
	C Substances with clearly-defined melting (or boiling) points are pure. If the melting or boiling of a substance occurs over a temperature range then it is impure.
Activity	**Toothpaste tales**
	Ingredients list and uses should include hydrated silica (removes plaque), sodium fluoride (prevents cavities), sodium lauryl sulfate (makes foam), carrageenan (thickens toothpaste), and titanium oxide (whitener).

Summary Questions	
	1a A mixture is made up of different substances that are **not** chemically joined together.
	b You **can** change the amounts of substances in a mixture. (**c** is correct.) (3 marks)
	2 Substance is pure because the phase change (melting or boiling) takes place at a clearly-defined temperature. (2 marks)
	3 QWC question (6 marks). Example answers:
	In a mixture substances are not joined together. In a compound the atoms of the substances are strongly joined together. Substances in mixtures keep their properties whereas compounds have different properties to the elements their made of. Substances in mixtures can be easily separated. Substances in compounds have to be separated by chemical reactions. The amount of each substance in a mixture can change, but in a compound the relative amount cannot change.

Starter	Support/Extension	Resources
An alternative question-led lesson is also available.		**Question-led lesson**: Mixtures
What is a mixture? (5 min) Students describe what they think a mixture is and give examples of any everyday mixtures they can think of. A common misconception is that mixtures cannot contain substances that appear to remain together, and students will often assume if a substance looks the same throughout (such as white toothpaste) then it cannot be a mixture, so this can cause confusion.	**Support**: Remind students of the definitions of atom, element, and compound before they proceed. **Extension**: Students recall and use the words pure and impure.	
Spot the mixtures (10 min) Students sort a list of common substances according to whether they are mixtures or not using the interactive resource. Students should justify their suggestions. Check their answers and ask students if there are any substances that they have found surprising in its category.	**Extension**: Students should suggest how mixtures are related to elements and compounds.	**Interactive**: Spot the mixtures
Main	**Support/Extension**	**Resources**
Identifying mixtures (15 min) Discuss the definition of a mixture, explaining that they contain parts which can easily be separated, and that they would be classified as impure. Explain that pure substances will have sharp melting points, whereas impure substances melt over a range of temperatures. Discuss the differences between elements, compounds, and mixtures.		
Separating mixtures (25 min) Students carry out simple experiments to separate different mixtures, choosing appropriate techniques using the apparatus provided, justifying their choice of techniques, and answer the questions that follow.	**Support**: The accompanying support sheet lists possible separation techniques and how they work.	**Practical**: Separating mixtures **Skill sheet**: Scientific apparatus
Plenary	**Support/Extension**	**Resources**
Defining mixtures (10 min) Draw particle diagrams of elements, compounds, and mixtures on the board. Students use their knowledge to decide on the category and use mini-whiteboards to display their answer. This activity will ensure full-class participation.	**Extension**: Students may draw other examples of their own, particularly if double-sided whiteboards are available.	
Pure or impure? (10 min) Draw sketch graphs for phase changes of hypothetical substances. Students use mini-whiteboards to say whether the graph shows a pure or impure substance. Select students to justify their answer.	**Extension**: Students should be able to suggest, using the direction of the line graph, whether the graph is showing the melting/boiling or freezing/condensing of a substance.	
Homework	**Support/Extension**	
Students write a list of five mixtures from around the home and local environment. Students explain how they decided the substances were mixtures.	**Extension**: Encourage students to offer suggestions on how to separate mixtures into individual substances.	

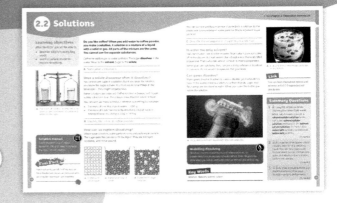

Chemistry NC link:

- mixtures, including dissolving
- the identification of pure substances.

Working Scientifically NC link:

- interpret observations and data, including identifying patterns and using observations, measurements, and data to draw conclusions.

Band	Outcome	Checkpoint	
		Question	Activity
Developing	Identify a solvent, solute, and solution in a given scenario (Level 4).	B, 1, 3	WS, Main 2, Plenary 1, Homework
	State a solution contains dissolved particles (Level 3).	A, C, 3	Plenary 2
	Use data to decide if a substance is a solution or not (Level 4).	2	Main 2
Secure	Describe solutions using key words (Level 5).	A, 3	WS
	Use the particle model to explain dissolving (Level 6).	C, 1, 3	WS, Plenary 2, Homework
	Use data to predict how much solute is dissolved in a solution or the mass of a solution (Level 6).	2	Maths, Main 2
Extending	Explain the relationship between solutes, solvents, and solutions (Level 7).	3	WS, Plenary 1
	Draw particle diagrams to represent solutions and pure substances (Level 7).	3	Main 2, Homework
	Explain the applications of solution chemistry to different contexts (Level 8).		Main 2

Maths
Students carry out subtractions to determine the mass of solutes in solution.

Students also interpret numerical data from a table to draw a line graph and answer questions.

Literacy
Students plan ways to explain dissolving to a KS2 audience in the student-book activity, using scientific terminology in the explanation.

APP
Students use models to explain how substances dissolve (AF1), record observations in tables and graphs (AF3), and draw conclusions from experimental data (AF5).

Key Words
solution, dissolve, solvent, solute

Answers from the student book

In-text questions	**A** A mixture of a liquid with a solid or gas dissolved in it.
	B coffee powder
	C Solvent particles surround solute particles. The particles are arranged randomly and can move around.
Activity	**Solution masses**
	mass of solution = 3 g + 100 g = 103 g
	Modelling dissolving
	Credit sensible suggestions for how a model for dissolving can be set up. For example, small handfuls of beans can be placed carefully at different intervals throughout a container of rice. The rice represents solvent particles and the beans represent solute particles. When mixed, the content is shaken until the beans are scattered throughout the rice.

Summary Questions	
	1 solution, solute, solvent, water, salt (5 marks)
	2 Since pure water has a density of 1 g/cm³, Laura should find the masses of each liquid on a mass balance. The liquid with a mass of 200 g will be pure water and the other two liquids will be solutions. (3 marks)
	3 Visual summary example answers (6 marks):
	Definitions of the key words solute, solvent, and solution
	How dissolving requires solvent particles to surround the solute particles
	All particles are freely moving in a solution
	Use of mass to identify solvents from solutions
	Examples of different solutions, stating the solutes and solvents used
	Particle diagrams to illustrate the points above

kerboodle

Starter	Support/Extension	Resources
When does dissolving occur? (5 min) Ask students to make a list of times when they dissolve something, and to describe in their own words what happens when substances are dissolved. This is a useful starting point to gauge student preconceptions before the lesson.	**Extension**: Encourage students to explain their observations using scientific terminology and in terms of particles.	
Do all substances dissolve? (5 min) Demonstrate salt dissolving in water in a beaker and ask the question 'Has the salt disappeared?'. This is a common misconception as the salt can no longer be seen. Some students should be able to point out that salt must still be present since the water would taste salty.	**Extension**: Encourage students to explain observations using particles.	

Main	Support/Extension	Resources
Introducing solutions (10 min) Using an everyday example such as adding coffee powder to water, define solute as the substance being dissolved (coffee powder), solvent as the substance doing the dissolving (water), and the resulting mixture as the solution (coffee). Demonstrate the conservation of mass by dissolving a known mass of coffee powder in a known mass of water (mass of coffee solution = mass of coffee powder + mass of water). Ask students to suggest possible applications of the conservation of mass (to identify pure solvents from solutions).		
Solution or not? (35 min) Students watch a demonstration (which can be turned into a student-led investigation if time) on the solubility of different solutes in a range of solvents, recording observations in a results table. Students then carry out a short task about the conservation of mass, plotting a graph, and identifying unknown substances as solvents or solutions given their volumes and masses.	**Support**: A support sheet is available with a graph grid for students to plot numerical data. **Extension**: Students should consider the advantages and disadvantages of the method investigated in deciding if an unknown sample is a solvent or a solution.	**Practical**: Solution of not? **Skill sheet**: Recording results **Skill sheet**: Drawing graphs

Plenary	Support/Extension	Resources
Solutes, solvents, and solutions (5 min) Students match the key words solute, solvent, and solution to images on the interactive resource. Students should then explain how the key words relate to one another.	**Extension**: Encourage students to link the three terms using the particle model.	**Interactive**: Solutes, solvents, and solutions
Modelling dissolving (10 min) Students design and perform role plays to describe what happens to particles when a solute dissolves. Students should ensure that their role plays illustrate the difference between solutes, solvents, and solutions.	**Extension**: Students should evaluate the strengths and weaknesses of each role play.	

Homework		
Students identify one example of dissolving that happens in the home, and draw particle diagrams to illustrate this process. They write a description of their observations, and identify the solute, solvent, and solution.		

2.3 Solubility

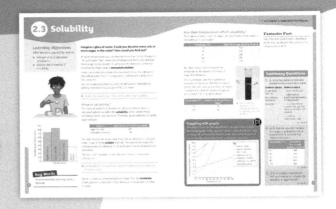

Chemistry NC link:
- mixtures, including dissolving.

Working Scientifically NC link:
- select, plan, and carry out the most appropriate types of scientific enquiries to test predictions, including identifying independent, dependent, and control variables, where appropriate.

Band	Outcome	Checkpoint	
		Question	**Activity**
Developing	Describe what happens when a solute dissolves (Level 4).		Starter , Homework
	Describe how temperature affects solubility (Level 4).	2	Main 1, Plenary 1
	Plan how to find out how much of a solute dissolves at a given temperature, with help (Level 4).	3	Main 2
Secure	Explain what a saturated solution is (Level 5).	A, 1	Plenary 1
	Explain the meaning of solubility (Level 5).	1, 2	Plenary 1
	Plan an investigation to compare solubility with temperature, considering variables (Level 5).	3	Main 2
Extending	Explain why temperature affects the amount of solute dissolved in a solution (Level 7).	2	Maths, Plenary 2
	Explain what a solubility graph shows (Level 7).	B, 2	Maths, Main 1, Plenary 2
	Justify the choice of method chosen to investigate solubility of salt in seawater (Level 7).	3	Main 2

Maths

Students will extract and interpret information from tables and graphs when completing the student-book activity and summary questions, describing trends shown in graphs and extrapolating data beyond the regions shown.

Literacy
Students use scientific terminology to explain the relationship between solubility of different solutes, and how solubility differs with changing temperatures.

APP
Students will plan an investigation to investigate how solubility changes with temperature (AF4), record results in a suitable table (AF3), and draw conclusions from experimental data (AF5).

Key Words
saturated solution, solubility, soluble, insoluble

Answers from the student book

In-text questions	**A** A solution where no more solute will dissolve.
	B lithium chloride (most), sodium chloride (least)
Activity	**Grappling with graphs**
	Solubility increases with temperature for straight-line graphs (sodium nitrate, lead nitrate, potassium chloride, and sodium chloride). Lead nitrate has the steepest gradient (solubility increases the most for each degree of temperature increase) while sodium chloride has the shallowest gradient.
	Curves for calcium chloride, potassium nitrate, and potassium chlorate (VII) show a slow increase in solubility with temperature at first, before a rapid increase after a certain temperature. Credit use of the correct temperature.
	The curve for cerium (III) sulfate is the only one to show a decrease in solubility with temperature, to a constant solubility of 3 g/100 g of water from 30 °C onwards.

Summary Questions	**1** A saturated solution is a solution that contains the greatest mass of solid that can dissolve. A saturated solution contains undissolved solid. An insoluble substance does not dissolve. Solubility is the mass of substance that dissolves in 100 g of water. (4 marks) **2** Graph should show an upward curve of decreasing gradient. This shows that solubility increases with temperature but up to a limit of approximately 700 g/100 g of water. (4 marks) **3** Credit sensible suggestions for comparing solubilities. For example, heating 100 ml of water in a beaker to different temperatures and adding known amounts of salt and sugar in each beaker. Form saturated solutions at each temperature for each solute and plot the results on graph. (6 marks)

kerboodle

Starter	Support/Extension	Resources
Describing dissolving (5 min) Ask students to write a simple description of what happens when sugar dissolves in water. The idea of particles should be used in the explanation. This activity will serve to dispel any remaining misconceptions about dissolving from the previous lesson. **Dissolving substances** (10 min) Demonstrate the differences in solubility in 20 cm³ of water for salt, calcium carbonate, and potassium permanganate. Explain that calcium carbonate is insoluble and hence all falls to the bottom, whilst the other two are both soluble, but a different amount of each can be added before the solid no longer dissolves and falls to the bottom. Explain when this happens a saturated solution has been made and that different substances have different solubility values.	**Extension**: Students may draw particle diagrams to explain the process of dissolving a particular solute. **Extension**: Ask students to suggest the relative solubilities of everyday substances, for example, sugar.	

Main	Support/Extension	Resources
Solubility graphs (10 min) Introduce the term solubility, and how this relates to saturated solutions. Explain that solubility graphs are used to compare solubility of different solutes, or to compare solubility at different temperatures. Discuss the solubility graphs on the corresponding student-book spread to ensure students are able to extract information and to quote solubility at given temperatures in the units g/100 g water. **Seawater solubility** (30 min) Students will plan a practical investigation to find out whether the solubility of salt in seawater differs according to the temperature of the region. Students carry out the investigation and record observations.	**Support**: Discuss the relevance of the units g/100 g water to facilitate students' understanding of solubility graphs and what the numbers mean. **Support**: Step-by-step guidance on writing a method and a partially filled results table are available on the support sheet.	**Activity**: Seawater solubility **Skill sheet**: Planning investigations **Skill sheet**: Recording results **Skill sheet**: Scientific apparatus

Plenary	Support/Extension	Resources
Understanding solubility (5 min) Students fill in the gaps in a short paragraph summarising solubility using the interactive resource.	**Extension**: Encourage students to give numerical examples of the difference in solubility at different temperatures using the graphs in the corresponding student-book spread.	**Interactive**: Understanding solubility
Solubility graphs (10 min) Discuss the solubility graphs shown in the corresponding student-book spread. Ask students to describe the trends shown in the graphs. Students should then use the graphs to state the solubility of particular solutes at given temperatures. This activity can be done on a mini-whiteboard.	**Extension**: Students should offer an explanation for why the solubility of different substances varies with temperature.	

Homework		
Students complete the questions on the practical sheet, and write a short paragraph to explain why sugar crystals can sometimes be found at the bottom of a teacup after the tea has been drunk.		

2.4 Filtration

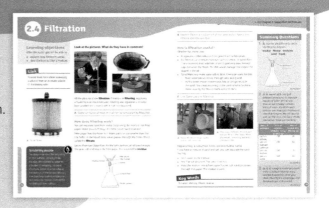

Chemistry NC link:

● simple techniques for separating mixtures: filtration, evaporation.

Working Scientifically NC link:

● use appropriate techniques, apparatus, and materials during fieldwork and laboratory work, paying attention to health and safety.

Band	Outcome	Checkpoint	
		Question	**Activity**
Developing	Name the filtrate and residue in given situations (Level 3).	B, 1	Maths, Main 2
	State some situations in which filtering is used (Level 4).	A, C	Maths, Main 1, Main 2, Homework
	Draw a labelled diagram of the apparatus needed to filter a solution (Level 4).		Main 2, Plenary 2
Secure	Explain how filtration works (Level 5).	3	Starter 2, Main 2, Plenary 1, Plenary 2, Homework
	Describe how to filter a mixture (Level 5).		Maths, Main 2, Plenary 2
	Label a diagram of apparatus used for filtration to show where the filtrate and residue are found (Level 5).	1	Main 2, Plenary 2
Extending	Use particle diagrams to illustrate how filtering works (Level 7).	3	Main 2, Homework
	Explain whether or not filtering can be used in given situations (Level 7).		Main 2
	Explain in detail how filtration apparatus can be used to separate salt from a mixture of salt and sand (Level 7).		Main 2, Plenary 2, Homework

Maths
Students carry out simple calculations and apply the concept of ratios when working through the student-book activity and summary questions.

Literacy
Students use scientific terminology to explain their experiment and in answering questions.

APP
Students use models to explain what happens to particles during filtration (AF1).

Students also plan and carry out an investigation to separate salt from a mixture of rock and salt (AF4).

Key Words
filtration, filtering, filtrate, residue

Answers from the student book

In-text questions	**A** A liquid or solution from an insoluble solid. **B** glitter = residue, water = filtrate **C** Removing coffee from ground-up coffee beans, removing solid impurities from oil, making water safe to drink.
Activity	**Solubility puzzle** Remove solid solute by filtering the solution into a pre-weighed beaker. Find the mass of the filtrate by: final mass of beaker − initial mass of beaker Pour the filtrate into a measuring cylinder to measure volume volume of solution = volume of solvent Covert volume of solvent to mass by using 1 cm³ of water = 1 g Solubility of zinc sulfate in the volume of solvent used can be found by: mass of solution − mass of solvent Scale up or down to give solubility in g/100 g of water

Summary Questions	
	1 residue and insoluble solid (top), filtrate and liquid (bottom) (4 marks)
	2 Amount of solute dissolved in 100 g of water:
	calcium chloride $= 100 - 25 = 75$ g
	calcium hydrogencarbonate $= 100 - 84 = 16$ g
	calcium bromide $= 100$ g
	calcium iodide $= 100 - 33 = 67$ g (4 marks)
	3 Students design a suitable model and identify at least one advantage and one disadvantage of their model. They have also included relevant diagrams that help describe their model. (6 marks)

Starter	Support/Extension	Resources
Filtration demonstration (10 min) Demonstrate the filtration of a mixture of sand and water. Explain that filter paper contains tiny holes, large enough for water molecules to pass through but not sand. Identify the apparatus names and introduce the terms filtrate and residue.	**Extension**: Ask students whether the residue is always discarded after filtration. Discuss that sometimes the residue is important (production of aspirin) and sometimes it can be discarded (ground coffee beans).	
Filter paper model (10 min) Introduce filtration apparatus and the terms filtrate and residue. Stretch a badminton net across the classroom, or arrange chairs with tiny gaps between them. Line up students on one side of the room and give them coloured balls. Ask students to approach the net (or chairs) and to pass the balls through the gaps. Ask students to explain this model of filtration (students = residue, coloured balls = filtrate).	**Extension**: Students should offer strengths and weaknesses of this model.	

Main	Support/Extension	Resources
Uses of filtration (15 min) Students work in pairs or small groups to gather as many ideas as possible on what filtration may be used for. Students then share these ideas as a class, before noting down two important uses of filtration in society (oil filters in cars and sand filters for drinking water).	**Extension**: Students should attempt the maths activity on the corresponding student-book spread to test their understanding and application of the concepts from this lesson and the last.	
Investigating filtration (25 min) Students solve a problem of separating salt from a mixture of rock and salt by filtration. Students start by planning the investigation, explaining why their plan works, and drawing a diagram of the filtration apparatus. They then answer the questions that follow about filtration.	**Support**: The accompanying support sheet includes diagrams of apparatus that can be used during filtration to help students draw their own labelled diagrams.	**Activity**: Investigating filtration **Skill sheet**: Planning investigations **Skill sheet**: Scientific apparatus

Plenary	Support/Extension	Resources
How does filtering work? (5 min) Students summarise key concepts and terminology from this lesson using a gap-fill exercise on the interactive resource.		**Interactive**: How does filtering work?
Filtering apparatus (5 min) Students draw a labelled diagram showing the apparatus for filtering on mini-whiteboards and define what the residue and filtrate are. Students should also give a brief description how filter paper works in separating the filtrate from the residue.	**Extension**: Students should offer detailed explanations that involve a discussion of relative particle sizes and solubility.	

Homework	Support/Extension	
Students research six uses of filtration. They should include three examples where the residue is useful, and three examples where the filtrate is useful. An explanation of how filtration works is required.	**Extension**: Students may use particle diagrams to explain this process.	

2.5 Evaporation and distillation

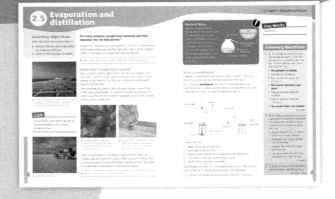

Chemistry NC link:
- simple techniques for separating mixtures: evaporation, distillation.

Working Scientifically NC link:
- interpret observations and data, including identifying patterns and using observations, measurements, and data to draw conclusions.

Band	Outcome	Checkpoint	
		Question	Activity
Developing	State some mixtures that can be separated using evaporation (Level 3).	A, B	Starter 1, Starter 2, Main, Plenary 2, Homework
	State some mixtures that can be separated using distillation (Level 3).	2, 3	Main, Plenary 2
	Label distillation apparatus (Level 4).		Main
Secure	Explain how to use evaporation to separate mixtures (Level 5).	A, 3	Starter 1, Starter 2, Homework
	Explain how distillation works (Level 6).	1, 3	Lit, Main, Plenary 1
	Explain observations made during distillation of inky water (Level 6).		Main
Extending	Compare evaporation and distillation (Level 7).	3	Plenary 1, Plenary 2
	Discuss whether evaporation or distillation would be suitable for separating a mixture (Level 7).	2, 3	Main, Plenary 2
	Consider the physical properties utilised during distillation when interpreting observations (Level 8).		Main

Maths
Students apply their understanding of the number scale when using boiling points of substances to explain distillation.

Literacy
Students discuss early scientific ideas and principles when suggesting possible ways the alembic could work.

Students also write an information leaflet explaining salt flats for a science magazine.

APP
Students draw conclusions from experimental observations (AF5) and from these observations, ask further questions that can be investigated (AF4).

Key Words
distillation

Answers from the student book

In-text questions	**A** Evaporation of water from seawater.
	B making copper sulfate crystals, drying of glue, obtaining lithium compounds from solution
Activity	**Ancient distillation** Credit sensible suggestions for how the alembic might work. Answers should include evaporation of the mixture and condensation once vapours reach the curved lid.

Summary Questions	1 correct order: B, D, F, A, E, C, G (4 marks)
	2 evaporation (a, d) and distillation (b, c) (4 marks)
	3 QWC question (6 marks). Example answers:
	Evaporation separates solute from a solution. The solvent evaporates and enters the atmosphere. The solvent cannot be obtained from evaporation. Distillation uses evaporation and condensation to obtain a solvent from a solution. Solids (main solute and other soluble impurities) remain. Only distillation can be used to obtain a solvent from solution. Both distillation and evaporation can be used to obtain solutes from solution, but evaporation uses much simpler apparatus and is therefore easier to set up, and to carry out.

Starter	Support/Extension	Resources
How do we get salt? (5 min) Ask students to suggest how salt can be obtained from seawater and why this may be a useful thing to be able to do. This is a useful recap of evaporation as students have met this in C1 Chapter 1.		
Evaporation apparatus (10 min) Show students the apparatus used for evaporation all set up. Ask students what this is used for before demonstrating the evaporation of salty water. Students should be able to see the presence of small salt crystals, but ask students where the water particles have gone and if there is any way to get them back. This activity is useful to highlight any misconceptions, such as the water particles 'disappearing'.	**Extension**: Students should compare evaporation to filtration.	

Main	Support/Extension	Resources
Distillation of inky water (40 min) Students carry out (or observe as a demonstration) how pure water is extracted from inky water. Students are required to draw a labelled diagram of the apparatus for the experiment, and answer the questions that follow.	**Support**: The accompanying support sheet contains labels students can use for their distillation diagram, as well as a suggested results table for their observations.	**Practical**: Distillation of inky water **Skill sheet**: Scientific apparatus **Skill sheet**: Recording results
If the distillation of inky water is carried out as a demonstration, time will be left over to attempt questions from the corresponding student-book spread, or to demonstrate distillation in separating mixtures using the extraction of limonene experiment. Further details of this experiment can be found on the RSC Learn Chemistry website.		

Plenary	Support/Extension	Resources
Describing evaporation and distillation (5 min) Students summarise the key stages in distillation, explaining when evaporation and distillation are used, using the gap-fill exercise on the interactive resource. This activity can also be used as a consolidation of the terms solute, solvent, and solution.		**Interactive**: Describing evaporation and distillation
Evaporation or distillation (10 min) Call out mixtures or solutions and ask students to decide if they would be suitable for separation by evaporation, distillation, or both. Students display their answers using mini-whiteboards. They should be able to justify their answers by explaining the distillation and evaporation processes.	**Extension**: Students offer an extensive comparison between the two processes.	

Homework		
Students write an article for a science magazine about why geographic areas called salt flats (huge expanses of salt) arise. Students should include scientific terminology wherever possible.		

2.6 Chromatography

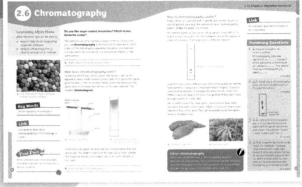

Chemistry NC link:
- simple techniques for separating mixtures: chromatography.

Working Scientifically NC link:
- interpret observations and data, including identifying patterns and using observations, measurements, and data to draw conclusions.

Band	Outcome	Checkpoint	
		Question	Activity
Developing	State what happens to mixtures when they undergo chromatography (Level 4).	A, 1	Lit, Main 2, Plenary 1
	Describe what a chromatogram looks like (Level 4).	2	Main 1, Plenary 1
	Identify the pen used to write a forged cheque by comparing chromatograms (Level 4).		Main 1
Secure	Explain how chromatography separates mixtures (Level 5).	A, 1	Lit, Main 2, Plenary 1, Plenary 2
	Analyse chromatograms to identify substances in mixtures (Level 6).	3	Main 1
	Explain how a chromatogram can be used to identify a suspect's pen (Level 6).	4	Main 1
Extending	Explain how chromatography can be used in different scenarios (Level 7).	3, 4	Lit, Main 1, Plenary 2
	Consider how chromatography can be used to monitor the progress of reactions (Level 8).		Main 1, Plenary 2
	Suggest possible issues with using chromatography (Level 8).	4	Main 1

Literacy
Students use scientific terminology when explaining what happens during chromatography, and in relation to how it can be used to aid crime-solving in the practical.

Students must also decide on the appropriate level to pitch their explanation of chromatography when writing to the general public for homework.

APP
Students will interpret chromatograms and draw conclusions from their observations (AF5).

Key Words
chromatography, chromatogram

Answers from the student book

In-text questions	**A** Chromatography separates substances in a mixture that are soluble in the same solvent.
	B The result from a chromatography experiment, where different colours have travelled up the chromatography paper by different amounts.
Activity	**Clever chromatography**
	Answers must include three uses of chromatography, for example, separating mixtures in solution, identifying coloured dyes, identifying the presence of vitamins and minerals, matching an unknown sample to a known specimen, and checking the progress of a reaction against a known product.
	Credit detailed descriptions of how chromatography is used, and check that scientific terminology has been used correctly.

Summary Questions	**1** a mixture, the same solvent, a chromatogram (3 marks) **2** Some substances are more soluble than others, and some stick to the chromatography paper more/better than others (better retention rate). (3 marks) **3** Plant A – all the pigments in the unknown plant match all the constituent pigments in plant A. (2 marks) **4** Example answers (6 marks): Place a sample of the unknown ink onto chromatography paper. Obtain samples from the three possible pens. Place dots of sample inks along a line with the unknown sample on the same piece of chromatography paper. Carry out the chromatography procedure to obtain a chromatogram. Compare chromatograms obtained and one of the samples will match the unknown ink. Possible issues: Obtaining the sample of the unknown ink from the note. If more than one person uses the same ink (same brand) then their chromatograms will look the same. Chromatography tests the ink for the soluble substances inside it, not the pen itself.

Starter	Support/Extension	Resources
How are different colours made? (5 min) Ask students to recall the primary colours and use these to explain how other colours can be made. Discuss how coloured felt-tip pens are made from a combination of dyes, and ask students to suggest ways in which we can separate the different coloured dyes. Students will most likely suggest methods they have met, such as filtration, evaporation, and distillation.	**Extension**: Students should explain why each of filtration, evaporation, and distillation, will not work for this problem.	
Colourful sweets (10 min) Place a coloured sugar-coated chocolate in the middle of a piece of filter paper. Place one drop of water on it very slowly using a pipette. Show students how the dyes in the sugar coating separate out. Discuss that the shell contains a mixture of colours and they dissolve in the water and travel outwards with the water. Discuss what this method of separation can be used for.	**Extension**: Students should predict colours they expect to see on the chromatogram based on previous knowledge about primary and secondary colours.	

Main	Support/Extension	Resources
Who stole the money? (25 min) Students carry out a short investigation using chromatography to solve a mystery involving a fraudulent cheque, before answering questions that follow.		**Practical**: Who stole the money?
Modelling chromatography (15 min) Give each student a different coloured ball or coloured piece of paper. Working in small groups, ask students to make a role play to model chromatography, which they will perform and explain to the rest of the class.	**Extension**: Students should offer strengths and weaknesses of the models demonstrated.	

Plenary	Support/Extension	Resources
Colourful sweets – part two (10 min) Students explain chromatography in terms of what they saw with the sugar-coated sweet using key ideas and scientific terminology used in this lesson. This can be done as a game of pair-share consequences, where each pair adds the next step in the chromatography procedure or explanation.		
Describing chromatography (5 min) Students re-order sentences on the interactive resource to explain what happens during chromatography.	**Extension**: Students share how chromatography is useful in determining whether a reaction has gone to completion or not.	**Interactive**: Describing chromatography

Homework		
Students prepare a newspaper article on how the fraudster from the practical was caught using chromatography.		
An alternative WebQuest homework activity is also available on Kerboodle where students research the use of chromatography in forensic science.		**WebQuest**: Chromatography and crime

Checkpoint lesson routes

The route through this lesson can be determined using the Checkpoint assessment. Percentage pass marks are supplied in the Checkpoint teacher notes.

Route A (support)
Resource: C2 Chapter 2 Checkpoint: Revision

Students work through a series of tasks that allows them to gradually revisit and consolidate their understanding of separation techniques. Students can keep this as a summary of the topic, and use this when revising for future assessments.

Route B (extension)
Resource: C2 Chapter 2 Checkpoint: Extension

Students prepare an information booklet for a trainee scientist explaining the use of separation techniques. This booklet should include particle diagrams to show how each technique works, how to set up each experiment, and how to carry out each procedure.

Progression to *secure*

No.	Developing outcome	Secure outcome	Making progress
1	State that parts of mixtures are not joined together.	Describe particle arrangements in mixtures.	In Task 1 students draw particle diagrams to describe the arrangement of particles in elements, compounds, and mixtures.
2	State that different substances in mixtures have their own melting points.	Explain how to identify pure substances.	In Task 1 students interpret heating curves for two substances, and use these to explain how pure and impure substances can be identified.
3	Identifying a solvent, solute, and solution in a given scenario.	Describe solutions using key words.	In Task 2 students use the key words solute, solvent, and solution to describe how a solution is formed.
4	State a solution contains dissolved particles.	Use the particle model to explain dissolving.	In Task 2 students use particle diagrams given (for solute, solvent, and solution) to explain what happens to a solute when it dissolves.
5	Describe what happens when a solute dissolves.	Explain what a saturated solution is.	In Task 2 students explain the term saturation and label this on a solubility curve.
6	Describe how temperature affects solubility.	Explain the meaning of solubility.	In Task 2 students use solubility data to explain and compare the solubility of different compounds in water.
7	Name the filtrate and residue in given situations.	Explain how filtration works.	In Task 3 students rearrange sentences to describe how to filter a mixture and explain how filtration works.
8	State some situations in which filtering is used.	Describe how to filter a mixture.	In Task 3 students rearrange sentences to describe how to filter a mixture and explain how filtration works.
9	State some mixtures that can be separated using evaporation.	Explain how to use evaporation to separate mixtures.	In Task 3 students complete a word fill on why evaporation can be used to obtain salt from sea water but not water from an inky solution.
10	State some mixtures that can be separated using distillation.	Explain how distillation works.	In Task 3 students complete a word fill on why evaporation can be used to obtain salt from sea water but not water from an inky solution.
11	State what happens to mixtures when they undergo chromatography.	Explain how chromatography separates mixtures.	In Task 3 students match sentences to explain how chromatography separates mixtures.
12	Describe what a chromatogram looks like.	Analyse chromatograms to identify substances in mixtures.	In Task 3 students use chromatograms provided to identify mystery substances.

Answers to end-of-chapter questions

1a Filtration. Sand would end up in the filter paper. (2 marks)

b Evaporation. Water would evaporate, leaving salt in the container/evaporating basin. (2 marks)

c Chromatography. The dye would end up on the chromatography paper, as a spot separate from spots of other colours mixed in ink from the felt-tip pen. (2 marks)

2a Mass of salt dissolved in 100 g of water. (1 mark)
 b Whether or not the golf ball floats. (1 mark)
 c Volume of solution or shape of container. (1 mark)
 d Total mass of solution = 100 g + 10 g = 110 g (2 marks)
 e 20 g (1 mark)
 f 20 g × 2 = 40 g
   Mass of water is twice what it was originally, so mass of salt dissolved must also be doubled to achieve the same concentration. (2 marks)
3a Graph should include (5 marks):
   x-axis labelled temperature (°C)
   x-axis labelled with an even scale from 0 to 100
   y-axis labelled mass of solute that dissolves in 100 g of water (g)
   y-axis labelled with an even scale from 0 to 180
   points for cerium (III) sulfate accurately plotted
   points for sodium nitrate accurately plotted
   a key given to show which points are for which solute
 b Smooth curve drawn for each data set that does not join every point. (2 marks)
 c Any four from:
   Overall, cerium (III) sulfate is less soluble than sodium nitrate.
   The solubility of cerium (III) sulfate decreases with temperature
   On the other hand, the solubility of sodium nitrate increases with temperature.
   For cerium (III) sulfate the change of solubility is greatest at lower temperatures
   However, for sodium nitrate the change of solubility is greatest at higher temperatures.
4 This is a QWC question. Students should be marked on the use of good English, organisation of information, spelling and grammar, and correct use of specialist scientific terms. The best answers will provide a detailed explanation of how distillation can be used to extract pure water from inky water (maximum of 6 marks).
   Examples of correct scientific points:
   Place the inky water in the round bottomed flask.
   Heat the contents of the flask with a Bunsen burner.
   At first, water evaporates from the inky water, since it has a lower boiling point than the other substances in this mixture.
   Water vapour enters the condenser, and cools.
   As its temperature falls below 100 °C, the water vapour condenses to form liquid water.
   Liquid water drips out form the condenser, and can be collected in a beaker.
   The more concentrated ink solution (with higher boiling point) remains in the round bottomed flask.

Answer guide for Big Write

Developing	Secure	Extending
1–2 marks	3–4 marks	5–6 marks
• Incorrectly labelled, or unlabelled, particle diagram showing a solution. • Meanings of **two** or more of the following key terms accurately given: solvent, solute, solution, dissolve, dissolving, saturated solution, solubility, soluble, and insoluble. • Page poorly organised.	• Correctly labelled particle diagram showing a solution of a solute in a solvent. • Meanings of **four** or more of the following key terms accurately given: solvent, solute, solution, dissolve, dissolving, saturated solution, solubility, soluble, and insoluble. • Some organisation of page apparent.	• Correctly labelled particle diagrams showing a solvent, a solute, and a solution of the solute in the solvent. • Meanings of **all** key terms clearly and accurately given. Terms include: solvent, solute, solution, dissolve, dissolving, saturated solution, solubility, soluble, and insoluble. • Page well-organised and attractively presented.

kerboodle

C2 Chapter 2 Checkpoint assessment (automarked)
C2 Chapter 2 Checkpoint: Revision
C2 Chapter 2 Checkpoint: Extension
C2 Chapter 2 Progress task (Risk assessment)

3.1 Acids and metals

Chemistry NC link:
- the order of metals and carbon in the reactivity series.

Working Scientifically NC link:
- interpret observations and data, including identifying patterns and using observations, measurements, and data to draw conclusions.

Band	Outcome	Checkpoint	
		Question	Activity
Developing	Describe what happens when metals react with acids (Level 3).	1	WS, Starter 1, Main 1, Plenary 2
	State that hydrogen gas makes a squeaky pop when lit (Level 3).	B, 2	WS, Main 1, Plenary 2
	State which metals produce bubbles when reacting with acid (Level 4).		Starter 1, Main 1
Secure	Compare the reactions of different metals with dilute acids (Level 5).	3	WS, Main 1, Main 2, Plenary 1
	Explain the test for hydrogen gas (Level 6).	3	Main 1, Plenary 2
	Decide which metals react more vigorously from practical observations (Level 5).		Main 1
Extending	Use formula equations to show what happens when metals react in different acids (Level 7).	3	Main 1, Main 2, Plenary 1, Homework
	Use word and formula equations to explain the test for hydrogen gas (Level 7).	3	Main 1, Plenary 2
	Suggest how temperature changes may be linked with differences in reactivity between metals with acid (Level 8).		Main 1

Literacy
Students use scientific terminology to explain observations in metal–acid reactions, suggesting relative reactivity between different metals.

Students also explain the naming convention of metal salts in their tutorial sheet that they write for homework.

APP
In the student-book activity students plan an experiment to compare reactivity of metals in hydrochloric and sulfuric acids, as well as testing for the presence of hydrogen gas (AF4).

Students carry out four metal–acid reactions, noting their observations in a table (AF3) and draw conclusions from data obtained (AF5).

Key Words
acid, metal

Answers from the student book

In-text questions	**A** metal salt and hydrogen gas
	B Hydrogen gas produces a squeaky pop when a lit splint is placed near it.
Activity	**Sulfuric similarities**
	Plan should include appropriate apparatus list, method, risk assessment, and consideration for different variables.
	An example method would be to place different metals that are known to react vigorously with HCl in H_2SO_4 to see if bubbles are produced at a similar rate. The gas produced can then be collected and tested with a lit splint. Hydrogen is present if a squeaky pop is produced.

Summary Questions	**1** a salt, hydrogen, lead, magnesium, silver (5 marks)
	2a Iron chloride and hydrogen. This is because all metal–acid reactions result in a salt and hydrogen being made. Hydrochloric acid forms chloride salts. (3 marks)
	b Presence of hydrogen can be tested with a lit splint. If hydrogen is present, a squeaky pop can be heard. (2 marks)
	3 Visual summary example answers (6 marks):
	Most metals react with acids to produce a salt and hydrogen. Bubbles of hydrogen are produced. Hydrogen can be tested for using the lit-splint test. If hydrogen is present, a squeaky pop is made. This is due to hydrogen reacting with oxygen to form water. Some metals react vigorously with acid, for example, magnesium. Some metals react steadily, for example, iron. Some metals do not react at all with acid, for example, gold. Common acids in the laboratory are hydrochloric, sulfuric, and nitric acids. Hydrochloric acid produces chloride salts.

Starter	Support/Extension	Resources
Do acids and metals react? (10 min) Show a strip of magnesium ribbon and a test tube containing dilute hydrochloric acid. Students predict if the two will react and recall the signs of a chemical reaction. Discuss the observations.	**Support**: Recap the differences between physical and chemical reactions.	
Testing for hydrogen gas (10 min) Demonstrate the reaction between magnesium and hydrochloric acid, collecting the hydrogen gas produced using an empty, inverted test tube. Hold a lit splint to the test tube containing the collected gas to demonstrate the characteristic squeaky pop as a test for hydrogen gas.	**Extension**: Students suggest what may have happened to the hydrogen gas to produce the squeaky pop.	

Main	Support/Extension	Resources
Reacting metals with acids (25 min) Introduce the idea of metal reactions with acids using word and balanced formula equations. Explain how all metal reactions with acid produce a metal salt and hydrogen, and describe the characteristic squeaky pop for testing for hydrogen. Students then carry out four reactions of metals with hydrochloric acid to practise testing for hydrogen. They note down the observations, discuss relative reactivity of the metals, and answer the questions on the practical sheet.	**Support**: A suggested results table is provided on the accompanying support sheet.	**Practical**: Reacting metals with acids **Skill sheet**: Recording results
What happens with other acids? (15 min) Summarise observations from the experiment, identifying the relative reactivity of each metal reaction observed. Discuss with students that most metals react with acids in the same manner, then give them the general equation for this reaction: metal + acid → salt + hydrogen Discuss how to name salts using the metal and the type of acid. Encourage students to practise writing word equations of metals reacting with different acids.		

Plenary	Support/Extension	Resources
Spot the salt (5 min) Students match reactants to products of different metal–acid reactions using the interactive resource. Ask students for the other product formed in all these reactions (hydrogen).	**Extension**: Give students mini-whiteboards and chemical formulae of compounds to write balanced formula equations.	**Interactive**: Spot the salt
Metal and acid facts (5 min) Students write the general equation for the metal–acid reaction on mini-whiteboards. Students then write down the signs of chemical reactions that would show the metal was reacting, and explain the test for hydrogen gas.	**Extension**: Students write the word and balanced formula equation for the reaction of hydrogen and water in the test for hydrogen.	

Homework
Students produce a tutorial sheet that teaches other students how to name the salts made when metals react with acids.

Chemistry NC link:
- the order of metals and carbon in the reactivity series.

Working Scientifically NC link:
- interpret observations and data, including identifying patterns and using observations, measurements, and data to draw conclusions.

Band	Outcome	Checkpoint	
		Question	Activity
Developing	State the product of the reaction between metals and oxygen (Level 3).	1, 2	Starter 1, Main 2, Plenary 1, Plenary 2, Homework
	Identify state symbols from an equation (Level 4).	A, 2	Main 1, Plenary 2
	Make observations about how different metals react with oxygen (Level 4).	C	Starter 1, Main 2
Secure	Compare the reactions of different metals with oxygen (Level 6).	B, C, 1, 4	WS, Starter 1, Main 2, Plenary 2, Homework
	Use state symbols in balanced formula equations (Level 5).	2	Main 1, Main 2, Plenary 2, Homework
	Rank metals in order of how vigorously they react with oxygen (Level 6).	C, 4	Main 2, Homework
Extending	Explain the reactivity of metals according to how they react with oxygen (Level 7).	B, C, 1, 3, 4	Starter 1, Main 2, Homework
	Construct balanced equations that include state symbols (Level 7).	2	Main 1, Main 2, Plenary 2, Homework
	Predict the reactivity of unfamiliar metals from information about their behaviour (Level 8).	3	Main 2

Literacy
Students use scientific terminology when explaining fair tests in the student-book activity, and when explaining experimental observations.

APP
Students record observations (AF3), and draw conclusions from experimental data (AF5).

Key Words
state symbol, reactive

Answers from the student book

In-text questions	**A** (s) for solid, (g) for gas **B** Two from: magnesium, zinc, and iron **C** magnesium, zinc, iron, lead, copper, and gold
Activity	**Fair test?** Jamilla should hold each metal sample using tongs over the Bunsen flame and time how long it takes for the metal to catch on fire. The metal that burns the quickest is the most reactive, whilst the one that does not burn will be the least reactive. Some metals may not burn but may char and appear with an oxide coating. Jamilla should time how long it takes to make that oxide coating instead. Possible improvements: Use the same mass of metal with the same surface area. Testing reactivity with acid as well, since metals demonstrate the same reactivity trends whether burning in oxygen or reacting with acid.

Summary Questions	1 magnesium, oxides, copper, gold (4 marks)
	2 $2Ca(s) + O_2(g) \rightarrow 2CaO(s)$ (3 marks)
	3 Potassium oxide will be made in an explosive/very vigorous reaction. This is because the reactivity trends of metals are the same whether burning in oxygen or reacting with acid. (4 marks)
	4 Key points song or rap should include (6 marks): Metals react with acids to make metal salts and hydrogen. Some metals react with acids vigorously (magnesium). Some react steadily (iron). Some do not react at all (gold). Metals follow a similar reactivity trend for reactions with oxygen. Metals react with oxygen to make metal oxides. Some burn (magnesium). Some form a layer of oxide on the surface (lead). Some do not react at all (gold).

kerboodle

Starter	Support/Extension	Resources
What is happening to these metals? (10 min) Demonstrate cutting a piece of lithium on a white tile. Show the shiny surface rapidly becoming dull. Also show a new iron nail and a rusty iron nail. Ask students to suggest what has happened to the metals in both examples. Discuss and lead to metals reacting with oxygen to produce metal oxides. Clarify that rusting only refers to the formation of iron (III) oxide; other metals corrode.	**Extension**: Students consider the rates of the oxidation reaction and how this is linked to reactivity. Explain that most metals require heating before tarnishing.	
What is in these compounds? (5 min) Give the names of several metal oxides and ask students to identify which elements the compounds are made from. This task will serve as good revision of naming of compounds, such as the ending '–ide' for compounds containing only two elements.	**Extension**: Give students the chemical formulae of compounds for them to state the number of atoms of each element.	

Main	Support/Extension	Resources
What are state symbols? (10 min) Discuss the state symbols (s), (l), (g), and (aq) with students. Explain that these tell you whether substances are solids, liquids, gases, or in aqueous solutions (dissolved in water). Give several examples of balanced formula equations containing state symbols, ask students to identify the state that each substance is in, before offering some examples of simple chemical equations for students to add state symbols to.	**Support**: The difference between liquids and aqueous solutions can be demonstrated by showing some water (liquid) and adding some salt to form an aqueous solution.	
How do metals react with oxygen? (30 min) Students carry out the reactions of four different metals with oxygen using a Bunsen flame, record their observations in a suitable results table and write formula equations, including, state symbols, to demonstrate their understanding. Students then answer the questions that follow based on reactivity.	**Support**: The support sheet has a suggested results table and hints on how to decide the correct state symbol in formula equations.	**Practical:** How do metals react with oxygen? **Skill sheet**: Recording results

Plenary	Support/Extension	Resources
Can this be true? (5 min) Interactive resource where students categorise statements on the reactions of metals and oxygen, according to whether they are true or false.	**Extension**: Students justify their answers by applying their scientific knowledge and understanding.	**Interactive**: Can this be true?
Revisiting lithium and iron (10 min) Revisit the starter demonstration involving the oxidation of lithium and iron. Students should now be able to explain what has happened to both metals and write word equations on mini-whiteboards. If a choice of chemical formulae is provided, students should write formula equations on mini-whiteboards instead, including state symbols.	**Extension**: Students should balance the equations they have written.	

Homework		
Students write a paragraph to explain why some metals lose their shine over time but why gold does not. Students should include examples of other metals, and include word and formula equations with state symbols.		

3.3 Metals and water

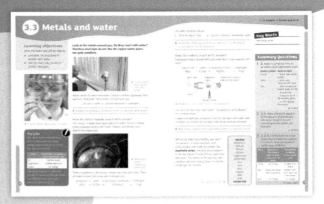

Chemistry NC link:

- the order of metals and carbon in the reactivity series.

Working Scientifically NC link:

- select, plan, and carry out the most appropriate types of scientific enquiries to test predictions, including identifying independent, dependent, and control variables, where appropriate.

Band	Outcome	Checkpoint	
		Question	Activity
Developing	State the products of the reaction between metals and water (Level 4).	A, 2	Plenary 2
	State whether a metal is more or less reactive than another metal (Level 4).	1, 4	Lit, Starter 2, Main, Plenary 1, Plenary 2
	Write a simple method to find out how easily metals react with acids or water (Level 4).		Main
Secure	Compare the reactions of metals with water (Level 5).	C, 1, 4	Lit, Starter 2, Main, Plenary 2
	Use the reactivity series to predict reactions (Level 6).	3	Main
	Plan a practical to compare the reactivity of three metals (Level 5).		Main
Extending	Link a metal's reactions with its place in the reactivity series (Level 7).	1, 3	Lit, Starter 2, Main, Plenary 2
	Explain predictions made about a metal's reactivity (Level 7).	3	Main
	Consider why it is important to be able to find out the reactivity of metals (Level 7).		Main

Literacy

Students use scientific terminology when explaining experimental observations and the uses of the reactivity series.

Students will also write a mnemonic for their homework to help them remember the order of metals in the reactivity series.

APP

Students will plan a practical to compare the reactivity of sodium, magnesium, and lithium (AF4), record observations in a table (AF3), and draw conclusions about relative reactivity based on the data obtained (AF5).

Key Words

reactivity series

Answers from the student book

In-text questions	**A** calcium hydroxide and hydrogen gas
	B substance in a liquid state (l), substance dissolved in water (aq)
	C zinc and iron
Activity	**Tim's tin** From Tim's data, tin is less reactive than magnesium but more reactive than copper. In order to learn more about the reactivity of tin, Tim should repeat the reaction with hydrochloric acid using other metals. He should also carry out the reactions of metals with water and metals with oxygen for all metals tested. This is because metals follow similar reactivity trends for all these reactions.

Summary Questions	
	1 Any six from:
	Sodium reacts very vigorously with water.
	Sodium is near the top of the reactivity series.
	Sodium is more reactive than copper.
	Iron is more reactive than copper.
	Gold is less reactive than copper.
	Gold does not react with oxygen, water, or acid.
	Gold is unreactive.
	2 $2Na(s) + 2H_2O(l) \rightarrow 2NaOH(aq) + H_2(g)$ (3 marks)
	3 QWC question (6 marks). Example answers:
	Nickel is less reactive than iron.
	Iron reacts with water and air but nickel does not.
	Iron reacts more vigorously with acid than nickel.
	Nickel is more reactive than lead.
	Neither nickel nor lead react with water and air, but nickel reacts with acid whereas lead does not.

Starter	Support/Extension	Resources
How do different metals react with water? (10 min) Remind students that metals react with water to produce metal hydroxides and hydrogen gas. This can be done by demonstrating the reactions of Group 1 metals in water again. This time the rate of reaction can be linked to reactivity. Show what happens when magnesium in placed in water, to show that some metals (less reactive than lithium) will only react if the water is heated up to steam.	**Extension**: Students may suggest reasons why steam triggers a reaction when water does not. This can lead to a gentle introduction of activation energy.	
Comparing metals (5 min) Ask students to predict the relative reactivity of gold compared to iron based on daily observations.	**Support**: Students may require hints, for example, why is jewellery made from gold, or why do we need to oil bike chains?	

Main	Support/Extension	Resources
Comparing the reactivity of metals (40 min) Students plan an investigation to test the reactivity of three metals (sodium, magnesium, and copper) in water and in acid. They then carry out this experiment, note down observations in a results table, and answer the questions that follow. There should be a class discussion after the experiment to go through experimental observations and conclusions regarding the order of reactivity. Students should also be encouraged to offer their experimental methods for peer assessment during the class discussion.	**Support**: The accompanying support sheet provides students with prompts when planning the investigation, as well as a suggested results table to fill in observations.	**Practical**: Comparing the reactivity of metals **Skill sheet**: Planning investigations **Skill sheet**: Recording results

Plenary	Support/Extension	Resources
Ordering metals (10 min) Students explain what the reactivity series is and what it can tell you about the reactions of elements. Students then re-order the metals given on the interactive resource according to their position in the reactivity series.		**Interactive**: Ordering metals
Guess who (5 min) Students make up a 'Guess Who'-style game about the identity of different metals using their existing knowledge about the reactions each metal can undergo as clues to their identities.	**Extension**: Students should give further details on each metal, for example, by giving word or balanced formula equations for each metal.	

Homework		
Students write a mnemonic to help them remember the order of metals in the reactivity series.		

3.4 Metal displacement reactions

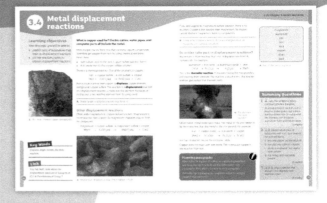

Chemistry NC link:
- combustion, thermal decomposition, oxidation, and displacement reactions
- the order of metals and carbon in the reactivity series.

Working Scientifically NC link:
- make predictions using scientific knowledge and understanding.

Band	Outcome	Checkpoint	
		Question	**Activity**
Developing	State which metal is more reactive in a pair of named metals (Level 4).	B, 1, 2	Starter 1, Main, Plenary 1, Plenary 2
	State where different metals are found in the reactivity series (Level 4).	B, 2	Lit, Starter 1, Plenary 1, Plenary 2
↓	Predict the trend displayed by displacement reactions (Level 4).	1, 2	Main
Secure	Predict if a given pair of substances will undergo displacement (Level 5).	1, 2	Starter 1, Main, Plenary 2
	Use the reactivity series to explain displacement reactions (Level 6).	A, B, 1–3	Lit, Plenary 1, Plenary 2, Homework
↓	Predict which combinations of metals and metal compounds will lead to displacement reactions (Level 6).	2	Main
Extending	Explain why given displacement reactions are predicted to occur or not occur (Level 7).	B, 1, 2	Main, Plenary 2, Homework
	Use particle models and diagrams to represent displacement reactions (Level 7).	3	Lit, Main, Homework
↓	Predict which combinations of metals and metal compounds will lead to displacement reactions, with scientific reasons (Level 7).	2	Main

Maths
Students use the mathematical symbol > when stating the order of reactivity of metals from their experiment.

Literacy
Students organise ideas and information in a coherent manner when completing the student-book activity.

Students use scientific terminology when explaining key concepts demonstrated in their experimental observations.

APP
Students use a model to describe and explain what happens during a displacement reaction (AF1).

Students record observations accordingly (AF3) and draw conclusions from their results (AF5).

Key Words
displace, displacement reaction, thermite reaction

Answers from the student book

In-text questions	**A** A reaction where a more reactive element displaces a less reactive element from a compound.
	B Copper is less reactive than magnesium (lower in the reactivity series).
Activity	**Planning paragraphs**
	Credit suitable prose to explain displacement reactions.
	Possible information to include in each paragraph:
	What a displacement reaction is.
	Displacement of metal salts.
	Displacement of metal oxides.
	Using the reactivity series to predict displacements.

Summary Questions	1 In a displacement reaction, a **more** reactive metal pushes out a **less** reactive metal from its compound. For example, **aluminium** displaces **iron** from **iron** oxide. (5 marks) 2 Reactions a, c, and d will occur, since the element on its own is more reactive (positioned higher in the reactivity series) than the metal found in the compound. (8 marks) 3 Credit cartoons that show a scientifically correct explanation of displacement. For example, Superman (stronger/more reactive element) appearing in front of a couple, and taking the damsel-in-distress away from the (weaker/less reactive) evil villain. (6 marks)

Starter	Support/Extension	Resources
Demonstrating displacement (10 min) Set up a boiling tube containing silver nitrate solution and a coiled-up piece of copper wire, hooked over the edge of the boiling tube. Ask students to find silver and copper in the reactivity series, and to predict what may happen in the boiling tube. Introduce the concept of displacement, and ask students to suggest what they will see in the boiling tube by the end of the lesson.	**Extension**: Students should offer the word equation for this reaction based on the definition of displacement.	
The thermite reaction (10 min) Demonstrate the thermite reaction. (Use video clips from the Internet as an alternative.) Explain that aluminium displaces iron from iron oxide, forming aluminium oxide and iron. Introduce this as a displacement reaction based on the positions of iron and aluminium in the reactivity series.	**Extension**: Encourage students to list the signs of a chemical reaction here (including the fact that this is a useful exothermic reaction that produces molten iron).	

Main	Support/Extension	Resources
Will a displacement reaction occur? (35 min) Students predict whether displacement reactions will occur between combinations of four metals and their nitrates (Mg, Zn, Cu, and Pb). Students then carry out the experiment, record their observations, and answer questions that follow.	**Support**: An access sheet is provided where students are not required to use the reactivity series to predict the possibility of reactions. Students carry out the experiment for only copper, magnesium, and their nitrates, before deleting the appropriate words to complete the conclusion for their experiment.	**Practical**: Will a displacement reaction occur? **Skill sheet**: Recording results

Plenary	Support/Extension	Resources
Revisiting the displacement demonstration (10 min) Look back at the demonstration of copper wire in silver nitrate, set up at the start of the lesson. Ask students to describe what they can see (they should see silver solid on the coiled wire or in the bottom of the boiling tube). Ask students to explain in their own words what has happened to the particles and why. Students should use the reactivity series, the word displacement, and a word equation in their explanation.	**Extension**: Students should offer a balanced formula equation for this reaction, and suggest how silver can be separated from copper nitrate solution.	
True or false? (10 min) Students use their knowledge of metal displacement to decide if statements given on the interactive resource are true or false. Mini-whiteboards may be used at this stage to encourage whole-class participation. Students should be asked to justify their answers using the reactivity series, and write word equations for the displacement reactions that occur.	**Extension**: Students may be able to suggest other sentences to add to the interactive resource, with the rest of the class deciding if the statement is true or false, and correcting if necessary.	**Interactive**: True or false?

Homework	Support/Extension	
Students draw a cartoon to show and explain what happens during a displacement reaction.	**Extension**: Students should write a short paragraph to explain the strengths and weaknesses of their cartoon model in explaining displacement.	

Chemistry NC link:
- the order of metals and carbon in the reactivity series
- the use of carbon in obtaining metals from metal oxides.

Working Scientifically NC link:
- interpret observations and data, including identifying patterns and using observations, measurements, and data to draw conclusions.

Band	Outcome	Checkpoint	
		Question	Activity
Developing	State where carbon is found in the reactivity series (Level 4).		Main 1, Plenary 1, Plenary 2, Homework
	Calculate the percentage of waste material in a metal ore (Level 4).	2	Maths
	State simple observations during a metal extraction (Level 4).		Main 1, Plenary 2
Secure	Use the reactivity series to decide which metals can be extracted from their ores by heating with carbon (Level 5).	3	Main 1, Plenary 1, Plenary 2, Homework
	Calculate the amounts of metals in ores (Level 6).	2	Maths, Main 2
	Link an example of metal extraction to knowledge of the reactivity series (Level 6).	3	Main 1, Main 2, Plenary 1, Plenary 2
Extending	Explain why metals can be extracted using carbon, using the idea of displacement (Level 7).	4	Main 1, Main 2, Plenary 1, Plenary 2, Homework
	Convert amounts of metals within ores from masses to percentages, or vice versa (Level 7).	2	Maths, Main 2
	Use balanced formula equations to illustrate examples of metal extraction (Level 8).	3	Main 2, Plenary 1

Maths
Students carrying out simple calculations involving percentages to find the amounts of waste material in ores in the student-book activity and on their activity sheets.

Literacy
Students draw on scientific knowledge gained over several lessons to link the reactivity series, displacement reactions, and metal extractions.

APP
Students construct balanced formula equations as models for unfamiliar situations (AF1), and extract information from secondary sources (AF3).

Key Words
ore

Answers from the student book

In-text questions	**A** A rock that metals can be extracted from.
	B Separate the desired metal compound from the compounds it is mixed with, then use chemical reactions to extract the desired metal from its compound **C** carbon + copper oxide → copper + carbon dioxide
Activity	**Ore waste**
	For an ore of 1000 kg with 50% iron:
	percentage wasted = 100% − 50% = 50% mass wasted = 0.5 × 1000 kg = 500 kg
	Ore with 16% iron:
	percentage wasted = 100% − 16% = 84% mass wasted = 0.84 × 1000 kg = 840 kg
	Ore with 70% iron:
	percentage wasted = 100% − 70% = 30% mass wasted = 0.3 × 1000 kg = 300 kg

Summary Questions	1 rock, compounds, mixed with (3 marks) 2 mass of copper = 0.06 × 100 kg = 6 kg (2 marks) 3 $C(s) + 2ZnO(s) \rightarrow 2Zn(s) + CO_2(g)$ (2 marks) 4 QWC question (6 marks). Example answers: Metals can be extracted from their compounds using carbon if the metal is below carbon in the reactivity series. This is because carbon is more reactive than the metal in its compound. A displacement reaction takes place. For example, carbon + lead oxide → lead + carbon dioxide If carbon is below the metal in its compound, it cannot be used to extract the metal. This is because carbon is less reactive. Displacement will not occur. For example, there will be no reaction between carbon and aluminium oxide. (Credit correctly balanced formula equations as examples of displacement.)

Starter	Support/Extension	Resources
An alternative question-led lesson is also available. **Where do metals come from?** (10 min) Students consider where metals are found, for example, can lumps of iron be found in the ground? Students consider why periods of history are named after metals, for example, the Iron Age. Explain that most metals are found combined with other elements in the Earth's crust, and that periods of time that saw developments in how to obtain and use these metals were often named after the metal in question. **Metal extraction wordsearch** (5 min) Interactive resource where students complete a wordsearch on key words of the lesson. They then suggest what they mean.		**Question-led lesson:** Extracting metals **Interactive:** Metal extraction wordsearch

Main	Support/Extension	Resources
How are metals extracted? (20 min) Show students a reactivity series with carbon slotted in between aluminium and zinc, and ask them to spot something odd in this series. (Students should be able to notice that carbon is not a metal.) Explain the presence of carbon in this series by introducing the displacement of metals using carbon. This can then be demonstrated to students with the extraction of iron from iron(III) oxide (rust) using charcoal. Students should state what they observe and write this down in their books.	**Support:** Students may need a reminder of displacement reactions before proceeding with the lesson. **Extension:** Students should name metals that can/cannot be extracted using carbon.	
How were metals extracted in the past? (20 min) Students will consider an early method for extracting iron by reading an old 'recipe', and applying their understanding of scientific concepts to answer the questions that follow, explaining the steps in iron extraction.	**Support:** The support sheet includes sentences students re-order to help them with the long question on the activity sheet.	**Activity:** How were metals extracted in the past?

Plenary	Support/Extension	Resources
Revisiting key words (10 min) Students write as many sentences as they can that involve the words found in the wordsearch at the beginning of the lesson. This activity helps students summarise what they have learnt about metal extraction. It is suitable for mini-whiteboards.	**Extension:** Students suggest reactions of some of the elements found in the wordsearch as balanced formula equations.	
Snowballing metal extraction (5 min) Ask students to work in pairs to describe why it is necessary to extract metals, the role carbon plays in metal extraction, and how the method of extraction relates to a metal's place in the reactivity series. Ask student pairs to compare their descriptions with other pairs, and to make improvements or changes to their descriptions.	**Extension:** Encourage students to use as many scientific terms as possible, drawing from their knowledge of the reactivity series and displacement reactions.	

Homework		
Students write an article for a newspaper about the history of metal extraction, linking in historical periods (Stone Age, Bronze Age, and Iron Age).		
An alternative WebQuest homework activity is also available on Kerboodle where students research how metals are extracted from their ores.		**WebQuest:** Extracting and using metals

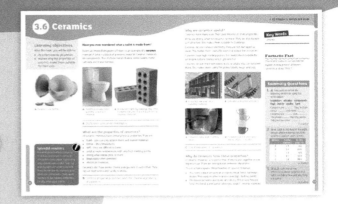

Chemistry NC link:

- properties of ceramics (qualitative).

Working Scientifically NC link:

- select, plan, and carry out the most appropriate types of scientific enquiries to test predictions, including identifying independent, dependent, and control variables, where appropriate.

Band	Outcome	Checkpoint	
		Question	**Activity**
Developing	List the properties of ceramics (Level 3).	B, 1, 2	Lit, Starter 2, Plenary 1, Plenary 2
	List some uses of ceramics (Level 3).	C, 3	Lit, Plenary 1, Plenary 2
	Suggest a simple method for comparing the strength of ceramic materials given a choice of apparatus (Level 4).		Main 2
Secure	Explain ceramic properties (Level 6).	A, 3	Lit, Plenary 2
	Explain why properties of ceramics make them suitable for their uses (Level 5).	C, 3	Lit, Main 1, Plenary 1, Plenary 2
	Plan a method for comparing the strength of ceramic materials, identifying the variables that need to be controlled (Level 5).		Main 2
Extending	Distinguish between chemical and physical properties of ceramics (Level 7).	B, 3	Lit, Main 1, Plenary 2
	Justify why you identify possible ceramics from data about material properties (Level 7).	2	Main 2
	Plan a method for comparing the strength of ceramic materials, justifying choices of experimental techniques and apparatus (Level 7).		Main 2

Maths
Students extract and interpret numerical data on hardness and melting points of ceramics from a table.

Literacy
Students organise ideas and information, adapting their writing style towards their target audience to write an interesting article on the properties and uses of ceramics in the student-book activity.

APP
Students plan an investigation to test the relative strengths of three ceramic materials, identifying variables and carrying out a risk assessment for their experiment (AF4).

Key Words
ceramic

Answers from the student book

In-text questions	**A** Compounds that include metal silicates, metals oxides, metal carbides, and metal nitrides.
	B Four physical properties from: hard, brittle, stiff, solid at room temperature, strong when forces press on them but break easily when stretched, are electrical insulators.
	One chemical property from: unreactive with water, unreactive with acids, unreactive with alkalis.
	C Three from: buildings, electrical power-line insulators, jet-engine turbine blades, plates, bowls, mugs, or jugs.
Activity	**Splendid ceramics**
	The article should include information on the usefulness of ceramics presented in an interesting way for a general audience.
	Possible areas of focus:
	What are ceramics?
	Properties of ceramics and where these properties come from.
	Uses of ceramics in technical equipment and in everyday lives.

Summary Questions	
	1 compounds, silicates, oxides, brittle, hard, high, insulators (7 marks)
	2 Materials B, D, and possibly E could be ceramics. This is because they possess high relative hardness and high melting points. (4 marks)
	3 Credit suitable tables with properties of ceramics in one column, and uses of ceramics in the other (6 marks). Extra credit should be given where uses are linked directly to the properties of ceramics, for example:
	Hardness and strength for bricks in buildings.
	Electrical insulation and lack of reactivity with water for power-line insulators.
	High melting points for jet-engine turbine blades.
	Unreactive nature of ceramics with water, acids, and alkalis for decorative ornaments, plates, and so on.

kerboodle

Starter	Support/Extension	Resources
Deduce the properties (5 min) Have an array of ceramic items around the room for students to look at, feel, and compare (bricks, roof tiles, pottery, porcelain, and bone china). They should be told that all the items are known as ceramics. Students should make suggestions of properties of ceramics before discussing as a class.	**Support**: Students may be able to describe properties of everyday ceramics, such as plates. **Extension**: Students should justify their predictions of ceramic properties from their observations.	
Finding the properties of ceramics (10 min) Using a range of ceramic materials as stimuli (bricks, roof tiles, pottery, porcelain, and bone china) students must find the properties of ceramics hidden in the wordsearch on the interactive resource.	**Extension**: Students should suggest reasons why they know ceramics exhibit these properties based on daily observations and general knowledge.	**Interactive**: Finding the properties of ceramics

Main	Support/Extension	Resources
What are ceramics? (15 min) Formally introduce ceramics, what they are, what they are made from, as well as their chemical and physical properties. Discuss reasons for these properties (strong bonds, strong intermolecular forces) and discuss common uses of ceramics. Students should then match uses of ceramics to their physical or chemical properties to explain why ceramics have been used this way.	**Extension**: Students should identify properties of ceramics as physical or chemical properties, justifying their answers.	
Comparing ceramic strength (25 min) Students plan an investigation to compare the strength of different ceramic materials using the guidelines on the practical sheet. Students are required to select the correct apparatus, decide on a suitable method, and carry out a risk assessment before having one procedure for testing ceramic strength demonstrated to them (unless another lesson is devoted to the testing of this experiment). Students then record their observations in the results table provided.	**Support**: The accompanying support sheet includes a list of suitable apparatus for students to use in their method for this experiment.	**Practical**: Comparing ceramic strength **Skill sheet**: Planning investigations **Skill sheet**: Scientific apparatus

Plenary	Support/Extension	Resources
Reviewing ceramics (10 min) Revisit the ceramic items available at the start of the lesson and ask students to describe why each item can be classified as a ceramic, in terms of the physical and chemical properties they have learnt about in the lesson. Students should also link common uses of ceramics with their properties.		
Ceramic properties and uses (5 min) Students prepare a list of the properties of ceramics and suggest one use of ceramics that utilises each property, while distinguishing between chemical and physical properties.	**Extension**: Students should explain the origin of some of these properties based on the internal structure of ceramics.	

Homework		
Students complete the questions on the practical sheet for homework.		

3.7 Polymers

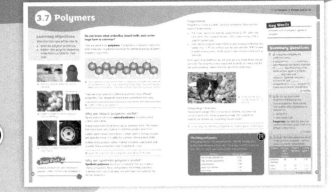

Chemistry NC link:

- properties of polymers (qualitative).

Working Scientifically NC link:

- interpret observations and data, including identifying patterns and using observations, measurements, and data to draw conclusions.

Band	Outcome	Checkpoint	
		Question	Activity
Developing	State the definition of a polymer (Level 3).	A, 1	Plenary 1, Homework
	State some uses of polymers (Level 3).	B, C, 2	Main 1, Main 2, Plenary 2, Homework
	Identify a suitable polymer to use when given simple information about the polymer (Level 4).		Main 2
Secure	Describe polymer properties (Level 6).	C, 2, 3	Maths, Main 1, Main 2, Plenary 2, Homework
	Explain how polymer properties make them suitable for their uses (Level 5).	C, 2	Main 1, Main 2, Plenary 2, Homework
	Interpret data on polymers to decide on the best polymer for a given purpose, justifying the choice (Level 6).		Main 2
Extending	Explain properties of different polymers (Level 7).	1	Main 1, Plenary 1
	Compare properties of different polymers (Level 7).	3	Maths, Main 1, Plenary 2
	Suggest advantages and disadvantages of using polymers (Level 7).		Main 2

Maths
Students extract numerical data from tables to draw bar charts, interpret the information given, and draw conclusions on trends.

Literacy
Students use and explain scientific terminology when discussing polymer properties and suitability.

APP
Students interpret experimental data from an investigation into polymers to draw conclusions and apply their properties to what these polymers may be used for (AF5).

Key Words
polymer, natural polymer, synthetic polymer

Answers from the student book

In-text questions	**A** A substance with very long molecules containing identical groups of atoms that are repeated many times.
	B One from: wool for jumpers and socks, cotton for summer clothing like T-shirts, and rubber for tyres.
	C They are flexible but strong.
Activity	**Plotting polymers** Bar charts should have names of the five polymers along the *x*-axis and density (g/cm³) on the *y*-axis. Axes should be labelled with labels at regular intervals. Bars should decrease in height from PVC, soft rubber, HDPE, LDPE, to poly(propene).

Summary Questions	**1** long, atoms, natural, synthetic, poly(ethene), flexible (6 marks)
	2a low density **b** poor conductor of heat (4 marks)
	3 QWC question (6 marks). Example answers:
	PVC is the weakest polymer of the three when pulled.
	PVC is harder than nylon but softer than acrylic.
	PVC is the densest of the three polymers.
	Nylon is stronger than PVC but weaker than acrylic when pulled.
	Nylon is the softest.
	Nylon is the least dense of the three polymers.
	Acrylic is the strongest of the three polymers when pulled.
	Acrylic has the highest relative hardness.
	Acrylic is less dense than PVC but more dense than nylon.

Starter	Support/Extension	Resources
Modelling polymers (10 min) Show students an array of polymers, both natural and synthetic (plastic bottles, carrier bags, wool, and nylon). Describe that polymers are long chains, made up of a huge number of repeating groups of atoms. Ask students to link arms in pairs, and then in one long chain. Explain that all the individual groups (pairs) have joined to become one polymer. Explain that the properties of polymers will depend on the repeating units, and this makes them extremely useful for many different products.	**Extension**: Students should suggest strengths and weaknesses of the model given the definition of a polymer.	
Making nylon (5 min) Make nylon by floating a solution of decanedioyl dichloride in cyclohexane on an aqueous solution of 1,6-diaminohexane. Use tweezers to extract a thread of nylon from the interface between the two solutions. Use this demonstration to introduce the terms polymer and polymerisation. (Further information on this practical can be found on the RSC website).	**Extension**: Students should classify nylon as a synthetic polymer, given the choice of synthetic polymer and natural polymer.	

Main	Support/Extension	Resources
Different polymer properties (15 min) Using an array of polymers as stimuli, discuss different polymers that are readily available and their uses. Ask students to deduce and compare differences in common properties (such as flexibility, strength, water resistance, and opaqueness) using the stimuli in front of them. Explain that by changing the groups that form polymer chains, properties of polymers can be changed. The differences in polymer properties can be explored numerically using the maths task in the student book if time.	**Extension**: Students should link the uses of polymers to their properties, and compare properties between different polymers.	
Choosing suitable polymers (25 min) Students interpret information on different polymers from a table in order to choose suitable polymers for different functions. Students explain their choices and answer questions that follow.	**Support**: The accompanying support sheet offers prompts for students to decide on suitable polymers to use in the first three cases of their task.	**Activity**: Choosing suitable polymers

Plenary	Support/Extension	Resources
Defining polymers (5 min) Students summarise the information they have learnt in this lesson using a gap-fill activity provided on the interactive resource.		**Interactive**: Defining polymers
Properties and uses of polymers (10 min) Students make a list of polymers they have learnt about in the lesson. They categorise these polymers according to whether they are natural or synthetic, then explain the properties they possess that make them suitable for their uses.	**Extension**: Students should compare polymer properties.	

Homework		
Students write a newspaper article about a polymer of their choice. In their article they must state what a polymer is, how it is made on a large scale in industry, and the range of uses that polymer has.		

Chemistry NC link:
- properties of composites (qualitative).

Working Scientifically NC link:
- present observations and data using appropriate methods, including tables and graphs.

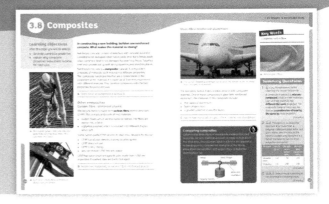

Band	Outcome	Checkpoint	
		Question	Activity
Developing	State some properties of composite materials (Level 3).	1–3	Main 1, Plenary 1, Plenary 2, Homework
	State some uses of composite materials (Level 3).	2, 3	Plenary 1, Plenary 2, Homework
	Plot a graph to show the strength of different composite materials (Level 4).		Main 2
Secure	Describe composite properties (Level 6).	1–3	Main 2, Plenary 1, Plenary 2, Homework
	Explain why composite properties make them suitable for their uses (Level 5).	2, 3	Main 2, Plenary 1, Plenary 2, Homework
	State the relationship shown on a graph of composite strengths (Level 5).		Main 2
Extending	Explain composite properties (Level 7).	1–3	Main 2, Plenary 1, Homework
	Suggest advantages and disadvantages of composite properties (Level 7).	2, 3	Plenary 2, Homework
	Suggest the role played by composite components when describing a graph of composite strengths (Level 8).		Main 2

Maths
Students plot a graph from numerical data provided, and use the information presented to answer questions that follow.

Literacy
Students use scientific terminology throughout the lesson to explain the properties and uses of composite materials, and organise scientific ideas and information appropriately when creating a visual summary of this topic.

APP
In the student-book activity students design an experiment to compare the strengths of different composite blocks, including the identification of variables (AF4).

Students also interpret numerical data from a table to plot a graph (AF3), and use the graph to inform a conclusion (AF5).

Key Words
composite, carbon fibre

Answers from the student book

In-text questions	**A** It is a mixture of materials, each with different properties. The composite material has properties that are a combination of these properties. **B** carbon fibre and a glue-like polymer **C** Two from: aluminium, glass fibre, and a glue-like plastic.
Activity	**Comparing composites** Callum can put different numbers of masses on the straw and mud blocks, and see how much force each block can take before breaking. Independent variable: amount of straw; dependent variable: force (N) taken by block before breaking; control variables to make the investigation fair: size of block, amount of mud in each block, method of testing strength, position the mass hanger is placed on the block each time

Summary Questions	1 mixture, different properties, a combination of (3 marks)
	2 Fibreglass has a greater strength when pulled and when squashed than polyester resin. It is the addition of glass fibres that modify the properties of polyester resin in these ways. (3 marks)
	3 Visual summary example answers (6 marks):
	Composites as mixtures of materials.
	Combined properties of individual materials in the mixture.
	Allows for a better combination of properties for their uses.
	Examples (CFRP, glass-fibre-reinforced-aluminium, or fibreglass).
	Components that make up the individual composite.
	Properties of that composite material.
	Uses for the composite material.

kerboodle

Starter	Support/Extension	Resources
Composite materials (10 min) Show students an image of an average bike and one that is made from carbon-fibre-reinforced plastic. Ask students to spot the difference. Explain that composites are mixtures of substances that, when combined, form a substance with particular properties that are better suited to a role than the individual substances alone, as the composite benefits from both properties.	**Support**: Give students further images of composite materials (fibreglass, glass-fibre-reinforced aluminium, concrete) to help with their answers.	
Composite key words (5 min) Students complete a wordsearch based on key words they will meet in this topic. Students should offer suggestions as to what each word means in the context of this lesson.	**Extension**: Students discuss why carbon-fibre bikes are better than the average bike.	**Interactive**: Composite key words

Main	Support/Extension	Resources
Mud bricks (10 min) Show students images of homes made from mud, and ones made from straw. Ask students for advantages and disadvantages of building houses in each of these ways, before introducing the idea of composite materials and showing an image of a house made from mud and straw. Explain that the mud and straw have unique properties but when combined the resulting brick will have a combination of these properties. Demonstrate the strength of a mud brick compared with a mud and straw brick, if time.		
Concrete properties (30 min) Students plot a graph of various composite mixtures of concrete, and describe how strength varies according to the mixture used. Students will then answer the questions that follow, ranging from comparing properties of concrete and reinforced concrete to using their graphs to predict the strength of a concrete mixture given a certain amount of aggregate in the mixture.	**Support**: The accompanying support sheet includes pre-drawn axes for their graph.	**Activity**: Concrete properties **Skill sheet**: Drawing graphs

Plenary	Support/Extension	Resources
Composing composites (10 min) Students use the key words identified in the wordsearch starter to write three sentences about what composite materials are, their properties, and why they are useful.	**Extension**: Students should use as many of the key words as possible in their answers.	
Composite examples (5 min) Ask students to describe one of the composite examples discussed in the lesson, describing the starting materials and the properties of these compared with the composite materials at the end.	**Extension**: Students should compare the advantages and disadvantages of the properties of composite materials compared to the individual starting materials.	

Homework	Support/Extension	
Students make a small-scale model of a composite material such as reinforced steel, using everyday craft materials. They should include some written information about what composite materials are, and how their properties change when starting materials are mixed.	**Extension**: Where possible, students should offer numerical data towards advantages and disadvantages of using composite materials.	

Checkpoint lesson routes

The route through this lesson can be determined using the Checkpoint assessment. Percentage pass marks are supplied in the Checkpoint teacher notes.

Route A (support)
Resource: C2 Chapter 3 Checkpoint: Revision

Students work through a series of tasks that allows them to gradually revisit and consolidate their understanding of metals and their reactions, ceramics, polymers, and composite materials. Students can keep this as a summary of the topic, and use this when revising for future assessments.

Route B (extension)
Resource: C2 Chapter 3 Checkpoint: Extension

Students design a board game that can be used by other KS3 students to test their knowledge, understanding, and application of different materials and their uses. Students not only have to prepare questions for this game but also plan answers and a scoring system.

Progression to *secure*

No.	Developing outcome	Secure outcome	Making progress
1	Describe what happens when metals react with acids.	Compare the reactions of different metals with dilute acids.	In Task 1 students are given observations for the reactions of different metals with dilute acids to compare.
2	State that hydrogen gas makes a squeaky pop when lit.	Explain the test for hydrogen gas.	In Task 1 students are asked to write a word equation to explain the hydrogen pop test.
3	State the product of the reaction between metals and oxygen.	Compare the reactions of different metals with oxygen.	In Task 1 students are given observations for the reactions of different metals with oxygen to compare.
4	Identify state symbols from an equation.	Use state symbols in balanced formula equations.	In Task 1 students are required to balance formula equations and add state symbols to these equations.
5	State the products of the reaction between metals and water.	Compare the reactions of metals with water.	In Task 1 students are given observations for the reactions of different metals with water and steam to compare.
6	State where different metals are found in the reactivity series, and use this to give the more reactive element in a pair of named metals.	Use the reactivity series to predict and explain if a pair of substances will undergo displacement.	In Task 2 students use the reactivity series to predict the metals that can be extracted using carbon by applying the principle of displacement.
7	State where carbon is found in the reactivity series.	Use the reactivity series to decide which metals can be extracted from their ores by heating with carbon.	In Task 2 students use the reactivity series to predict the metals that can be extracted using carbon by applying the principle of displacement.
8	Calculate the percentage of waste material in a metal ore.	Calculate the amounts of metals in ores.	In Task 2 students are given an example of how to calculate the amount of a metal in an ore before carrying out some calculations for themselves.
9	List the properties of ceramics.	Explain ceramic properties.	In Task 3 students explain ceramic properties and why these properties make ceramics suitable for their uses.
10	State the definition of a polymer.	Describe polymer properties.	In Task 3 students link ceramics, polymers, and composite materials to descriptions of their properties.
11	State some properties of composite materials.	Describe composite properties.	In Task 3 students link ceramics, polymers, and composite materials to descriptions of their properties.
12	List some uses of ceramics, polymers, and composite materials.	Explain how properties of ceramics, polymers, and composite materials make them suitable for their uses.	In Task 3 students explain why each of ceramics, polymers, and composite materials are chosen for their particular uses.

Answers to end-of-chapter questions

1 copper – no change

potassium – moves on surface of water, lilac flame

calcium – bubbles vigorously (2 marks)

2a Two from: same sized pieces of metal, same volume of acid, same concentration of acid. (2 marks)

b Wear eye protection to prevent corrosive acid entering his eye and causing damage. (2 marks)

c zinc – closest to the top of the reactivity series. (1 mark)

d hydrogen (1 mark)

3 hard, brittle, electrical insulator, high melting point (4 marks)

4a lithium hydroxide, hydrogen **b** magnesium, oxygen **c** zinc chloride, hydrogen **d** sulfuric acid, hydrogen (8 marks)

5a X and Z – because the metal elements are more reactive than the metals in the compounds. In each case the metal element can displace the metal in the compound. (4 marks)

b iron + copper oxide → iron oxide + copper/iron + lead oxide → iron oxide + lead (2 marks)

6 This is a QWC question. Students should be marked on the use of good English, organisation of information, spelling and grammar, and correct use of specialist scientific terms. The best answers will provide a methodical approach to the correct identification of the three solutions (maximum of 6 marks).

Examples of correct scientific points:

Add a small sample of magnesium to each solution.

Those solutions that react are of metal compounds that include a metal that is less reactive than magnesium.

This is because more reactive metals displace less reactive metals from their compounds in solution.

The solution that does not react with magnesium is magnesium chloride.

Then add a small sample of zinc to the remaining solutions (zinc chloride and copper chloride).

The solution that reacts is copper chloride.

This is because copper is less reactive than zinc.

Zinc displaces copper from its compounds in solution.

The solution that does not react is therefore zinc chloride.

Credit answers that state the coloured/blue/green solution is copper chloride.

Answer guide for Case Study

Developing	Secure	Extending
1–2 marks	3–4 marks	5–6 marks
• Instructions are given for one test, such as adding the metals to water, to acid, or heating the metal in air.	• The instructions include two tests such as adding the metals to water, to acid, or heating the metal in air.	• The instructions include three tests such as adding the metals to water, to acid, and heating the metal in air.
• The instructions do not state how the test results show the order of reactivity.	• The instructions state that the metals that react most vigorously with these reagents are the most reactive.	• The instructions state that the metals that react most vigorously with these reagents are the most reactive.
• The instructions give one way of making the test fair, for example, using similarly-sized pieces of metal, or acid samples of the same concentration.	• The instructions give two ways of making the tests fair, for example, by using similarly-sized pieces of metal or samples of acid of the same concentration.	• The instructions state that the tests can be made fair by using similarly-sized pieces of metal, samples of acid of the same concentration, Bunsen flames of the same temperature, and so on.
• The instructions are not clear, and would be difficult to follow.	• The instructions lack detail, but overall are clear and easy to follow.	• The instructions are detailed, clear, and easy to follow.
• There is no results table, or one that is poorly laid out. Some variables may be missing from the results table.	• The results table is clearly laid out with all variables involved. Some units may be missing.	• The results table is clearly set out with all variables involved including their units.

kerboodle

C2 Chapter 3 Checkpoint assessment (automarked)

C2 Chapter 3 Checkpoint: Revision

C2 Chapter 3 Checkpoint: Extension

C2 Chapter 3 Progress task (Literacy)

4.1 The Earth and its atmosphere

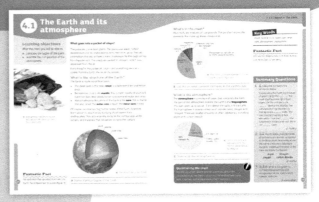

Chemistry NC link:
- the composition of the Earth
- the structure of the Earth
- the composition of the atmosphere.

Working Scientifically NC link:
- present observations and data using appropriate methods, including tables and graphs.

Band	Outcome	Checkpoint	
		Question	**Activity**
Developing	Name the layers of the Earth (Level 3).	A, 1	Starter 2, Main 2, Plenary 1, Plenary 2
	Name the main components of the atmosphere (Level 3).	2	Lit, Plenary 2
	Design a simple model of the Earth using information about its structure (Level 4).		Main 2
Secure	Describe properties of the different layers of the Earth's structure (Level 5).	B, 1, 3	Starter 2, Main 2, Plenary 1, Plenary 2
	Describe the composition of the atmosphere (Level 5).	2	Lit, Plenary 2
	Describe advantages and disadvantages of a given model of the Earth's structure (Level 5).		Starter 2, Main 2
Extending	Compare the different layers of the Earth in terms of their properties (Level 7).	3	Starter 2, Main 2, Plenary 1, Plenary 2
	Describe the composition of the atmosphere in terms of abundance of components (Level 7).	2	Lit, Main 2, Plenary 2
	Explain why models are good or poor representations of the Earth's structure in terms of materials used (Level 8).		Starter 2, Main 2

Maths
Students interpret numerical data in tables and charts to extract information, draw conclusions, and ask questions.

Literacy
Students use scientific terminology when describing the composition and properties of the Earth's structure and atmosphere.

APP
Students design and evaluate models to represent the Earth's structure and atmosphere (AF1).

Key Words
crust, mantle, core, outer core, inner core, atmosphere, troposphere

Answers from the student book

In-text questions	**A** From the outer layer: crust, mantle, outer core, inner core
	B oxygen, silicon, aluminium, iron, calcium, sodium
	C The mixture of gases that surrounds the Earth.
Activity	**Questioning the crust** Questions should be linked to the data in the pie charts, ideally asking for quantitative comparisons.

Summary Questions	**1** atmosphere, crust, solid, nickel, liquid (5 marks)
	2 most abundant element: nitrogen; most abundant compound: carbon dioxide (2 marks)
	3 QWC question (6 marks). Example answers:
	The crust and mantle are both made up of solid rock.
	The mantle can flow and the crust cannot flow.
	Like the crust, the inner core is solid.
	The outer core is the only liquid layer of the Earth.
	It can flow, as can the mantle.
	The outer core and inner core are both mainly iron and nickel.

kerboodle

Starter	Support/Extension	Resources
Imagining the scale of the Earth (10 min) Display pictures of mountain ranges and ocean trenches from the Internet and tell students that these landforms can be around the height of 140 double-decker buses for mountains, and over 380 double-decker buses deep for ocean trenches. Ask students to consider how big these are in comparison to the size of the Earth. Explain that these structures are part of a small layer on the outside of the Earth called the crust, and would account for less than 0.5% of the overall planet.	**Extension**: Students should suggest what they think lies beneath the crust, justifying their suggestions.	
Why is the Earth like an apple or a Scotch egg? (5 min) Show students an apple cut in half, and a Scotch egg cut in half. Ask students to give ideas about how these are similar to Earth (if the Earth were also cut in half). Some students may be able to offer suggestions before the cross-section of the Earth is shown.	**Extension**: Students should give advantages and weaknesses of the models shown. For example, a weakness of the apple model is that the flesh of the apple (the mantle) does not flow.	

Main	Support/Extension	Resources
The Earth's atmosphere (10 min) Introduce that, as well as having a layered structure inside the Earth, the Earth also possesses a layered atmosphere (which includes a mixture of gases that are vital for life). Explain that the first layer of the atmosphere, approximately 10 km high, is the troposphere, and that it contains predominantly oxygen and nitrogen.		
Modelling Earth's structure (30 min) Students label a diagram showing the structure of the Earth and include a brief description of each layer. They will then consider a student's model of the Earth in terms of how well it represents the internal structure. Students answer questions based on this model, before suggesting improvements and designing their own model of the Earth's structure.	**Support**: Prompt students to think about how different properties of the layers can be shown using materials in their proposed models.	**Activity**: Modelling Earth's structure

Plenary	Support/Extension	Resources
The Earth and the atmosphere (5 min) Students place the layers of the Earth given on the interactive screen into the correct order, starting from the inner core. This step can be carried out using mini-whiteboards to increase class participation. Students should then offer descriptions of each layer.	**Extension**: Students may be able to re-order the layers of the Earth according to their depths, starting with the largest.	**Interactive**: The Earth and the atmosphere
Describing the Earth (10 min) Provide students with mini-whiteboards and call out a layer of the Earth, including the atmosphere. Students write down as many facts as they can about that layer. Discuss answers given. This can be done as a competition to see who can give unique facts about each layer.		

Homework		
Students make models showing the structure of the Earth, as described in their activity sheet.		

4.2 Sedimentary rocks

Chemistry NC link:
- the formation of sedimentary rocks.

Working Scientifically NC link:
- interpret observations and data, including identifying patterns and using observations, measurements, and data to draw conclusions.

Band	Outcome	Checkpoint	
		Question	**Activity**
Developing	State a property of sedimentary rocks (Level 3).	B, 2	Starter 1, Starter 2, Plenary 1
	Describe simply how sedimentary rocks are made (Level 4).	C, 1, 3	Lit, Main 2, Plenary 1, Homework
	State the processes shown by different models of the stages in sedimentary rock formation (Level 4).		Main 2
Secure	Explain two properties of sedimentary rocks (Level 6).	2	Starter 2, Homework
	Explain how sedimentary rocks are made (Level 5).	C, 1, 3	Lit, Main 2, Plenary 1, Homework
	Describe how models are representing sedimentary rock formation processes (Level 6).		Main 2
Extending	Explain two properties of sedimentary rocks by linking them to the rock structure and formation (Level 7).	2	Starter 2, Homework
	Give a detailed explanation of the sedimentary rock cycle (Level 7).	3	Lit, Main 2, Homework
	Evaluate strengths and weaknesses for models of sedimentary rock formation, giving reasons (Level 8).		Main 2

Literacy
Students organise and sequence information to explain the formation of sedimentary rocks in the student-book activity and for homework.

APP
Students evaluate models demonstrating the different processes of sedimentary rock formation (AF1).

Key Words
sedimentary, igneous, metamorphic, porous, weathering, sediment, physical weathering, freeze–thaw, chemical weathering, biological weathering, erosion, transport, deposition, compaction, cementation

Answers from the student book

In-text questions	**A** igneous, sedimentary, metamorphic
	B Sedimentary rocks are porous. They are usually soft and can be scratched easily.
	C weathering, transportation (erosion), deposition, compaction/cementation
Activity	**Sedimentary sequence**
	Give credit for accuracy, clarity, and engagement of audience during the talk.
	Talk should include the individual stages of the sedimentary rock formation process: weathering (physical, chemical, or biological), transportation (by water, ice, wind, or gravity), deposition, compaction/cementation.

Summary Questions	**1** Weathering breaks rock into pieces.
	Erosion breaks rock into smaller pieces and moves them away from their original rock.
	Transportation moves sediments far away from their original rock.
	Deposition is the settling of sediments.
	Compaction involves the weight of sediment above making sediments stick together. (5 marks)
	2 Sedimentary rocks are porous because they are made up of separate grains. There are gaps between the grains. Air and water can get into these gaps.
	Sedimentary rocks are soft because they are made up of separate grains. The forces holding the grains together are relatively weak. This is also why sedimentary rocks can be scratched easily. (4 marks)
	3 Flow diagram should include the names of the main processes, correctly sequenced. (6 marks)

kerboodle

Starter	Support/Extension	Resources
Sediments and rocks (5 min) Show students some sediment, for example sand, and a sedimentary rock, for example, sandstone. State that the sediment can be turned into the stone. Ask students to give ideas on how they think this happens.	**Support**: Show students wet sand as a visual aid. **Extension**: Students compare the properties of sand and sandstone.	
Observing rock types (10 min) Provide students with hand lenses and examples of sedimentary rocks (sandstone), metamorphic rocks (slate), and igneous rocks (granite). Ask them to list features they can see for each rock type and ask whether they think the rocks come from the same 'family' given their observations.	**Support**: Give students rock samples grouped by rock type, to justify the groupings using observations. **Extension**: Students sort rocks into different types, comparing similarities and differences in properties.	

Main	Support/Extension	Resources
Sedimentary rocks (10 min) Explain that rocks form over thousands of years. There are three types of rock: igneous, metamorphic, and sedimentary. Explain that the different rock types form under different conditions and have unique features. Introduce sedimentary rocks as rocks that form from small fragments of other rocks and matter, called sediments. Explain the properties of sedimentary rock, with examples, and introduce the stages of formation: weathering, transportation (erosion), deposition, and compaction/cementation. Animations to show the stages of formation are readily available on the Internet.		
Modelling sedimentary rock formation (30 min) Students carry out simple experiments that model sedimentary rock formation processes, and then answer the questions that follow.	**Extension**: Students offer reasoned evaluations of the models in this activity.	**Practical**: Modelling sedimentary rock formation

Plenary	Support/Extension	Resources
Sedimentary rocks (10 min) Interactive resource where students complete a crossword on key words from the topic. They then place the key words in order to describe sedimentary rock formation.	**Extension**: Students improve the clues by adding more detail.	**Interactive**: Sedimentary rocks
Guess the process (5 min) Give simple descriptions of a stage of sedimentary rock formation. Students write the stage name on a mini-whiteboard. This can be turned into a competition where the first person to hold up the correct answer will get to make up the next question.		

Homework	Support/Extension	
Students draw a cartoon strip to show how a small pebble that was loosened by weathering goes on to form a new sedimentary rock.	**Extension**: Students explain in their cartoons why sedimentary rocks have properties such as softness and porosity.	

4.3 Igneous and metamorphic rocks

Chemistry NC link:
- the formation of igneous and metamorphic rocks.

Working Scientifically NC link:
- make predictions using scientific knowledge and understanding.

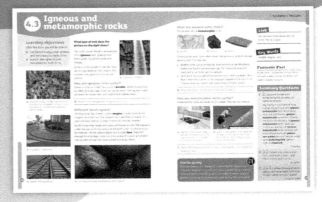

Band	Outcome	Checkpoint	
		Question	Activity
Developing	State one difference between igneous and metamorphic rocks (Level 3).	1, 3	Main 1, Plenary 1, Plenary 2, Homework
	Describe very simply how igneous and metamorphic rocks are formed (Level 4).	B, 1, 3	Starter 2, Main 1, Main 2, Plenary 2, Homework
	State what you expect to see when a substance representing lava is cooled (Level 4).		Main 2
Secure	Compare the ways that igneous and metamorphic rocks form (Level 6).	1, 3	Main 1, Main 2, Plenary 2, Homework
	Explain how igneous and metamorphic rocks form (Level 6).	1, 3	Main 1, Main 2, Plenary 2, Homework
	Predict observations when a substance representing lava is cooled at different temperatures (Level 6).		Main 2
Extending	Discuss examples of rocks that illustrate the different methods of formation of igneous and metamorphic rocks (Level 7).	B, 1–3	Main 1, Plenary 2, Homework
	Link properties of igneous and metamorphic rocks to their methods of formation (Level 7).	1–3	Main 1, Homework
	Predict observations when a substance representing lava is cooled, using knowledge about igneous rock formation to explain the answer (Level 8).		Main 2

Maths
Students calculate the mean amount of granite quarried per week at Rubislaw quarry when completing the student-book activity.

Students record numerical comparisons of crystal sizes in salol for their experimental observations.

Literacy
Students organise ideas and information using scientific terminology when giving reasons for their hypotheses in their experiment.

APP
Students carry out an experiment using salol to mimic the formation of igneous rock (AF4), record observations in a results table (AF3), and draw conclusions from experimental data (AF5).

Key Words
durable, magma, lava

Answers from the student book

In-text questions	**A** hard, durable, and not porous **B** Marble is formed when limestone below the Earth's surface is heated. Slate is formed when high underground pressure squashes mudstone. **C** Not porous and made up of layers so easily split into thin sheets.
Activity	**Granite quarry** Years = 1971 − 1740 = 231; weeks = 231 × 52 = 12 012; mass/week = 6 000 000 ÷ 12 012 = 500 tonnes/week
Summary Questions	**1** metamorphic, igneous, metamorphic, non-porous, crystals, hard (6 marks) **2** Igneous rocks form when liquid rock cools and freezes. When liquid rock freezes slowly the particles have time to arrange themselves into big crystals. When liquid rock freezes quickly the crystals are small because there is less time for particles to arrange themselves into crystals. (3 marks)

3 QWC question (6 marks). Example answers:

Igneous rocks form when liquid rock cools and freezes/solidifies. For example, lava cooling to form basalt. But metamorphic rock formation does not involve substances in the liquid state. Instead, metamorphic rocks may form as a result of high pressure acting on existing rock. This process changes mudstone (a sedimentary rock) into slate (a metamorphic rock). Metamorphic rocks may also form as a result of heat acting on existing rock, without causing it to melt. This process changes limestone (a sedimentary rock) into marble (a metamorphic rock).

Starter	Support/Extension	Resources
Giant's Causeway (5 min) Display a photograph of the Giant's Causeway. Students consider how the natural landmark was formed. Discuss that the causeway is actually a collection of basalt columns, which formed when lava cooled rapidly. This rapid cooling and contraction formed the shapes seen.	**Extension**: Ask students about the 'formation' of Stonehenge. They offer similarities and differences between the sites.	
What happens when a volcano erupts? (5 min) Show a video clip from the Internet of lava erupting from a volcano. Students recap where the lava comes from and what happens to it once it leaves the volcano. This recaps the structure of the Earth, before introducing the other two types of rock. Introduce the difference between magma (liquid rock underground) and lava (on the surface).	**Extension**: Students say where magma is found relative to the other layers that form the structure of the Earth.	

Main	Support/Extension	Resources
Igneous and metamorphic rocks (20 min) Introduce igneous and metamorphic rocks. Discuss that igneous rocks are formed when liquid rock cools down. This can happen slowly within the Earth's crust or rapidly outside the crust (including under water). Metamorphic rocks are formed when other types of rocks are under high pressures and/or temperatures but do not melt. Samples of slate, basalt, and granite could be passed around so that students can observe the different properties of each rock type (e.g., both have crystals but metamorphic rocks have layers, neither are porous, and metamorphic rocks may contain distorted fossils whilst igneous rocks do not).	**Support**: Students recap properties of sedimentary rocks before moving on. They should focus on identifying properties of each rock under a hand lens. **Extension**: Students use observations to group the rock samples, and to compare differences in properties between the rock types.	
What determines crystal size in igneous rock? (20 min) Students read a short text that gives information about the formation and crystal sizes of granite and basalt, before writing a hypothesis on the relationship between crystal sizes in igneous rock and the temperature of the environment during formation. Students carry out a practical to mimic igneous rock formation using salol, and use their observations to answer questions that follow.	**Support**: The support sheet offers students a simpler text and a writing frame to help with their hypothesis.	**Practical**: What determines crystal size in igneous rock? **Skill sheet**: Hypothesis

Plenary	Support/Extension	Resources
Properties of rock types (10 min) Interactive resource where students complete a paragraph on the properties of the three types of rocks.	**Support**: Students explain how each property is observed.	**Interactive**: Properties of rock types
Modelling rock formation (10 min) Students walk randomly around the room whilst staying in contact with each other. Give 30 seconds for students to order themselves into lines. Repeat the process but only give 10 seconds. Students are likely to be in smaller lines. Moving one end of a line forces students to move to new places. Students describe how these models represent igneous and metamorphic rock formation.	**Extension**: Students should offer strengths and weaknesses of these models.	

Homework	Support/Extension	
Students complete the practical sheet. They then find names and pictures of a sedimentary, igneous, and metamorphic rock. Describe the properties and uses of each.	**Extension**: Students link the properties of the rocks to their formation.	

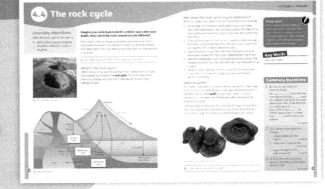

Chemistry NC link:
- the rock cycle.

Working Scientifically NC link:
- interpret observations and data, including identifying patterns and using observations, measurements, and data to draw conclusions.

Band	Outcome	Checkpoint	
		Question	Activity
Developing	Give simple facts about how a rock can be changed from one type to another (Level 4).	A, B, 1–3	Lit, Main 1, Main 2, Plenary 1, Plenary 2, Homework
	State what happens to wax in a model rock cycle (Level 3).		Main 2
Secure	Use the rock cycle to explain how the material in rocks is recycled (Level 5).	A, 1–3	Lit, Main 1, Plenary 1, Plenary 2, Homework
	Describe how changes in the wax used to represent a rock represent the real rock cycle (Level 5).		Main 2
Extending	Give a detailed description and explanation of a rock's journey through the rock cycle (Level 7).	3	Lit, Main 1, Plenary 1, Plenary 2, Homework
	Explain the steps used to model the rock cycle and evaluate the results of this model (Level 8).		Main 2

Maths
Students consider the timescales taken for a rock to travel through the rock cycle, during this lesson.

Literacy
Students adapt their writing style in order to write a drama to communicate the rock cycle to a general audience. They must also organise information effectively and in a logical order for this purpose, and for the student-book activity.

APP
Students carry out an experiment to model the rock cycle (AF4), record observations in tables (AF3), and evaluate the models used (AF1).

Key Words
rock cycle, uplift

Answers from the student book

In-text questions	**A** One from: weathering breaks down existing rock, sediments join together to make new rock, lava freezes to make rock, high pressure and temperature deep within the crust alters rocks of all types. **B** Uplift is the process by which huge forces inside the Earth push rocks upwards.
Activity	**Rock route** Paragraphs should describe processes of the rock cycle, be clearly organised, and have events in the rock cycle occurring in a logical order. An example is provided in the corresponding page in the student book.
Summary Questions	**1** rock cycle, recycles, uplift, mountains, limestone (5 marks) **2a** melting (1 mark) **b** cooling and freezing (2 marks) **c** cementation or compaction (1 mark) **3** Script should include clear descriptions of routes around the rock cycle and be entertaining. The route should include all three types of rock going from one to another. (6 marks)

Starter	Support/Extension	Resources
The rock cycle (10 min) Students find key words in the wordsearch on the interactive resource that they will need to describe the rock cycle throughout the lesson. Students should suggest what they think new words mean and, as a recap, state the definition of words they have already met. This activity allows you to gauge the confidence levels of students in terms of their understanding of the topic so far.	**Support**: If this activity reveals gaps in students' knowledge of this topic, time should be spent recapping words that are not fully understood.	**Interactive**: The rock cycle
Chocolate rocks (5 min) Provide students with cut-up chunks of three different chocolate bars or cakes. Ask them to decide which rock type they best describe and why. Students should be considering the arrangement of grains, presence of fossils, and so on. (A layered chocolate bar = sedimentary, marble effect chocolate = metamorphic, and chocolate honeycomb = igneous.) Ensure that students do not eat in the laboratory.		

Main	Support/Extension	Resources
Introducing the rock cycle (20 min) Display a diagram of the rock cycle on the board. Discuss that rocks are constantly recycled over millions of years and will therefore be changed from one type to another over and over again. Ask students to work in pairs or small groups to identify a possible route around the rock cycle, using as many scientific key words (from Starter 1) as possible before presenting possible routes in a class discussion.	**Support**: Students may be prompted to use a specific starting point for their routes.	
Modelling the rock cycle (20 min) Students carry out a short practical where they use wax to model the processes in the formation of sedimentary, metamorphic, and igneous rocks as part of the rock cycle. They will then answer questions that follow, linking parts of the model to different rock formations, and evaluating the strengths and weaknesses of the models used.	**Support**: The accompanying support sheet provides students with a suggested table to record their observations during the experiment.	**Practical**: Modelling the rock cycle **Skill sheet**: Recording results

Plenary	Support/Extension	Resources
Rock cycle sentences (5 min) Students use as many key words as possible from the interactive wordsearch to write sentences about the processes within the rock cycle in a logical order. Students should present their answers as part of a class discussion.	**Support**: Allow students to work in small groups.	
Rock cycle describing game (10 min) In a clear open space, have the three rock type names written on large pieces of paper laid on the floor, placed as vertices of a triangle. Divide students in the class to make three groups and place each group on one vertex. Students must describe to another student how they move from one rock type to another. A correct answer allows the student to move; an incorrect answer means the student must sit back down. The winner is the person who can move around the rock cycle in the shortest amount of time.	**Extension**: Students must describe the difference between intrusive and extrusive igneous rocks during their path.	

Homework	Support/Extension	
Students produce a coloured poster of the rock cycle, with full labels and descriptions of each possible stage.	**Extension**: Students must include the difference between intrusive and extrusive igneous rocks in their diagrams.	

4.5 The carbon cycle

Chemistry NC link:

- the carbon cycle
- the production of carbon dioxide by human activity and the impact on climate.

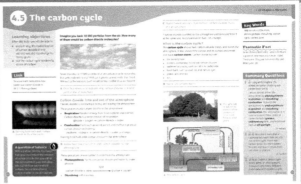

Band	Outcome	Checkpoint	
		Question	**Activity**
Developing	State the changes in levels of carbon dioxide over time (Level 4).	1	Main 1, Homework
	Name one place carbon dioxide may be stored (Level 3).	D, 1, 2	Starter 1, Starter 2, Main 2, Plenary 2, Homework
Secure	Explain why the concentration of carbon dioxide in the atmosphere did not change for many years (Level 5).	1	Main 1, Homework
	Use the carbon cycle to identify reservoirs of carbon (Level 5).	D, 1–3	Starter 1, Starter 2, Main 2, Plenary 2, Homework
Extending	Explain changes in the levels of carbon dioxide using stages of the carbon cycle (Level 7).	1	Main 1, Homework
	Use equations to explain processes that exchange carbon dioxide to and from the atmosphere (Level 7).	2, 3	Main 1, Main 2, Plenary 2, Homework

Maths
Students calculate the percentage of carbon dioxide found in the atmosphere based on parts per 10 000.

Literacy
Students interpret a diagram of the carbon cycle in order to organise scientific information and answer questions based on this topic.

Students also identify ways to reduce the amount of carbon dioxide released into the atmosphere to explain how these link to the carbon cycle in the student-book activity.

APP
Students interpret a diagram of the carbon cycle to suggest possible routes carbon particles may take as they are recycled (AF1).

Key Words
respiration, combustion, photosynthesis, dissolving carbon cycle, carbon store

Answers from the student book

In-text questions	**A** Carbon dioxide is vital for plants to make their own food. It also keeps the Earth warm enough for living things to flourish. **B** respiration and combustion **C** photosynthesis and dissolving of carbon dioxide in the oceans **D** atmosphere, oceans, sedimentary rocks, fossils fuels, plants and animals, soil
Activity	**A question of balance** Credit any four sensible methods of reducing the amount of carbon dioxide added to the atmosphere. Give credit for relevant explanations. For example: Burn smaller quantities of fossil fuels by replacing fossil fuels in cars or generating electricity using renewable sources, because fossil fuels release carbon dioxide during combustion. Plant more trees (or other plants) to remove carbon dioxide from the atmosphere during the process of photosynthesis.

Summary Questions	1 respiration, combustion, photosynthesis, dissolving, sedimentary, oil (6 marks)
	2 Route around the carbon cycle, including the names of four carbon stores, described clearly and in detail. Students must include how the carbon atom moves from one store to the next. (5 marks)
	3 Credit sensible game that correctly describes possible routes around the carbon cycle. Each game must have an accompanying set of rules and a clear method of determining the winner. (6 marks)

kerboodle

Starter	Support/Extension	Resources
How much carbon dioxide? (5 min) Explain to students that less than 4 in every 10 000 air particles are carbon dioxide. Ask them to calculate what percentage this represents (0.04%).	**Support**: Students may need to be shown how to calculate percentages before introducing this task.	**Skill sheet**: Calculating percentages
Carbon and its compounds (10 min) Ask students to write a list of substances that consist of carbon, and places they know that contain carbon or its compounds. Students should discuss why carbon is important to all of us, using ideas such as organic matter (in living things), oceans, and the atmosphere. A common misconception is that the existence of carbon dioxide causes global warming, when without carbon dioxide there would be no greenhouse effect and the Earth would no longer be hospitable.	**Extension**: Students should then demonstrate their understanding of this knowledge by explaining the difference between global warming and the greenhouse effect.	

Main	Support/Extension	Resources
What is the carbon cycle? (10 min) Describe how carbon moves through a cycle continuously, just like rocks and water. Carbon dioxide can rapidly move within the carbon cycle, for example, during combustion of fossil fuels, or extremely slowly, for example, being locked within fossil fuels during their formation.	**Support**: Students may require an in-depth explanation of how the carbon cycle can be interpreted. This can be done by following several routes through the cycle.	
Introduce the carbon cycle as a cycle, not just for elemental carbon but mainly for carbon as part of compounds. It is important to point out the importance of carbon dioxide in the carbon cycle (as well as the useful side of the greenhouse effect), and the available carbon stores in the cycle. This can be done using a diagram on the board. Students then discuss the relative rates of each step in the carbon cycle to keep the overall composition of carbon dioxide at approximately 0.04% (despite fluctuations).	**Extension**: Students should use equations to describe the processes involved in the carbon cycle, for example, methane + oxygen → carbon dioxide + water	
Interpreting the carbon cycle (30 min) Students complete a diagram of the carbon cycle, before using this to draw a storyboard showing a possible journey of one particular carbon atom.	**Support**: The support sheet includes a diagram of the carbon cycle with labels for students to complete as a word-fill.	**Activity**: Interpreting the carbon cycle

Plenary	Support/Extension	Resources
In or out? (5 min) Students decide whether each of the processes shown on the interactive resource puts carbon dioxide into the atmosphere or removes it from the atmosphere.	**Extension**: Students should describe the processes in full, giving equations for the processes where applicable.	**Interactive**: In or out?
Recall the carbon cycle (10 min) Students make a rough sketch of the carbon cycle on a mini-whiteboard and label as many processes and carbon stores as possible without help. They should then compare their diagrams with a complete version (which can be displayed on the whiteboard), and decide how much they missed. Repeat the process to improve recall.		

Homework		
Students write a catchy rhyme, rap, or song to describe the different routes available in the carbon cycle, and how the levels of carbon in the atmosphere change over time.		

4.6 Climate change

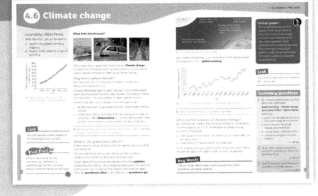

Chemistry NC link:
- the production of carbon dioxide by human activity and the impact on climate.

Working Scientifically NC link:
- present observations and data using appropriate methods.

Band	Outcome	Checkpoint	
		Question	**Activity**
Developing	State a cause of global warming (Level 3).	2	Maths, Starter 1, Starter 2, Plenary 1
	State one impact of global warming (Level 3).	3	Main 1, Plenary 1, Plenary 2
	Suggest one good point and one bad point about a given model of global warming (Level 4).		Main 2
Secure	Explain why global warming happens (Level 6).	2	Maths, Starter 1, Starter 2, Main 2, Plenary 1
	Explain some impacts of global warming (Level 5).	3	Main 1, Plenary 1, Plenary 2
	Design a model to represent global warming, and describe how it represents the real situation (Level 6).		Main 2
Extending	Use a model to explain why global warming happens (Level 7).	2	Main 2
	Discuss in detail the impacts of global warming, identifying primary and secondary problems (Level 8).	3	Main 1, Plenary 2
	Design and evaluate a model to represent global warming (Level 8).		Main 2

Maths
Students extract and interpret information from graphs in order to find possible correlation between carbon dioxide concentrations and temperature in the student-book activity.

Literacy
Students organise scientific ideas to suit audiences from primary-school children to the general public, when teaching them about ideas relating to the greenhouse effect, global warming, and climate change.

APP
Students use models to represent global warming (AF1), and evaluate the effectiveness of using models in teaching primary-school children about this concept (AF5).

Key Words
climate change, deforestation, radiation, greenhouse effect, greenhouse gas, global warming

Answers from the student book

In-text questions	**A** burning more fossil fuels, deforestation
	B The increase in global average air temperature due to extra carbon dioxide in the atmosphere.
Activity	**Global graphs**
	Both graphs have a similar shape. They show that there is a correlation between the increasing concentration of carbon dioxide in the atmosphere and the increasing global average air temperature.
	Scientists use thermometers to collect temperature data. To collect carbon dioxide concentration data that is fair to compare, they must make measurements at the same place each time and in a place unaffected by local contributions to the carbon dioxide concentration, for example, a power plant.
Summary Questions	**1** global warming: the increase in the global average air temperature
	climate change: changes to long-term
	weather patterns greenhouse effect: gases in the atmosphere increasing the global average air temperature
	deforestation: cutting down or burning forests (4 marks)

2 Diagrams should include (4 marks):

The paths of thermal radiation entering and exiting the Earth's atmosphere. Some of the radiation is prevented from escaping the Earth due to the presence of greenhouse gases. Possible examples of greenhouse gases (methane, carbon dioxide). The increasing concentration of carbon dioxide in the atmosphere (global warming) over time, caused by deforestation and burning increasing amounts of fossil fuels.

3 QWC question (6 marks). Example answers:

One cause is the increasing concentration of carbon dioxide in the atmosphere as a result of deforestation and burning increasing amounts of fossil fuels. Increasing amounts of carbon dioxide in the atmosphere absorb more of the heat radiated by Earth. This keeps the temperature of Earth higher than it would otherwise be. Effects of global warming include melting polar ice caps (making sea levels rise leading to flooding) and changing weather patterns, including more droughts, heavier rainfall, and heat waves.

Starter	Support/Extension	Resources
An alternative question-led lesson is also available.		**Question-led lesson**: Climate change
What is climate change and global warming? (5 min) Students list what they know about global warming and climate change. Students should have touched on the differences between these two terms and it is important to ensure students are secure in this knowledge before progressing.	**Support**: Discuss in detail the difference between global warming and the greenhouse effect, and that carbon dioxide is only harmful in the atmosphere.	
The greenhouse effect (10 min) Introduce the greenhouse effect using an animation of from the Internet. (The BP Educational Resources website for Secondary Science offers animations and a quiz on the topic.) Follow up with a recap of the difference between the greenhouse effect and global warming in a class discussion.		

Main	Support/Extension	Resources
The causes and effects of global warming (15 min) Recap how the level of CO_2 in the atmosphere has remained approximately constant at 0.04% for a very long time (with fluctuations), and discuss the processes involved in the carbon cycle to maintain this CO_2 level. Introduce the rising levels of CO_2 concentration since the 1800s, and invite possible reasons from students. Students should then go on to suggest consequences of sustained global warming.	**Extension**: Students should distinguish between primary and secondary consequences of sustained global warming.	
Modelling global warming (25 min) Students design a model to illustrate the greenhouse effect, global warming, and climate change that can be used to explain these concepts to primary-school children. They will then draw a labelled diagram of their model, and present this as a poster. Students then evaluate the strengths and weaknesses of their models.	**Support**: The access sheet has an existing model that students answer the questions on.	**Activity**: Modelling global warming

Plenary	Support/Extension	Resources
Describing global warming (10 min) Students re-order phrases given on the interactive resource to summarise the greenhouse effect, global warming, and climate change. Students should then use the completed summary to give definitions of the three key terms in this lesson.	**Extension**: Students give causes/effects of climate change, giving the consequences in terms of primary/secondary effects.	**Interactive**: Describing global warming
Consequences of global warming (5 min) Students list consequences of global warming on a mini-whiteboard as primary or secondary effects.	**Extension**: Students explain why the consequences arise.	

Homework		
Students produce an informative leaflet for the general public about the differences between the greenhouse effect, global warming, and climate change. The leaflet should teach the public why global warming occurs, and what steps can be taken to try and combat it.		

4.7 Recycling

Chemistry NC link:
- Earth as a source of limited resources and the efficacy of recycling.

Working Scientifically NC link:
- apply mathematical concepts and calculate results.

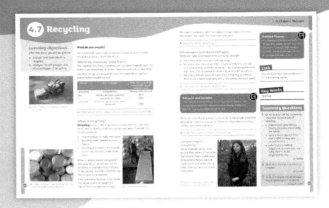

Band	Outcome	Checkpoint	
		Question	Activity
Developing	Describe how aluminium is recycled (Level 4).	2	Main 1, Plenary 1
	Give one advantage and one disadvantage of recycling (Level 4).	C, D, 3	Starter 1, Plenary 2
	Use data to decide which of the two towns recycles more (Level 4).		Main 2
Secure	Explain how aluminium is recycled (Level 5).	2	Main 1, Plenary 1
	Analyse the advantages and disadvantages of recycling (Level 6).	3	Starter 1, Plenary 2
	Plot a bar chart of recycling rates for two towns (Level 5).		Main 2
Extending	Compare how other materials are recycled with the recycling of aluminium (Level 7).	1, 2	Main 1, Plenary 1
	Use data to discuss the relative benefits and drawbacks of recycling materials (Level 7).	3	Plenary 2
	Calculate and compare the amount recycled per person in two towns (Level 8).		Main 2

Maths
In the student-book activity students calculate the number of plastic bottles required for recycling in order to make fleeces for all the students in their school.

Students also plot bar charts, interpret data given, and manipulate numerical data in calculations to answer questions on recycling in fictional towns.

Literacy
Students organise information in a coherent and logical manner when evaluating the advantages and disadvantages of recycling.

APP
Students display secondary data as bar charts (AF3), extracting information from the graph to draw conclusions (AF5), and use the scientific evidence provided to evaluate the advantages and disadvantages of recycling (AF1).

Key Words
recycling

Answers from the student book

In-text questions	**A** The Earth's crust or atmosphere.
	B Collecting and processing materials that have already been used so that they can be used again.
	C Resources last longer, less energy is required to produce a certain amount of a material, waste and pollution are reduced.
	D Two from: nuisance, using (fossil) fuels, pollution.
Activity	**Recycle and remake**
	Energy to extract 1 kg of Al = 255 MJ Energy to recycle 1 kg of Al = 15 MJ; 255 ÷ 15 = 17
	So for the same amount of energy used to extract 1 kg of Al from its ore, you can recycle 17 kg of Al.
	Bottled fleeces
	Answer depends on number of students in school: number of fleeces = 25 bottles × number of people in school

116

Summary Questions	
	1 collecting old bottles, melting the glass, and making new bottles collecting and melting poly(propene) bottle tops, and using them to make poly(propene) rope (2 marks) **2** Old aluminium objects are collected and taken to a factory. Machines shred the objects and remove their decoration. A furnace melts the shreds. The liquid cools and freezes in a mould, an aluminium ingot. This is then heated to 600 °C to soften it. It is rolled into thin sheets which are made into new aluminium objects. (4 marks) **3** QWC question (6 marks). Students include two advantages, two disadvantages, and a reasoned conclusion. Advantages: Resources last longer. Less energy required to produce a certain amount of material. Waste and pollution are reduced. Disadvantages: Some people think that recycling is a nuisance. Energy is required to collect objects for recycling. This also creates pollution.

kerboodle

Starter	Support/Extension	Resources
Do you recycle? (5 min) Ask students if they recycle at home. If they do, list the substances they recycle. Students then discuss the differences between reusing and recycling, and give advantages and disadvantages of recycling. **How does recycling happen?** (10 min) Discuss how various items are recycled. Use the RecycleNow website to show animations of the recycling process, and to look up the postcode of the school to show the range of materials that can be recycled in the local area.	**Support**: Show a list of materials that are recycled to identify which they recycle at home. **Extension**: Students consider how properties of individual materials are used at the sorting stage.	
Main	**Support/Extension**	**Resources**
Recycling aluminium (20 min) Discuss where aluminium is used and where it is originally obtained from. Students explain how each step is achieved based on the properties of aluminium. Compare the energy required to extract aluminium (around 255 MJ/kg) with the energy required to recycle it (15 MJ/kg). Discuss advantages and disadvantages of recycling and compare the recycling of aluminium with at least one other type of recycling. Animations for other types of recycling can be found on the RecycleNow website.	**Extension**: Students should evaluate the relative benefits of recycling compared with its disadvantages for a reasoned conclusion.	
Which town is better at recycling? (20 min) Students plot a graph to compare recycling data for two different towns, and use this to consider which town is better at recycling. Students then answer questions based on the graphs they have drawn, carrying out multi-stepped calculations.	**Support**: A bar chart is available on the support sheet, so that students can focus on the calculations.	**Activity**: Which town is better at recycling? **Skill sheet**: Drawing graphs
Plenary	**Support/Extension**	**Resources**
Recycling aluminium (5 min) Students re-order sentences given on the interactive resource to explain the steps required in the recycling of aluminium.	**Support**: Allow students to work in small groups. **Extension**: Students compare recycling of a different material.	**Interactive**: Recycling aluminium
Is it worth it? (10 min) Show students a recycling calculator on the Internet (for example, on the environment section of the Coca-Cola website). Students can then use this tool to calculate the amount of resources they have saved based on the items they have recycled in the last week, discussing the advantages and disadvantages of recycling.	**Extension**: Students decide if the information provided on energy values supports the case for recycling. Do some materials contribute to a higher proportion of energy savings than others?	
Homework		
Students complete questions on their activity sheet. They then write a short paragraph to explain why it is better to compost kitchen waste rather than send it to landfill, even though it would rot in both locations.		
An alternative WebQuest homework activity is also available on Kerboodle where students research recycling.		**WebQuest**: Recycling plastics

Checkpoint lesson routes

The route through this lesson can be determined using the Checkpoint assessment. Percentage pass marks are supplied in the Checkpoint teacher notes.

Route A (support)

Resource: C2 Chapter 4 Checkpoint: Revision

Students work through a series of tasks that allows them to gradually revisit and consolidate their understanding of Earth science. Students can keep this as a summary of the topic, and use this when revising for future assessments.

Route B (extension)

Resource: C2 Chapter 4 Checkpoint: Extension

In this activity students take the role of a teacher, planning a revision lesson on the topic of Earth science at KS3. Students must include activities that will recap and practise what they have learnt in this topic. Students should include answers to any tasks they design.

Progression to *secure*

No.	Developing outcome	Secure outcome	Making progress
1	Name the layers of the Earth.	Describe properties of the different layers of the Earth's structure.	In Task 1 students complete a word fill to describe the properties of the different layers of the Earth and the composition of the atmosphere.
2	Name the main components of the atmosphere.	Describe the composition of the atmosphere.	In Task 1 students complete a word fill to describe the properties of the different layers of the Earth and the composition of the atmosphere.
3	State a property of sedimentary rocks.	Explain two properties of sedimentary rocks.	In Task 2 students explain two properties of sedimentary rocks after assigning properties to the three different rock types.
4	Describe simply how sedimentary rocks are made.	Explain how sedimentary rocks are made.	In Task 2 students assign the three different methods of rock formation to the three types of rock that they make.
5	State one difference between igneous and metamorphic rocks.	Compare the ways that igneous and metamorphic rocks form.	In Task 2 students assign the three different methods of rock formation to the three types of rock that they make.
6	Describe very simply how igneous and metamorphic rocks are formed.	Explain how igneous and metamorphic rocks form.	In Task 2 students assign the three different methods of rock formation to the three types of rock that they make.
7	Give simple facts about how a rock can be changed from one type to another.	Use the rock cycle to explain how the material in rocks is recycled.	In Task 3 students complete a diagram of the rock cycle to illustrate and explain how material in rocks is recycled.
8	State the changes in levels of carbon dioxide over time.	Explain why the concentration of carbon dioxide in the atmosphere did not change for many years.	In Task 4 students attribute actions as adding CO_2 into the atmosphere or removing it, using this to explain why the concentration of CO_2 in the atmosphere did not change for many years.
9	Name one place carbon dioxide may be stored.	Use the carbon cycle to identify reservoirs of carbon.	In Task 3 students use a diagram of the carbon cycle to identify carbon reservoirs.
10	State one cause of global warming.	Explain why global warming happens.	In Task 5 students work through statements provided to explain the causes of global warming, deciding whether the statements given are true or false.
11	State one impact of global warming.	Explain some impacts of global warming.	In Task 5 students work through a list of statements explaining some impacts of global warming, deciding if the statements provided are true or false.
12	Describe how aluminium is recycled.	Explain how aluminium is recycled.	In Task 6 students reorder sentences to explain the process of aluminium recycling.
13	Give one advantage and one disadvantage of recycling.	Analyse the advantages and disadvantages of recycling.	In Task 6 students are given information on how different actions save resources. Students must then discuss the advantages and disadvantages of these actions.

Answers to end-of-chapter questions

1   78% = nitrogen

21% = oxygen

crust

inner core   (4 marks)

2a Any three from: fossil fuels, land-based organisms, atmosphere, carbon compounds
dissolved in oceans, or sedimentary rock (3 marks)

b photosynthesis (1 mark)

c respiration, combustion (2 marks)

d Greater amounts of fossils fuels burnt, releasing carbon dioxide during combustion. Deforestation
meaning there are fewer trees to remove carbon dioxide from the atmosphere by photosynthesis. (2 marks)

3a C (1 mark)   **b** A (1 mark)

c Igneous rock is formed from cooled magma that solidified/froze. (3 marks)

d The sedimentary rocks around granite (igneous) were softer, and eroded. (2 marks)

e Metamorphic rock is made under heating and pressure. The marble shown in the diagram was probably
made from sedimentary rock that was heated by the cooling magma (that formed granite). (2 marks)

4a temperature of microscope slide (1 mark)

b size of crystals (1 mark)

c To make the investigation fair. (1 mark)

d Small crystals are made quickly. Larger crystals are formed more slowly. (2 marks)

5   This is a QWC question. Students should be marked on the use of good English, organisation of information,
spelling and grammar, and correct use of specialist scientific terms. The best answers will fully explain the
different stages of the rock cycle (maximum of 6 marks).

Examples of correct scientific points:

Rocks are broken down by weathering.

Transportation moves the sediments formed as a result of weathering away from the parent rock.

Sediments are deposited.

These form new sedimentary rocks as a result of compaction or cementation.

Some rock melts to form magma.

Magma cools and solidifies to make igneous rocks.

Some rock is changed as a result of heat or pressure to make metamorphic rocks.

Answer guide for Maths Challenge

Developing	Secure	Extending
1–2 marks	3–4 marks	5–6 marks
• Axes of the graph labelled incorrectly, or not labelled at all. Title of the graph not given. A clear key not given to show that the different bars represent 2001 and 2010. • Some bars plotted accurately. • No or little attempt to explain how resources are recycled.	• x-axis labelled with the country and y-axis labelled with the percentage of waster recycled. A title of the graph not given. A key is given explaining which bars represent 2001 and 2010. • Most bars plotted accurately. • Explanation of how resources are recycled is attempted, although many details are missing.	• x-axis labelled with the country, y-axis labelled with the percentage of waste recycled. A title for the graph is given and and a key which explains which bars represent 2001 and 2010. • All bars plotted accurately, in order of increasing or decreasing percentage of waster recycled. The graph is attractively presented. • A detailed explanation of how resources are recycled is provided.

kerboodle

C2 Chapter 4 Checkpoint assessment (automarked)

C2 Chapter 4 Checkpoint: Revision

C2 Chapter 4 Checkpoint: Extension

C2 Chapter 4 Progress task (Handling information and problem solving)

Physics (2)

National curriculum links for this unit	
Chapter	**National Curriculum topic**
Chapter 1: Electricity and magnetism	Current electricity Static electricity Magnetism
Chapter 2: Energy	Calculation of fuel uses and costs in the domestic context Energy changes and transfers Changes in systems
Chapter 3: Speed and motion	Describing motion Forces Pressure in fluids Forces and motion

Preparing for Key Stage 4 Success

Knowledge

Underpinning knowledge is covered in this unit for KS4 study of:

- Current, potential difference
- Resistance
- Series and parallel circuits
- Static electricity – forces and electric fields
- Permanent and induced magnetism
- Conservation of energy
- National and global energy sources
- Work done and energy transfer
- Speed, velocity, and acceleration
- Distance-time and velocity-time graphs
- Pressure

Maths

Skills developed in this unit.
(Topic number)

- Quantitative problem solving (1.3, 3.5, 3.6).
- Extract and interpret information from charts, graphs, and tables (1.4, 1.7, 2.3, 2.5, 3.2, 3.6).
- Calculate arithmetic means (2.4, 2.5, end-of-chapter 2).
- Plot and draw graphs selecting appropriate scales for the axes (1.5, 2.3, 3.2).
- Understand and use direct proportion and simple ratios. (2.4, 2.7, 3.3).
- Understand number size and scale and the quantitative relationship between units. (2.1, 2.7).
- Understand when and how to use estimation (2.1, 3.4, 3.6).
- Substitute numerical values into simple formulae and equations using appropriate units (1.2, 1.3, 1.5, 2.7, 2.8, 3.1, 3.5, 3.6).
- Carry out calculations involving $+, -, \times, \div$, either singly or in combination (2.2, 2.4, 2.7, 2.8, 3.1, 3.5, 3.6).

Literacy

Skills developed in this unit.
(Topic number)

- Select, synthesise, and compare information from a variety of sources (2.2, 2.7, 3.3, 3.4, 3.5).
- Use scientific terms confidently and correctly in discussions and writing (all spreads).
- Organisation of ideas and evidence (1.6, 1.8, 2.4, 3.1, 3.2, 3.4).
- Identify ideas and supporting evidence in text (1.7, 3.2, 3.3).
- Use correct forms of writing styles and include information relevant to the audience (1.8, 2.1, 2.5, 3.2).
- Ideas are organised into well-developed, linked paragraphs (1.8, 2.6, end-of-chapter 2 Big Write, 3.4, end-of-chapter 3 Big Write).

Assessment Skills

- QWC questions (1.1, 1.2, 1.3, 1.4, 1.5, 1.7, 1.8, 2.1, 2.2, 2.3, 2.4, 2.7, 2.8, 3.1, 3.2, 3.3, 3.4, 3.5, 3.6) (end-of-chapter 1 Q8, Q10, end-of-chapter 2 Q10, end-of-chapter 3 Q8, Q11).
- Quantitative problem solving (1.4, 1.5, 2.1, 2.5, 2.7, 2.8, 3.1, 3.2, 3.5, 3.6) (end-of-chapter 1 Maths Challenge, Q6, end-of-chapter 2 Q3, Q7, Q8, end-of-chapter 3 Q3, Q6, Q10).
- Application of Working Scientifically (1.3, 1.6, 1.8, 2.4, 3.3) (end-of-chapter 1 Maths Challenge, Q5, end-of-chapter 2 Q3, end-of-chapter 3 Q7).

KS2 Link	Check before:	Checkpoint	Catch-up
Names of the basic parts in simple series circuits, for example, bulb, cell, and switch.	P2 1.2 Circuits and current	Show circuit components and their symbols for students to name and match up.	Provide names of components for students to label on a circuit diagram.
A complete loop is required for a circuit to work.	P2 1.2 Circuits and current	Show students a range of circuits with bulbs. Ask them to explain whether the bulbs will light up in each case.	Demonstrate building a simple series circuit with a bulb. Show students that the bulb does not light until the circuit is complete.
A switch opens and closes a circuit.	P2 1.2 Circuits and current	Students explain why bulbs light up depending on the position of the switch.	Students build a simple series circuit with a switch, a cell, and a bulb.
The brightness of a lamp depends on the number and voltage of cells used in a circuit.	P2 1.3 Potential difference	Students predict the brightness of bulbs in difference circuits.	Demonstrate a simple circuit making changes to the number of bulbs, cells, or potential difference of cells.
Metals are good conductors of electricity.	P2 1.5 Resistance	Ask students what sorts of materials they would use to make wires.	Demonstrate a simple series circuit, adding conductors and insulators to the circuit to show the effect on a bulb in the circuit.
Magnets have two poles.	P2 1.6 Magnets and magnetic fields	Students label a bar magnet.	Demonstrate labelled magnets.
Magnets will attract or repel each other, depending on which poles are facing.	P2 1.6 Magnets and magnetic fields	Students predict if magnets will attract or repel.	Suspend magnets from a clamp stand. Students bring other magnets close and explain what happens.
Some changes result in the formation of new materials	P2 2.1 Food and fuels	Students describe what happens to fuels that are burned.	Students watch a candle burn. They describe what happens by choosing from a list of products.
There are three states of matter: solid, liquid, and gas.	P2 2.3 Energy and temperature	Students label a diagram showing particles arranges as solids liquids and gases.	Students categorise different objects as solids, liquids, and gases.
Light travels in a straight line.	P2 2.5 Energy transfer: radiation	Students predict the path of a light beam reflecting off a mirror.	Students shine a torch on a mirror and predict which object will light up based on relative positions.
Friction slows down moving objects.	P2 3.1 Speed	Students describe motion of objects shown to them in a video clip.	Students label a force diagram of a moving object, explaining the effect of resultant forces.
Unsupported objects fall towards Earth because of the force of gravity.	P2 3.2 Motion graphs	Students explain why a ball falls towards Earth when thrown in the air.	Use force arrows to label forces acting on supported and unsupported objects.
Some mechanisms, including levers, pulleys, and gears, are force multipliers.	P2 3.6 Turning forces	Students predict what happens when a force is applied to a simple machine.	Students lift objects with and without simple machines and use labels to show where the force is being transmitted and in which direction.

kerboodle

P2 Unit pre-test
P2 Big practical project (foundation)
P2 Big practical project (higher)
P2 Big practical project teacher notes
P2 Practical project hints: graph plotting
P2 Practical project hints: planning

P2 Practical project hints: writing frame
P2 End-of-unit test (foundation)
P2 End-of-unit test (foundation) mark scheme
P2 End-of-unit test (higher)
P2 End-of-unit test (higher) mark scheme

Answers to Picture Puzzler
Key Words

Everest, newtonmeter, Earth, remote, gear, yellow
The key word is **energy**.

Close Up

copper wires

1.1 Charging up

Physics KS3 NC link:

- separation of positive or negative charges when objects are rubbed together: transfer of electrons, forces between charged objects
- the idea of electric field, forces acting across the space between objects not in contact
- non-contact forces: forces due to static electricity
- using physical processes and mechanisms, rather than energy, to explain the intermediate steps that bring about changes in systems.

Working Scientifically NC link:

- interpret observations and data, including identifying patterns and using observations, measurements, and data to draw conclusions.

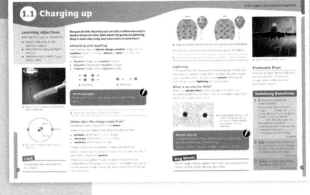

Band	Outcome	Checkpoint	
		Question	Activity
Developing	Describe how to charge insulators (Level 4).	1	Starter 1, Plenary 1
	State the two types of charge (Level 4).	A, 1	Lit, Main
	State what surrounds charged objects (Level 4).		Main
	Explain simply observations linked to charge (Level 4).		Main
Secure	Explain how objects can become charged (Level 5).	1	Main, Starter 1, Plenary 1
	Describe how charged objects interact (Level 5).	1	Main, Starter 1, Plenary 1, Plenary 2
	Describe what is meant by an electric field (Level 5).	3	Main
	Interpret observations, identifying patterns linked to charge (Level 5).		Main
Extending	Explain, in terms of electrons, why something becomes charged (Level 7).	1, 2	Main, Starter 1, Plenary 1, Plenary 2
	Predict how charged objects will interact (Level 7).	2	Main
	Compare a gravitational field and an electric field (Level 7).	3	
	Use observations to make predictions (Level 7).		Main

Maths

Students use the relative positions of materials in the triboelectric series to predict whether friction will cause an object to become positively or negatively charged.

Literacy

In the student-book activity students must unscramble anagrams of key words, pair them up, and explain why they have done so.

APP

Students use abstract ideas when describing processes in static electricity (AF1).

They use existing ideas about electrostatics to inform further predictions (AF5).

Key Words

electric charge, positive, negative, attract, repel, atom, proton, electron, neutron, neutral, current, lightning, electric field

Answers from the student book

In-text questions	**A** positive, negative **B** electron: negative; proton: positive; neutron: no charge
Activity	**Atomic puzzle** proton: positive; neutron: neutral; electron: negative; These are the charges on the particles.

Summary Questions	
	1 positive, negative, electrons, repel, attract (5 marks)
	2 Electrons are transferred between the balloon and the jumper. The balloon is charged, but the wall is neutral. The charge of the balloon repels like charges from the surface of the wall. (3 marks)
	3 QWC question (6 marks). Example answers: Gravitational and electric fields produce forces. You cannot see or feel a gravitational or electric field. They produce non-contact forces. Gravitational fields are produced by masses. Electric fields are produced by charges. Gravitational fields produce forces that only attract. Electric fields produce forces that attract and repel.

Starter	Support/Extension	Resources
Charges on a balloon (15 min) Rub a balloon (or a plastic straw) on cloth and hold it near some hair. For the best results, hair should be clean, fine, and not too long. Ask students to describe what they observe (the hairs are attracted to the balloon; when the balloon is removed, the hair strands remain repelling each other). Discuss why this is happening as a class. **Non-contact forces** (10 min) Students list as many non-contact forces as possible, describing their effects in terms of attraction/repulsion (gravitational, magnetic, electrostatic). Discuss their ideas and explain that electrostatic forces are between charged objects, and they will be investigating these forces during this lesson.	**Extension**: Demonstrate the effect of a charged object on a stream of water. Students should apply their existing ideas. **Support**: Give examples that students group by the non-contact force they experience. Note that some objects experience more than one non-contact force. **Extension**: Students identify common features of non-contact forces.	

Main	Support/Extension	Resources
Electrostatics (35 min) Demonstrate several effects of electrostatics, for example, repulsion between charged balloons and the attraction between scraps of paper and a charged balloon. Students should see that a non-contact force exists between charged objects. Explain why the balloon becomes charged (electric charge moves from hair to the balloon in the example in Starter 1) and use the idea of an electric field creating forces to explain each demonstration. Ask students for their own suggestions of effects they have already seen. Students then complete the tasks on the activity sheet.	**Support**: A support sheet is available with a partially filled table for observations. **Extension**: Introduce the triboelectric series. This lists materials and their tendency to lose or gain charge. It can be used to predict which becomes negatively charged, which becomes positively charged, and which will not gain a charge.	**Activity**: Electrostatics **Skill sheet**: Recording results

Plenary	Support/Extension	Resources
What happens with the balloon? (5 min) Students use the interactive resource to re-order sentences to explain the effect of a charged balloon on hair. **Draw it** (10 min) Students make labelled drawings showing what they think happens when something is charged. Use their drawings to explain any remaining misconceptions.	**Support**: Students should focus on illustrating key words from this lesson. **Extension**: This activity can be extended to electric fields.	**Interactive**: What happens with the balloon?

Homework		
Students research the uses of static electricity, at home or in industry, and write a short summary paragraph.		

1.2 Circuits and current

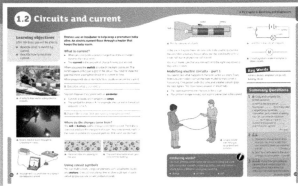

Physics KS3 NC link:

- electric current, measured in amperes in circuits
- current as a flow of charge
- using physical processes and mechanisms, rather than energy, to explain the intermediate steps that bring about changes in systems.

Working Scientifically NC link:

- use appropriate techniques, apparatus, and materials during fieldwork and laboratory work, paying attention to health and safety.

Band	Outcome	Checkpoint	
		Question	Activity
Developing	Name what flows in a circuit (Level 3).	1	Lit, Main, Plenary 1
	Name the equipment used to measure current (Level 3).	B, 1	Main, Plenary 2
	Use an ammeter to measure current (Level 4).		Main
Secure	Describe what is meant by current (Level 5).	A, 1	Lit, Main, Plenary 1
	Describe how to measure current (Level 5).	B, 1	Main, Plenary 2
	Set up a circuit including an ammeter to measure current (Level 5).		Main
Extending	Use a model to explain how current flows in a circuit (Level 7).	3	Plenary 1
	Predict the current in different circuits (Level 8).		Main
	Measure current accurately in a number of places in a series circuit (Level 7).		Main

Maths

Students must demonstrate their understanding of the number scale if reading current in a circuit using an analogue ammeter.

Students will also use the appropriate units for current values.

Literacy

In the student-book activity students must explain key words using scientific understanding, and relate this to how the key words may be used differently in everyday life.

APP

Students apply the rope model and the water pipe analogy to understand current (AF1).

Students select the appropriate combination of equipment when carrying out the practical to investigate current (AF4).

Key Words

current, switch, ammeter, amps, cell, battery, motor

Answers from the student book

In-text questions	**A** charge flowing per second	
	B ammeter	
Activity	**Confusing words**	
	charge: the electron has a negative charge; there is a charge to go into a theme park	
	current: current is the amount of charge flowing per second; there can be a strong current in the river	
	cell: component that pushes charge around a circuit; the smallest functional unit in an organism/American term for a mobile phone; a police or prison cell	

Summary Questions	
	1 charge, second, electrons, ammeter, amps, A (6 marks)
	2a Series circuit with battery of cells, motor, and switch. Students should annotate the switch, and explain how this can be switched on and off to control the circuit. (2 marks)
	b The electrons move/a current flows. (1 mark)
	3 QWC question (6 marks). Example answers:
	Start with a small series circuit with a switch, lamp, and cell. Show that the light comes on as soon as you press the switch. Make the leads longer, and show that this has no effect. Make a really big circuit, and show that the lamp comes on straight away. Use the rope model to show that the bulb comes on straight away if the charges are already in the wires. It does not matter how long the wire is, the bulb still comes on straight away. If the charges were in the battery, there would be a time delay.

Starter	Support/Extension	Resources
Drawing circuits (5 min) Review circuit symbols from KS2. Check students can draw circuit symbols when given a names component, and vice versa. If the existing knowledge is good, they can draw simple series circuits using the correct circuit symbols. Remind them that most connecting leads are drawn with straight lines.	**Support**: Cards can be used for students to match circuit symbols to the name of the component.	
Comparing currents (10 min) Introduce current and that some appliances use larger currents than others. Explain that larger currents flow in more powerful equipment and equipment that heats things. List appliances that plug into the mains. Students to rank these in order of the current they use. If a current meter is available, the current drawn by different appliances can be demonstrated.	**Support**: Group equipment as mains and battery-operated. **Extension**: Students explain their rank order in terms of the function of the appliance.	

Main	Support/Extension	Resources
Investigating current (40 min) Introduce students to the idea that current is a flow of charge. The water pipe analogy can be used to facilitate understanding. Explain the use of an ammeter, introduce the unit of charge (the ampere), and demonstrate how to set up a simple series circuit (including the ammeter). Students carry out a practical to measure current using simple series circuits and answer the questions that follow on the practical sheet. Ensure that at the end of the experiment, students are aware of the conclusion. There is only one path in the (series) circuit so the current must be the same in all places. If more cells are used the current increases, and if more components are placed in the circuit for the same number of cells, the current will decrease but will still be the same in all places.	**Support**: Draw circuits on a sheet of paper. Students place components in the correct positions and link them up using wires. A partially filled results table is available on the support sheet that gives combinations students should test in their series circuit. **Extension**: Students predict changes in current if the number of components in a circuit is changed. This links to resistance, which is covered later.	**Practical**: Investigating current

Plenary	Support/Extension	Resources
Rope model (10 min) Explain that charge is spread throughout the circuit, and as soon as it turns on, the charge moves at the same time, transferring energy. Use the rope model, as described in the student book, to show this phenomenon. Students should discuss what each part of the model represents in a circuit.	**Extension**: Students should suggest limitations and improvements to this model.	
Function of circuit components (5 min) This interactive resource can be used as a quick recap of the functions of five circuit components. In this activity, students match the names of circuit components with their functions.	**Extension**: Students should draw the symbol for each circuit component on a mini-whiteboard.	**Interactive**: Function of circuit components

Homework		
Students draw the circuit diagrams for simple pieces of equipment, for example, a torch, a handheld fan, or a hairdryer.		

1.3 **Potential difference**

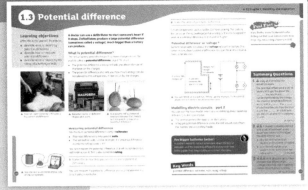

Physics KS3 NC link:
- potential difference, measured in volts
- battery and bulb ratings.

Working Scientifically NC link:
- use appropriate techniques, apparatus, and materials during fieldwork and laboratory work, paying attention to health and safety.

Band	Outcome	Checkpoint	
		Question	Activity
Developing	State the unit of potential difference (Level 4).	B	Main, Plenary 1
	Name the equipment used to measure potential difference (Level 3).	A, 1	Main, Plenary 1
	Describe the effect of a larger potential difference (Level 4).	1	
	Use appropriate equipment to measure potential difference (Level 4).		Main
Secure	Describe what is meant by potential difference (Level 5).	B, 1	Starter 1, Starter 2, Plenary 1
	Describe how to measure potential difference (Level 5).	A, 1	Main
	Describe what is meant by the rating of a battery or bulb (Level 6).	1	
	Set up a simple circuit and use appropriate equipment to measure potential difference (Level 6).		Main
Extending	Explain the difference between potential difference and current (Level 7).	3	Plenary 2
	Explain why potential difference is measured in parallel (Level 7).		Starter 1, Starter 2, Main, Plenary 1
	Predict the effect of changing the rating of a battery or bulb in a circuit (Level 7).	2	Plenary 1
	Set up and measure potential difference across various components in a circuit (Level 7).		Main

Maths
Students show understanding of number scales and relative sizes when ranking items in order of p.d. and when recording voltage readings on analogue voltmeters.

They use the correct units when measuring in the practical activity.

Literacy
Students use scientific key terms in the discussions of analogies, models, and their practical results.

APP
Students plan an experiment to investigate the relationship between battery size and p.d. in the student-book activity (AF4).

Key Words
potential difference, voltmeter, volts, rating, voltage

Answers from the student book

In-text questions	**A** voltmeter **B** volt
Activity	**Are bigger batteries better?** Plan should include how to measure the size of the batteries, decision on diameter/weight/volume, use of voltmeter to measure the potential, difference across the battery, collect a selection of different batteries, measure the 'size' and potential difference, record results in a table, plot the correct graph type.

Summary Questions	**1** push, energy, voltmeter, rating, rating (5 marks)
	2a The potential difference is bigger because the extra cell supplies more energy. (2 marks)
	b The buzzer would not work, the cells cancel out. (2 marks)
	3 QWC question (6 marks). Example answers:
	Charges flow when you connect a cell or battery. The charges are already in the wires/component. The battery pushes the charges. The size of the push is related to the potential difference. The charges flowing per second are the current. You measure the current with an ammeter. You measure the potential difference with a voltmeter.

Starter	Support/Extension	Resources
Comparing potential difference (10 min) Hand round five to six battery-powered items, and show images of appliances, including their operating potential difference (p.d.). Explain that p.d. indicates energy used by the equipment, and is measured in volts. Group items as battery operated (mainly low p.d.) or mains operated (mainly high p.d.), and rank all items from the lowest to the highest p.d. It is useful at this stage to use only the term potential difference, and not voltage, to avoid confusing students with additional terminology.	**Support**: Provide cards with the p.d. written on the back of each item. Students place the images on a number line. **Extension**: Students suggest dangers of high p.d., and understand that high current is the cause of fatalities.	
Looking at potential difference (10 min) Introduce sources of p.d. (e.g., lightning, power lines, railway lines). Explain that in each case a different amount of energy is used, which is linked to p.d. The interactive resource can then be used to link the operating p.d. with objects.		**Interactive**: Looking at potential difference

Main	Support/Extension	Resources
Investigating potential difference (40 min) Set up a simple circuit to demonstrate the position of the voltmeter in a circuit. Emphasise the difference between an ammeter (connected in series) and a voltmeter (connected in parallel). It is important to refer to p.d. **across** components, rather than inside each component. Students set up simple circuits to investigate p.d. in a range of different circuits, and answer the questions on their activity sheet. At the end of the experiment, ensure students understand the conclusions: p.d. is shared between components (depending on the component's resistance). The p.d. across the battery is the same as the sum of the p.d. across all the components in a series circuit.	**Support**: Provide enlarged circuit diagrams on A3 or A4 paper for students to place components on before linking them with wires. A support sheet is also available with suggested combinations of components to investigate in a results table.	**Activity**: Investigating potential difference **Skill sheet**: Recording results

Plenary	Support/Extension	Resources
Rope model for potential difference (10 min) Explain that energy is transferred through the circuit from cells to components. As soon as the circuit is complete, energy is transferred in all parts of the circuit at the same time, by charge. Revisit the rope model for current, and change the analogy to that for p.d. Details can be found in the student book.	**Extension**: Students can explain the effect of changing things in this circuit, offering limitations and improvements to this model.	
Comparing current and voltage (5 min) Students list similarities and differences between current and voltage, for example, how they are measured, their value in different parts of a series circuit, and what they are.	**Support**: Give students a list of statements describing current or p.d. for them to group.	

Homework	Support/Extension	
Students prepare a list of at least 10 pieces of electrical equipment used at home and the voltage supplied, either from batteries or the mains (230 V). Students should get parental permission to move/unplug equipment.	**Extension**: Students should rank these in order of p.d., and suggest why this is the case.	

1.4 Series and parallel

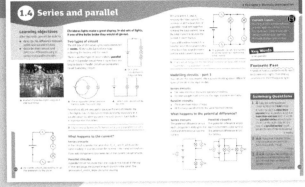

Physics KS3 NC link:
- series and parallel circuits, currents add where branches meet.

Working Scientifically NC link:
- interpret observations and data, including identifying patterns and using observations, measurements, and data to draw conclusions.

Band	Outcome	Checkpoint	
		Question	Activity
Developing	State one difference between series and parallel circuits (Level 4).	A, 1	Starter 2, Plenary 2
	State how current varies in series and parallel circuits (Level 4).	B, 2	Maths, Main
↓	Identify the pattern of current in series and parallel circuits (Level 4).		Main
Secure	Describe the difference between series and parallel circuits (Level 5).	A, 1	Starter 2, Plenary 2
	Describe how current and potential difference vary in series and parallel circuits (Level 6).	B, 2	Maths, Main, Plenary 1
↓	Identify the pattern of current and potential difference in series and parallel circuits (Level 6).		Main
Extending	Explain the most suitable type of circuit for the domestic ring main (Level 7).		Starter 2, Main, Homework
	Explain why current and potential difference vary in series and parallel circuits (Level 7).		Maths, Main, Plenary 1
↓	Explain the pattern in current and potential difference readings for series and parallel circuits, drawing conclusions (Level 7).		Main

Maths
Students should identify numerical patterns in the data obtained for current and p.d. from their experiment.

Literacy
Students should apply existing knowledge to explain the numerical patterns observed in their experiment using scientific key words.

APP
Students should use the rope model to compare similarities and differences between series and parallel circuits (AF1).

Students identify patterns in their data for current and p.d. to draw conclusions (AF5).

Key Words
series, parallel

Answers from the student book

In-text questions	**A** Two from: in a parallel circuit if one bulb breaks the others stay on; components can be turned on and off independently; parallel circuits have more than one loop or branch.
	B increases
Activity	**Current issues** 0.2 ÷ 2 = 0.1 A This is because current is shared between components in a series circuit.

Summary Questions	1 one, more than one, parallel, series (4 marks)
	2 The current increases. (1 mark)
	3 QWC question (6 marks). Example answers (three for each type of circuit): Series circuit: current is the same around the whole circuit, ammeter reading stays the same, p.d. is shared between components, voltmeter readings for components will add up to the p.d. of the power supply (cell/battery). Parallel circuit: current is split for each branch, the sum of the ammeter readings in the branches will add up to the ammeter reading from the main branch (by the power supply), p.d. is the same for each branch of the parallel circuit, voltmeter readings will be the same on each branch of the parallel circuit.

kerboodle

Starter	Support/Extension	Resources
What do you know? (10 min) Students write down what they already know about circuits, and then share their ideas. Identify misconceptions and correct mistakes at this stage.	**Support**: Prepare a short list of true/false statements about series circuits for students to categorise. **Extension**: Students should include explanations as well as descriptions.	
Series or parallel? (10 min) Ask students to list circuits where equipment or components can be controlled separately or together. For example, lighting circuits in the home or car, controls on a music system, cooker, or hairdryer. Explain how this can be done using series and parallel circuits. Students then apply this knowledge to group items into two categories: those that use series circuits, and those that use parallel circuits.	**Support**: Concentrate on if components require separate controls. Introduce key words in the main activity. **Extension**: Students justify why a series or parallel circuit is required in each case.	**Interactive**: Series or parallel?

Main	Support/Extension	Resources
Series and parallel circuits (35 min) Explain to students that the circuits they have been working with so far are series circuits, and introduce the idea of parallel circuits. Large diagrams of each type of circuit can be used to highlight similarities and differences, and will facilitate the tracing of electron paths around the circuits. Students then investigate circuit rules regarding current and p.d. in series and parallel circuits, by carrying out mini-experiments as part of an activity circus. Students must visit each station, each with a different circuit, and note down their observations. They then answer the questions that follow using their results.	**Support**: Diagrams of experimental setup are provided for students to add observations, current, and p.d. readings. **Extension**: Students should look for readings that are nearly the same, or that add up to roughly the same amount as another reading in the circuit.	**Practical**: Series and parallel circuits

Plenary	Support/Extension	Resources
Making predictions (10 min) Present students with circuit diagrams of simple series and parallel circuits. Each circuit will have partially filled data for current. Students must predict and complete the missing value for current in each case.	**Support**: Provide multiple-choice answers for predictions. **Extension**: Repeat the exercise for p.d. readings.	
Rope model revisited (10 min) Revisit the rope model to demonstrate current and p.d. in a series circuit. Ask students to contribute ideas as to how this model can be used to demonstrate parallel circuits. This model shows that adding more loops increases the current, that p.d. is supplied in all places of the circuit at the same time, and the same p.d. is supplied by the battery to both loops.	**Extension**: Once again, students can identify limitations and improvements to this model.	

Homework	Support/Extension	
Students consider what they have learned about series and parallel circuits, and use these ideas to draw a circuit for lighting in the home. This can be for several rooms in the home or for a staircase, for which the set-up for (two-way) switches should also be included.	**Support**: Students decide whether lights can be controlled independently or not, and draw a simple circuit diagram to explain their choice of circuit.	

1.5 Resistance

Physics KS3 NC link:

- resistance, measured in ohms, as the ratio of potential difference (p.d.) to current
- differences in resistance between conducting and insulating components (quantitative).

Working Scientifically NC link:

- select, plan, and carry out the most appropriate types of scientific enquiries to test predictions, including identifying independent, dependent, and control variables, where appropriate.

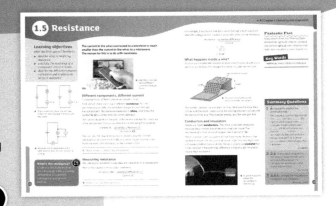

Band	Outcome	Checkpoint	
		Question	Activity
Developing	State the unit of resistance (Level 4).	B	Main
	Compare simply the resistance of conductors and insulators (Level 4).	1	Main
	List examples of conductors and insulators (Level 3).		Main
	Identify some of the variables in the investigation (Level 4).		Main
Secure	Describe what is meant by resistance (Level 5).	1	Main
	Calculate resistance of a component and of a circuit (Level 6).	2	Maths, Plenary 1, Homework
	Describe the difference between conductors and insulators in terms of resistance (Level 5).	1, 3	Main
	Identify independent, dependent, and control variables (Level 5).		Main
Extending	Explain the causes of resistance (Level 7).	1	Main
	Explain what factors affect the resistance of a resistor (Level 7).		Starter 2, Main
	Compare the effect of resistance in different materials (Level 7).	3	Starter 2, Main
	Independently select and control all the variables in the investigation, considering accuracy and precision (Level 7).		Main

Maths

Students calculate resistance using simple equations, giving units for their answers. Higher-ability students will be required to rearrange this equation.

They plot a graph of resistance against length of wire using experimental results.

Literacy

Students use key words correctly when suggesting a conclusion for their experiment, and when discussing aspects of working scientifically.

APP

Students identify key variables in their experiment (AF4), present experimental results using appropriate tables and graphs (AF3), and suggest reasons for the trends observed between variables (AF5).

Key Words

resistance, ohms, conductor, insulator

Answers from the student book

In-text questions	**A** How easy or difficult it is for the charges to pass through a component in a circuit. **B** ohms
Activity	**What's the resistance?** $$\text{resistance} = \frac{\text{voltage}}{\text{current}} = \frac{12\text{ V}}{0.6\text{ A}} = 20\ \Omega$$

Summary Questions	
	1 potential difference, resistance, resistance, electrons, energy, conductors, insulators (7 marks)

2 lamp resistance $= \dfrac{\text{voltage}}{\text{current}}$ motor resistance $= \dfrac{\text{voltage}}{\text{current}}$

$\qquad\qquad\quad = \dfrac{3\text{ V}}{0.4\text{ A}}$ $\qquad\qquad\qquad = \dfrac{3\text{ V}}{0.1\text{ A}}$

$\qquad\qquad\quad = 7.5\ \Omega$ $\qquad\qquad\qquad = 30\ \Omega$ (4 marks)

3 QWC question (6 marks). Example answers:

Both conductors and insulators have resistance.

Conductors have many charges that can move readily.

Conductors have low resistance.

Insulators do not contain many charges that are free to move.

Insulators have high resistance.

Most conductors are metals that have electrons that are free to move.

Current in an insulator would be smaller than the current through a conductor (for the same potential difference).

kerboodle

Starter	Support/Extension	Resources
What do you know already? (5 min) This interactive resource asks students to match circuit components to their functions. This can be used as a consolidation task, before introducing students to the more abstract concept of resistance.	**Extension**: Students draw circuit symbols or diagrams to illustrate each key word or phrase.	**Interactive**: What do you know already?
What affects resistance? (10 min) Explain what resistance is in general, for example, resistance makes it harder for something to happen. Remind students that current is the flow of charge, so electrical resistance makes it harder for charge to flow. Discuss changes you could make in a circuit to increase resistance. This is a useful activity to highlight student misconceptions.	**Support**: Use the analogy of water flowing in a hosepipe. How can water flow be reduced? For example, it is harder for water to flow if the hosepipe is narrower.	

Main	Support/Extension	Resources
Investigating the resistance of a wire (40 min) Introduce the idea of electrical resistance, including the equation to calculate resistance, and the difference in resistance between conductors and insulators. Students will investigate how changes in a wire affect its resistance. They should list the factors they can change, for example, length, diameter, material, and temperature. It is important at this point to remind students of independent, dependent, and control variables. Students will then carry out an experiment to investigate the relationship between resistance and the length of a wire. The practical sheets provided can easily be adapted to investigate other independent variables as described above.	**Support**: The support sheet contains a partially filled results table. **Extension**: Students can use ammeters and voltmeters instead of a multimeter, in order to use their readings to calculate resistance for each length of wire.	**Practical**: Investigating the resistance of a wire **Skill sheet**: Recording results **Skill sheet**: Choosing scales

Plenary	Support/Extension	Resources
Calculating resistance (5 min) Draw a circuit diagram including an ammeter and voltmeter. Add sample readings for students to calculate the correct value of resistance. This can be a quiz dividing the class into three teams, and giving marks for correct calculations.	**Support**: Provide a multiple-choice selection of resistance values. **Extension**: Provide circuit diagrams with resistance values but current or potential difference readings missing. Students should calculate the missing information.	
Evaluating my experiment (10 min) Students individually list two things that went well, and two things they would change if they repeated their experiment. They then compare these choices in their practical groups, and decide overall which factors had the greatest effect on the experiment.		**Skill sheet**: Evaluation

Homework	Support/Extension	
Provide students with further examples of resistance calculations, for them to complete at home.	**Support**: Provide multiple-choice answers. **Extension**: Include calculations involving rearrangements.	

1.6 Magnets and magnetic fields

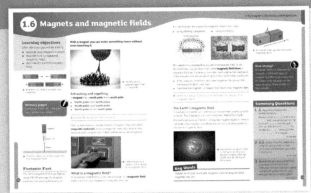

Physics KS3 NC link:

- magnetic poles, attraction and repulsion
- magnetic fields by plotting with compass, representation by field lines
- Earth's magnetism, compass, and navigation
- non-contact forces: forces between magnets
- using physical processes and mechanisms, rather than energy, to explain the intermediate steps that bring about changes in systems.

Working Scientifically NC link:

- make and record observations and measurements using a range of methods for different investigations; and evaluate the reliability of methods and suggest possible improvements.

Band	Outcome	Checkpoint	
		Question	Activity
Developing	Describe features of a magnet (Level 3).	A, 1	Starter 2, Main
	Draw the magnetic field lines around a bar magnet (Level 4).		Starter 2, Main
	State the Earth has a magnetic field (Level 4).	2	Main, Plenary 1
	Record the shape of field lines round a magnet (Level 4).		Main
Secure	Describe how magnets interact (Level 5).	1, 3	Starter 2
	Describe how to represent magnetic fields (Level 6).	B, 1	Starter 2, Main
	Describe the Earth's magnetic field (Level 5).	2	Main, Plenary 1
	Draw field lines round a magnet in detail (Level 6).		Main
Extending	Explain how magnets can be used (Level 7).	1, 4	Homework
	Compare magnetic field lines and a magnetic field (Level 7).	2	Starter 1, Main
	Explain how a compass works (Level 7).	1, 2	Main, Plenary 1, Plenary 2
	Suggest improvements to an experiment to observe field lines around a magnet (Level 7).		Main

Literacy
Students use scientific terminology correctly when describing magnetic fields and materials.

APP
Students use models when explaining the abstract concept of magnetism (AF1), and communicate observations relating magnetic fields using appropriate diagrams (AF3).

Key Words
magnet, north pole, south pole, magnetic material, magnetic field, magnetic field lines

Answers from the student book

In-text questions	**A** north and south **B** use a compass/iron filings
Activity	**How strong?**

Type of magnet	Distance between paperclip and magnet to get it to float (cm)

Summary Questions	1 north, south, repel, attract, compass, magnetic field (6 marks)
	2 A compass needle always points in a north–south direction.
	The compass needle lines up in the Earth's magnetic field (which does not change). (2 marks)
	3 The game instructions and scoring system should include (6 marks):
	Clear list of instructions.
	Using magnets to pick up or guide things.
	Correct use of north/south poles in the game.
	Scoring system linked to completion/difficulty.
	Linking scoring system to magnetic field strength/attraction/repulsion.
	Correct use of magnetic field strength/attraction/repulsion in scoring system.

kerboodle

Starter	Support/Extension	Resources
Changing fields (15 min) Attach a paperclip to thread and fix the thread firmly to the bench using sticky tape. Use a clamp stand to hold a magnet above the paperclip so it levitates with 3–5 cm between the paperclip and magnet. Students predict the effect of sliding different materials between the paperclip and magnet. Show that sliding non-magnetic materials between the paperclip and magnet has no effect, but magnetic materials disrupt the field so the paperclip falls.	**Extension**: Students suggest reasons for their observations using scientific terminology.	
What is a magnet? (15 min) Snowballing activity where students describe magnets in two or three sentences individually, then share ideas in small groups to come up with one description. Demonstrate field lines around a magnet using iron filings. This can be shown in 3-D if enough iron filings are used. (Ferrofluids can be used to show the 3-D nature of magnetic fields, if available.) Use students' ideas and the demonstration to identify the main features of a magnet (e.g., it attracts certain materials, it attracts/repels other magnets).	**Support**: Provide a list of true/false statements about magnets and magnetic fields. **Extension**: Make certain key words taboo in their description, for example, magnetic, north, and south.	

Main	Support/Extension	Resources
Drawing magnetic fields (30 min) Students are generally familiar with the concept of magnets and magnetic fields, but a short recap will aid students in their understanding of more abstract concepts. Demonstrate the difference between a magnet and a magnetic material, and their effect on a compass. Discuss the nature of the Earth's magnetic field, and explain that most magnets held close to an object have stronger fields than Earth, which is why compasses point towards a nearby magnet. Students can suggest the properties of the materials used to make a compass needle (magnetic, magnet, or non-magnetic) and the outer casing. Students then carry out a short practical where they use a compass to plot field lines around a bar magnet, and investigate field lines for magnets of different shapes. They then answer the questions that follow.	**Support**: The support sheet provides students with a step-by-step guide on drawing field lines around a bar magnet using a compass. **Extension**: Students predict the shapes of magnetic fields for different-shaped magnets.	**Practical**: Drawing magnetic fields

Plenary	Support/Extension	Resources
Which way does it point? (10 min) Students choose the correct words to explain how a compass works when filling in the gaps on the interactive resource.	**Extension**: Students should compare the strength of the Earth's magnetic field with a bar magnet.	**Interactive**: Which way does it point?
Navigating with magnets (10 min) Show a video clip from the Internet of migrating birds or homing pigeons. Students suggest how they can navigate. Discuss different theories (bird brains have sensors that respond to the Earth's magnetic field or their eyes respond to directional sunlight). Suggest why people need to use a compass to navigate.	**Extension**: Students suggest other ways to navigate if a compass is not available, or factors that can disrupt a bird's navigational system.	

Homework		
Students investigate magnets at home, finding as many uses as possible for permanent magnets and identifying magnetic materials around the home. Then write a paragraph explaining why magnets are used in these cases.		

1.7 Electromagnets

Physics KS3 NC link:
- the magnetic effect of a current, electromagnets, D.C. motors (principles only).

Working Scientifically NC link:
- make predictions using scientific knowledge and understanding.

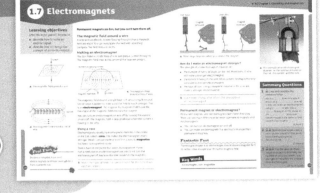

Band	Outcome	Checkpoint	
		Question	**Activity**
Developing	State the main features of an electromagnet (Level 4).	1	Starter 1
	State one difference between permanent magnets and electromagnets (Level 4).	1	Starter 1
	Test the effect of changing an electromagnet (Level 4).		Starter 2, Main
Secure	Describe how to make an electromagnet (Level 5).	1, 2	Starter 2
	Describe how to change the strength of an electromagnet (Level 6).	B, 3	Starter 2, Main
	Predict and test the effect of changes to an electromagnet (Level 6).		Main, Plenary 1
Extending	Explain how an electromagnet works (Level 7).	3	Homework
	Predict the effect of changes on the strength of different electromagnets (Level 7).		Main, Plenary 1, Homework
	Predict the effect of changes made to an electromagnet, using scientific knowledge to justify the claim (Level 8).		Main, Plenary 1

Maths
Students calculate the quantitative relationship between changes made to an electromagnet and the increase in its strength, demonstrating an understanding of simple ratios.

Literacy
Students use scientific terminology correctly when discussing observations and conclusions from their experiment.

APP
Students identify quantitative relationships between variables in an experiment (AF5).

Key Words
electromagnet, core, magnetise

Answers from the student book

In-text questions	**A** magnetic
	B type of core, number of turns, current
Summary Questions	**1** current, magnetic field, coil, current, magnetic field (5 marks)
	2 Wind a wire around the nail.
	Attach the ends of the wires to the battery using the leads and crocodile clips. (2 marks)
	3 QWC question (6 marks). Example answers:
	There is a magnetic field around a wire carrying a current.
	The field is stronger if there are more loops of wire.
	This is because the fields add together.
	A bigger current produces a stronger magnetic field.
	The magnetic material inside the coil becomes magnetised when you put it in a magnetic field.
	This increases the strength of the electromagnet.

Starter	Support/Extension	Resources
An alternative question-led lesson is also available. **What is an electromagnet?** (10 min) Demonstrate an electromagnet in the laboratory or using a video clip. Show that it can be switched on and off, and that it can be adjusted in strength. Students prepare a list that compares features of an electromagnet with a magnet. **Changing the strength** (10 min) Introduce the idea of an electromagnet using a diagram. Discuss as a class the factors affecting the strength of an electromagnet, encouraging students' ideas in the meantime. Students then recap what they have learnt using a gap-fill summary on the interactive resource.	**Support**: Provide a list of statements for students to match to magnets or electromagnets. **Support**: Prepare a list of variables from the interactive resource. Students can decide if any of these variables apply to a permanent magnet. **Extension**: Students evaluate the factors given, stating those that will cause the biggest change in strength.	**Question-led lesson**: Electromagnets **Interactive**: Changing the strength
Main	**Support/Extension**	**Resources**
Changing the strength of electromagnets (35 min) Students carry out a practical to investigate the effects on the strength of electromagnets of changing different variables, by taking part in a circus activity. Students will change the current, the number of turns on the coil, and the material used as the core of the electromagnet in their experiments. Students form their own predictions before carrying out the experiment, compare results to their predictions, and answer questions that follow on the practical sheet.	**Support**: A support sheet is available that includes partially filled results tables. **Extension**: Students should be encouraged to suggest quantitative predictions based on scientific understanding.	**Practical**: Changing the strength of electromagnets **Skill sheet**: Recording results
Plenary	**Support/Extension**	**Resources**
Testing predictions (10 min) Students compare their original prediction with what actually happened during their experiment. They identify the factors that had the biggest effect on the strength of an electromagnet and list features of a really strong electromagnet on a mini-whiteboard. **What have I learned?** (10 min) Students list three things they learnt in this lesson, including the three factors that affect the strength of an electromagnet. Use this as a chance to check and correct misconceptions.	**Support**: Students focus on general trends. **Extension**: Students should offer quantitative examples when explaining the trends observed.	
Homework		
Provide students with information regarding costs of materials to make an electromagnet (e.g., copper costs 10p per metre; 1 m = 20 turns in the coil). Ask students to make the strongest but cheapest electromagnet possible based on prices provided.		

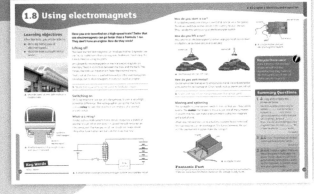

Physics KS3 NC link:

- the magnetic effect of a current, electromagnets, D.C. motors (principles only).

Working Scientifically NC link:

- identify further questions arising from their results.

Band	Outcome	Checkpoint	
		Question	**Activity**
Developing	State some uses of electromagnets (Level 4).	A, B, 1	Starter 2, Lit, Plenary 2
	State the main parts of a motor (Level 4).	2	Main
	Ask simple questions about motors (Level 4).		Main
Secure	Describe some uses of electromagnets (Level 5).	2, 3	Lit, Starter 2, Plenary 2
	Describe how a simple motor works (Level 5).	2	Main, Homework
	From your experiment, pose scientific questions to be investigated (Level 6).		Main
Extending	Apply existing knowledge about electromagnets to design a circuit (Level 7).	3	Lit
	Suggest ways to make a motor turn faster (Level 7).		Main, Homework
	Suggest investigations about electromagnets used in different applications (Level 7).		Main

Literacy
Students use scientific terms correctly when explaining observations in their experiment, when explaining the uses of motors for their homework, and when writing a letter in the student-book activity to persuade the use of electromagnets to sort soft-drinks cans for recycling.

APP
Students make further predictions on electromagnets and motors, based on experimental results (AF5).

Key Words
relay, motor

Answers from the student book

In-text questions	**A** electromagnets
	B To lift cars/sort metals.
Activity	**Recycle those cans!**
	The letter should explain the basic construction of an electromagnet, and that the electromagnet will attract steel cans but not aluminium.
Summary Questions	**1** trains, relay, current, spins, motor (5 marks)
	2 A simple motor contains a coil of wire and two permanent magnets.
	A current flows in the coil of wire.
	The coil becomes an electromagnet.
	The forces between the coil and the permanent magnets make it spin. (4 marks)

3 QWC question (6 marks). Example answers:
Electromagnet is on the two walls.
A magnetic material is on the doors.
When a current flows in the electromagnet there is a magnetic field around it.
The magnetic material on the doors is attracted to it.
The doors stay open while a current flows.
When the fire alarm sounds, the current to the electromagnet is cut.
There is no longer a magnetic field around the electromagnet.
The magnetic material on the doors is no longer attracted to it.
The doors close.

Starter	Support/Extension	Resources
Introducing motors (10 min) Explain that a motor uses electricity to make something spin. Students list as many pieces of equipment that use motors in the home as possible. This can be done as a competition in small groups.	**Extension**: Students rank their list of equipment by their prediction of the strength of the motor they use.	
Uses of electromagnets (10 min) Students sort uses of electromagnets into three categories (electromagnets that turn on and off, those that vibrate, and those that are very strong) using the interactive resources.	**Support**: Allow students to work in groups to discuss possible answers before a class discussion.	**Interactive**: Uses of electromagnets

Main	Support/Extension	Resources
Using electromagnets (35 min) Compare properties of permanent magnets and electromagnets, and introduce the different uses of electromagnets, leading to motors. Demonstrate equipment that uses a motor, and explain that motors need magnets and an electric current to spin. Students should be able to spot that both a permanent magnet and an electromagnet are required in a motor. Students then carry out a simple practical to make a motor of their own, answering questions that follow on the practical sheet. Students may choose to use different thicknesses of wire, different batteries, or different magnets if time permits. Students should explain their observations and try to relate their results to their work from previous lesson on electromagnets.	**Support**: The support sheet contains hints for students when writing further questions they can investigate in this practical. **Extension**: Students may be able to repeat the experiment, changing one variable in a methodical way, in the same time it takes the rest of the class to carry out the practical once.	**Practical**: Using electromagnets

Plenary	Support/Extension	Resources
Your questions (10 min) Students share their questions from the practical sheet with a partner, and decide in groups/pairs if they can suggest answers to these questions. If there is time, demonstrate the effect of some of their changes and see if they were right.	**Extension**: Students share their hypothesis for each change suggested.	
Uses of electromagnets revisited (10 min) Students should work independently to name as many uses of electromagnets as possible. They then join up in small groups to add to their existing ideas. Groups can then compete with each other in a competition for the longest list.	**Extension**: Students may earn bonus points if they list uses of electromagnets by category (e.g., transport: car engine and levitating train; kitchen: microwave turntable and electric whisk).	

Homework		
Students find out about one application of motors in detail. They write a paragraph explaining how the motor works, explaining the roles of the permanent and electromagnet in the motor, and how to make the motor stronger. Students can decorate their work using an image of a motor.		
An alternative WebQuest homework activity is also available on Kerboodle where students research the use of electromagnets in metal-recycling.		**WebQuest**: Metal-recycling and electromagnets

Checkpoint lesson routes

The route through this lesson can be determined using the Checkpoint assessment. Percentage pass marks are supplied in the Checkpoint teacher notes.

Route A (support)
Resource: P2 Chapter 1 Checkpoint: Revision

Students work through a series of tasks that allows them to gradually revisit and consolidate their understanding of electricity and magnetism. Students can keep this as a summary of the topic, and use this when revising for future assessments.

Route B (extension)
Resource: P2 Chapter 1 Checkpoint: Extension

Students prepare a leaflet describing some of the different household circuits to a primary-school audience. Students are required to draw labelled diagrams of series and parallel circuits, explaining current and potential difference rules.

Progression to *secure*

No.	Developing outcome	Secure outcome	Making progress
1	State the two types of charge.	Describe how charged objects interact.	In Task 1 students fill in a table to show whether two charges will attract or repel.
2	Describe how to charge insulators.	Explain how objects can become charged.	In Task 1 students reorder sentences to explain how hair becomes charged when it is combed.
3	State what surrounds charged objects.	Describe what is meant by an electric field.	In Task 5 students describe the difference between a magnetic and an electric field.
4	State what flows in a circuit.	Describe what is meant by current.	In Task 2 students fill in a table to give the definitions of current and potential difference, as well as naming the circuit components that measure these.
5	Describe the effect of a larger potential difference.	Describe what is meant by the rating of a battery or bulb.	In Task 4 students predict what would happen to a bulb rated 6 V in a circuit of 10 V.
6	State one difference between series and parallel circuits.	Describe the difference between series and parallel circuits.	In Task 3 students decide if the circuit diagrams given show series or parallel circuits, explaining their answers.
7	State how current varies in series and parallel circuits.	Describe how current and potential difference vary in series and parallel circuits.	In Task 4 students use their knowledge of series and parallel circuit rules to a calculation on resistance and complete the missing values on a circuit diagram.
8	State the unit of resistance.	Describe what is meant by resistance.	In Task 4 students complete the missing words in a paragraph describing resistance.
9	List examples of conductors and insulators, comparing simply their difference in resistance.	Calculate resistance of a component in a circuit and describe the difference between conductors and insulators.	In Task 4 students explain whether wires in an electric circuit are made from conductors or insulators using the idea of resistance.
10	Describe features of a magnet.	Describe how magnets interact.	In Task 5 students explain whether a given arrangement of two magnets will attract or repel, giving reasons for their answer.
11	Draw the magnetic field lines around a bar magnet and the Earth.	Describe how to represent magnetic fields.	In Task 5 students draw the magnetic field around a bar magnet and around the Earth.
12	State the main features of an electromagnet and give some examples of their uses.	Describe how to make an electromagnet and describe some of its uses.	In Task 5 students describe two uses of electromagnets, using the main features of an electromagnet in their description.

13	State one difference between permanent magnets and electromagnets.	Describe how to change the strength of an electromagnet.	In Task 5 students are required to describe two ways to make an electromagnet stronger.
14	State the main parts of a motor.	Describe how a simple motor works.	In Task 6 students reorder sentences to explain how a motor works.

Answers to end-of-chapter questions

1a B (1 mark)

  b Circuit A: connect a lead from the bulb to the battery.
Circuit C: turn one of the cells around. (2 marks)

2a Diagram as in page 133 of student book. (2 marks)   **b** A: attract B: repel (2 marks)

  c You can turn an electromagnet on and off but you cannot turn a permanent magnet on and off.

3 A current flows in a coil of wire, the coil of wire spins in a magnetic field. (1 mark)

4a Credit suitable parallel circuits with two cells on one branch, with a bulb and a switch on two other branches. (2 marks)

  b parallel (1 mark)   **c** X, Y, X and Y   **d** Attach an ammeter between the bulbs and the switches. (2 marks)

5a Circuit diagram as described. (2 marks)

  b The push of the battery/energy transferred in a component. (1 mark)

  c The potential difference that the lamp is designed to work at. (1 mark)

  d resistance $= \dfrac{\text{voltage}}{\text{current}}$

$$= \frac{12\ \text{V}}{0.4\ \text{A}}$$

$$= 30\ \Omega \qquad\qquad \text{(2 marks)}$$

6a Reading on the ammeter is halved, because there is twice the resistance. (2 marks)

  b The voltmeter reading is halved, there is less energy transferred to the lamp because the current is less. (2 marks)

7 This is a QWC question. Students should be marked on the use of good English, organisation of information, spelling and grammar, and correct use of specialist scientific terms. The best answers will explain in detail how the rod becomes charged and is able to attract the small pieces of paper (maximum of 6 marks).
Examples of correct scientific points:

Both the rod and cloth contain atoms.

Atoms contain electrons, protons, and neutrons.

Electrons are negatively charged.

Protons are positively charged.

When you rub the rod, electrons move from the cloth to the rod (or vice versa).

The rod becomes negatively charged/cloth becomes positively charged (or vice versa, as above)

The rod repels the electrons on the top of the pieces of paper.

The top of the pieces of paper become positively charged.

The paper is attracted to the rod.

Answer guide for Maths Challenge

Developing	Secure	Extending
1–2 marks	3–4 marks	5–6 marks
• Identifies at least one of the variables.	• Identifies most of the variables.	• Identifies all of the variables.
• Draws one table but with some or all units missing from the headers.	• Draws at least one table with some units in the headers.	• Draws all the relevant tables with the correct units in the headers.
• Draws one bar chart but with labels on the axes missing.	• Draws at least one bar chart or line graph with correctly labelled axes.	• Draws appropriate line graphs and bar charts with correctly labelled axes, including units.
	• States that tungsten has the biggest resistance because the electromagnet is weaker.	• Explains why tungsten has the biggest resistance in terms of current.

kerboodle

P2 Chapter 1 Checkpoint assessment (automarked)
P2 Chapter 1 Checkpoint: Revision
P2 Chapter 1 Checkpoint: Extension
P2 Chapter 1 Progress task (Literacy)

2.1 Food and fuels

Physics NC link:

- comparing energy values of different foods (from labels) (kJ)
- fuels and energy resources.

Working Scientifically NC link:

- present reasoned explanations, including explaining data in relation to predictions and hypotheses.

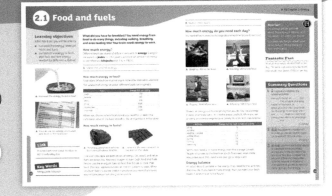

Band	Outcome	Checkpoint	
		Question	Activity
Developing	Identify energy values for food and fuels (Level 3).	A, 1	Main
	Describe energy requirements in different situations (Level 4).	1, 2	Maths, Starter 2, Main, Plenary 1
	Interpret data on food intake for some activities (Level 4).		Main
Secure	Compare the energy values of food and fuels (Level 5).	2	Starter 1, Main, Plenary 2
	Compare the energy in food and fuels with the energy needed for different activities (Level 5).	2, 3	Maths, Starter 2, Main, Plenary 1, Plenary 2
	Explain data on food intake and energy requirements for a range of activities (Level 6).		Main
Extending	Calculate energy requirements for various situations, considering diet and exercise (Level 7).	2, 3	Maths, Starter 2, Main, Plenary 1
	Suggest different foods needed in unusual situations, for example, training for the Olympics (Level 7).	3	Starter 2, Main
	Explain why an athlete needs more energy from food using data provided (Level 7).		Main

Maths

In the student-book activity students carry out simple calculations involving multiplication and division to deduce the energy expenditure per minute for different activities.

Students are also required to convert between joules and kilojoules in this lesson.

Literacy

Students extract and use information from different resources to describe situations where food and activities need to be matched.

APP

Student present data from secondary sources using tables (AF3).

Key Words

energy, joule, kilojoule

Answers from the student book

In-text questions	**A** joules
	B Three from: wood, oil, coal, gas
Activity	**How far?**
	50 g of chocolate contains: 0.5 × 1500 = 750 kJ
	You would need to run for: 750 ÷ 60 = 12.5 minutes
	This means you will need to run: 12.5 × 150 = 1875 m

Summary Questions	
	1 food, fuels, joules, breathing, bones, muscles, brains (6 marks)
	2 20 minutes (2 marks)
	3 Example answers (6 marks):
	Identifies a range of activities.
	Identifies the time that he/she spends doing each activity.
	Identifies the energy used per minute for the activities using the table.
	Calculates the energy for each activity by multiplying the time by the energy per minute.
	Identifies the energy stored in bananas, peas, chips, and chocolate from the table.
	Works out the mass of each that would be needed for the daily activities.
	Comments on the contrast in mass between fruit and chips/chocolate.

kerboodle

Starter	Support/Extension	Resources
Energy stored in foods (5 min) A list of statements relating to the energy stored in foods is given on the interactive resource. Students must categorise these statements according to whether they are true or false.	**Extension**: Students correct the statements that are false, and prepare three more statements (true or false) to share with the class.	**Interactive**: Energy stored in foods
Food and activity (10 min) Students consider how the food requirements change for different people engaged in different activities. These can be ranked in order of energy used.	**Extension**: Students suggest how energy requirements change for different people or activity levels. They predict the effect of keeping the amount of food eaten constant.	

Main	Support/Extension	Resources
Food and fuels (35 min) This activity uses props to demonstrate the size of a joule to students. Students extract information from food labels about energy intake per portion, suggest foods that could be eaten to provide their daily amount of energy, and rank energy requirements for carrying out different activities in order.	**Support**: The accompanying access sheet has simplified questions. **Extension**: Students can suggest similar activities that use the same amount of energy (or 10 times the amount of energy).	**Activity**: Food and fuels **Skill sheet:** Converting units

Plenary	Support/Extension	Resources
What used the most energy today? (10 min) Students decide which activity they do during a typical school day has the greatest energy requirement, and give a justification for their answer. Students compare their choices. Ask students 'Do you adjust your food intake to allow for an active school day?'.	**Support**: Provide a data sheet listing approximate energy requirements by activity for a fixed duration, which students can refer to.	
Energy in fuel (10 min) Provide students with information about the energy supplied by burning fuels. Students compare the amount of energy supplied by fuel with the energy supplied by food. Explain that fuels are often a more concentrated form of energy than food.	**Extension**: Students compare reasons for using fuels in different situations (e.g., coal is not used in cars because it leaves ash).	

Homework	Support/Extension	
Students keep track of what they do during a 24-hour period (activity and duration), and estimate their energy requirements for that day.	**Support**: Provide a table listing approximate energy requirements by activity and duration, which students can complete based on their own activity.	

2.2 Energy adds up

Physics NC link:

- energy as a quantity that can be quantified and calculated; the total energy has the same value before and after a change
- comparing the starting with the final conditions of a system and describing increases and decreases in the amounts of energy associated with movements, temperature, changes in positions in a field, in elastic distortions and in chemical compositions
- other processes that involve energy transfer: changing motion, dropping an object, completing an electrical circuit, stretching a spring, metabolism of food, burning fuels
- energy changes on deformation.

Working Scientifically NC link:

- make and record observations and measurements using a range of methods for different investigations.

Band	Outcome	Checkpoint	
		Question	Activity
Developing	State the definition of the conservation of energy (Level 4).	A, 1	Starter 2, Main
	State how energy is transferred (Level 4).	B	Starter 2, Main, Plenary 2
↓	Present simple observations of energy transfers (Level 4).		Main
Secure	Describe energy before and after a change (Level 6).	2, 3	Starter 1, Main, Plenary 2
	Explain what brings about transfers in energy (Level 6).	2, 3	Starter 2, Main, Plenary 2
↓	Present observations of energy transfers in a table (Level 6).		Main
Extending	Account for energy dissipation during transfers (Level 7).	2, 3	Starter 2, Main, Plenary 2
	Compare energy transfers to energy conservation (Level 7).	3	Starter 2, Main, Plenary 2
↓	Present detailed observations of energy transfers in a table, including useful and non-useful transfers (Level 8).		Main

Literacy
Students use scientific terminology to explain the Law of conservation of energy, describing energy transfers in different situations.

Students are also required to create their own mnemonics for remembering the names of energy stores in the student-book activity.

APP
Students present practical observations in a table (AF3).

Key Words
law of conservation of energy, chemical store, energy store, thermal, kinetic, gravitational potential, elastic, dissipated

Answers from the student book

In-text questions	**A** Energy cannot be created or destroyed. It can only be transferred.
	B light, sound, electricity
Activity	**Remember those stores!**
	Credit suitable mnemonics using the letters C, T, K, G, and E.

Summary Questions	**1** created, destroyed, chemical, thermal, cannot (5 marks)
	2a The battery has chemical energy. (2 marks)
	b Chemical energy transferred to thermal energy by electricity and light. (2 marks)
	3 QWC question (6 marks). Example answers.
	There is a chemical store associated with the wood (and oxygen).
	The wood burns in the oxygen.
	Energy is transferred to the sausages.
	Because the fire heats the sausages.
	There is more energy in the thermal store associated with the sausages.
	There is more energy in the thermal store associated with the air.
	There is less energy in the chemical store associated with the wood.

Starter	Support/Extend	Resources
Energy stores (10 min) Introduce energy stores (chemical, thermal, kinetic, gravitational potential, and elastic) to students giving examples of each type. Students, suggest another example of each type of energy store by trying to use examples in the room.	**Support**: Provide sort cards with named energy sources to match against types of energy stores. **Extension**: Students suggest reasons for differences between electricity, light, sound, and energy stores.	
Energy changes (10 min) Show some examples of energy changes and ask students to describe in words what is happening, for example, an antacid rocket, burning an indoor sparkler, and dropping a ball. Introduce the idea of energy stores and that energy is transferred from a store when anything happens. Explain that all energy must be accounted for (law of conservation of energy).	**Extension**: Students should point out unwanted energy transfers during each activity, and discuss the differences between electricity, light, sound, and energy stores.	

Main	Support/Extend	Resources
The conservation of energy (35 min) It is extremely important to introduce/recap the types of energy store and transfer, as well as the law of conservation of energy before the practical. Students will then carry out a circus activity where they identify energy stores before and after an energy transfer, in addition to the energy transfers taking place during the experiment. Students then answer questions that follow to consolidate their knowledge and understanding.	**Support**: The support sheet allows students to record their observations in words, choosing the type of energy store each time from two possible answers. **Extension**: Students start to write out energy transfers in words as equations, filling in details of the transfer between energy stores.	**Practical**: The conservation of energy

Plenary	Support/Extend	Resources
Energy stores and transfers (10 min) Students sort a list of items and scenarios into energy stores or energy transfers using the interactive resource. **Is it conserved?** (10 min) Ask students to write the law of conservation of energy on their mini-whiteboards. Students should then use an example from the practical and account for all the energy during the transfer.	**Extension**: Students should match each energy store to a corresponding energy transfer, offering the energy transfer in full for each example.	**Interactive**: Energy stores and transfers

Homework		
Students describe five energy changes that take place during a normal school day and the changes in the energy content of corresponding energy stores. For example, eating breakfast increases the chemical store of energy, while climbing stairs increases the gravitational (potential) energy.		

Physics NC link:

- heating and thermal equilibrium: temperature difference between two objects leading to energy transfer from the hotter to the cooler one
- changes with temperature in motion and spacing of particles.

Working Scientifically NC link:

- evaluate data, showing awareness of potential sources of random and systematic error.

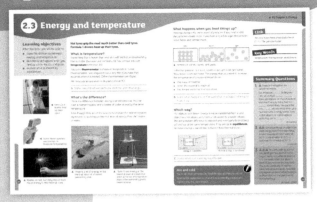

Band	Outcome	Checkpoint	
		Question	**Activity**
Developing	State how energy and temperature are measured (Level 4).	A, 1	Starter 2
	Describe how energy is transferred through solids, liquids, and in air (Level 4).	B, 3	Lit, Main
	State what is meant by the term 'equilibrium' (Level 4).	C, 1	Main
	Identify a source of error (Level 4).		Main, Plenary 2
Secure	State the difference between energy and temperature (Level 6).	A, 1	Starter 2
	Describe what happens when you heat up solids, liquids, and gases (Level 6).	B, 1, 3	Main
	Explain what is meant by equilibrium (Level 6).	1, 3	Main
	Describe how to reduce error in experimental apparatus (Level 6).		Main, Plenary 2
Extending	Give an example to show that energy and temperature are different (Level 7).	2	Starter 2
	Explain, in terms of particles, how energy is transferred (Level 7).	B, 3	Lit, Main, Plenary 1
	Give examples of equilibrium (Level 7).	3	Main
	Describe sources of error as systemic or random, and suggest ways to minimise these (Level 7).		Main, Plenary 2

Maths
Students use estimation for temperatures in familiar situations, and compare these to temperatures in unfamiliar situations.

Literacy
Students use scientific terminology when forming hypotheses and analysing and evaluating data from the experiment.

In the student-book activity students correct a scientifically incorrect phrase and justify this change.

APP
Students use abstract ideas and models when explaining heating and cooling (AF1).

Students collect experimental data (AF4), and suggest improvements to the experiment based on their observations (AF5).

Key Words
temperature, thermometer, equilibrium

Answers from the student book

In-text questions	**A** temperature: degrees Celsius (°C); energy: joules (J) **B** They move/vibrate faster.
	C When objects end up at the same temperature after energy transfer.
Activity	**Hot and cold** Shut the door, you will let the warm air out. (Energy moves from hot places to cold places.)

Summary Questions	**1** temperature, thermometer, temperature, energy, solids, equilibrium (6 marks)
	2 a cup of water at 30 °C, a saucepan of water at 30 °C, a saucepan of water at 50 °C (1 mark)
	3 QWC question (6 marks). Example answers:
	The particles in the metal tray vibrate. The hotter the tray the more they vibrate. When the tray goes into the oven the metal heats up. The particles on the outside of the tray vibrate more. They pass the vibrations on. The tray reaches the same temperature as the inside of the oven. The tray is in equilibrium. When you take the tray out of the oven it cools down. The energy moves from the thermal store of the tray to the thermal store of the air. The air heats up. The tray reaches the same temperature as the air. The particles in the tray vibrate less.

kerboodle

Starter	Support/Extension	Resources
Matching temperatures (10 min) Hand students different items to estimate the temperature of each object, and list them in rank order. For example, a warm filled hot water bottle, an ice pack, a metal spoon, a wooden spoon, and a beaker of tap water. Use the interactive resource to match examples of different objects to their temperatures.	**Support**: Simpler objects can be suggested in an alternative matching exercise, using boiling water, body temperature, and freezing point of water.	**Interactive**: Matching temperatures
Energy and temperature (10 min) Light a match and explain it burns at about 250 °C. Ask students to estimate how much it could heat a beaker of water. Dip the burning match in the water and show, using a thermometer, that the temperature rise is negligible. Explain that energy (J) stored in the match depends on temperature (°C), as well as mass and material.	**Extension**: Students can apply this idea to the difference in water temperature after heating 100 ml of water for 10 minutes, compared with heating 1 litre of water for 10 minutes.	

Main	Support/Extension	Resources
Energy and temperature (35 min) Explain the difference between temperature (°C) and energy in a thermal store (J). The energy stored in something hot depends on its temperature, its size, and the material it is made from. Demonstrate how to use a thermometer, describing sources of error. Explain that the thermometer is in equilibrium (the same temperature as) with its surroundings when its reading stops changing. Review the particle model of solids, liquids, and gases briefly. Explain that changes of state change the particle arrangement. The particles themselves do not change but the spacing between them does. Students then carry out short experiments as part of an activity circus, recording their observations, and answering questions that follow.	**Support**: A support sheet is available with a partially filled results table and a list of possible observations students should look out for during their experiments.	**Practical**: Energy and temperature **Skill sheet**: Recording results

Plenary	Support/Extension	Resources
Extreme temperatures (10 min) Explain why objects warm up (particles vibrate more, storing more energy). Explain that absolute zero is the temperature at which particles stop moving and nothing can get colder. This is −273 °C. There is no limit on the hottest temperature. Discuss where we may find extreme temperatures (e.g., in stars).	**Support**: Students may find particle diagrams of the three states of matter useful for this exercise.	
Types of thermometer (10 min) Students compare different thermometers used to make measurements, ranking them in order of ease of use, accuracy of measurements, and range of temperatures measured. Then have a class discussion.	**Support**: Allow groups of students to work together. **Extension**: Students offer their evaluation based on different uses of each thermometer.	

Homework		
Students investigate the temperature of different items in the home, making a list. Students should use a thermometer to make measurements if possible, or compare the temperature of some items with known temperatures.		

Physics NC link:

- heating and thermal equilibrium: temperature difference between two objects leading to energy transfer from the hotter to the cooler one, through contact (conduction); such transfers tending to reduce the temperature difference; use of insulators.

Working Scientifically NC link:

- interpret observations and data, including identifying patterns and using observations, measurements, and data to draw conclusions.

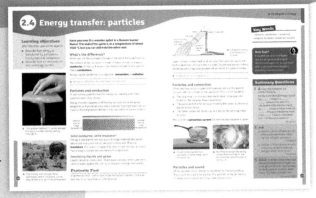

Band	Outcome	Checkpoint	
		Question	**Activity**
Developing	Describe simply what happens in conduction and convection (Level 4).	1, 2	Starter 2, Plenary 1
	State that insulators reduce heat loss compared to conductors (Level 4).	1	Main, Plenary 1, Homework
↓	State the pattern in conduction shown in results (Level 4).		Main
Secure	Describe how energy is transferred by particles in conduction and convection (Level 6).	1, 2	Starter 2, Plenary 1, Plenary 2
	Describe how an insulator can reduce energy transfer (Level 6).		Starter 1, Main, Plenary 1, Homework
↓	Describe the pattern in conduction shown by results, using numerical data to inform a conclusion (Level 5).		Main
Extending	Explain in detail the processes involved during heat transfers (Level 7).	3	Starter 2, Main, Plenary 1, Plenary 2
	Explain why certain materials are good insulators (Level 7).	2	Starter 1, Main, Plenary 1, Homework
↓	Explain the pattern in conduction shown by experimental results (Level 7).		Main

Maths
Students record numerical data in tables and calculate means, before interpreting this data to identify patterns and draw conclusions.

Literacy
Students explain observations and conclusions using scientific terminology.

APP
Students record observations in suitable tables (AF3), and draw conclusions from patterns in their experimental data (AF5).

Key Words
conductor, conduction, convection, radiation, insulator, convection current

Answers from the student book

In-text questions	**A** A material that transfers energy quickly.
	B A material that does not transfer energy quickly.
Activity	**How fast?**
	The plan should include timing how long it takes for water at a certain temperature to cool down, the need for repeat measurements, how variables are controlled, and a range of measurements of temperature.
	Risk assessment should include sensible suggestions to avoid damage/injury from hot water.

Summary Questions	**1** conduction, temperature difference, convection, move, slowly (6 marks)
	2a The particles in a solid are close together, so can pass on the vibration; the particles in a gas or in a liquid are too far apart. (2 marks)
	b The particles in a gas or in a liquid can move; the particles in a solid cannot. Convection involves the movement of particles to transfer energy. (2 marks)
	3 QWC question (6 marks). Example answers: The metal element gets hot. The particles in the metal vibrate more. Energy moves from the element to the water in contact with the element. The hot water molecules move faster. The hot water becomes less dense. Hot water floats up. Cooler (denser) water sinks to replace it. A convection current forms. The water circulates until all the water is hot.

kerboodle

Starter	Support/Extension	Resources
Keeping warm (10 min) Briefly introduce the difference between conduction and convection. Ask students to describe how they dress to keep warm. Use their suggestions to identify features reducing heat loss by conduction (e.g., insulators or trapped layers of air) and by convection (e.g., elasticated cuffs or using scarves to block gaps).	**Support**: Use items of clothing as examples, and point out the main insulating features. **Extension**: Encourage students to use the terms conductor and insulator in their ideas.	
Conduction and convection (15 min) Demonstrate and explain convection (including the concept of density) using potassium permanganate crystals. Students then apply their knowledge to reorder sentences on the interactive resource to explain what happens to soup when it is heated. A common misconception is that particles themselves change in size.	**Support**: Use diagrams or simulations to aid understanding when explaining the concept of density. These are readily available on the Internet.	**Interactive**: Conduction and convection

Main	Support/Extension	Resources
Investigating conduction (35 min) At this stage it is important to remind students of the particle models of solids, liquids, and gases. Mini-whiteboards can be used for students to draw these particle models on, to check for retention of previous knowledge. Explain how metals have delocalised electrons that help not only to conduct electricity but also to conduct thermal energy. Introduce the concepts of conduction and convection, and demonstrate how this can be done using a thermistor and resistor, a thermometer, or thermofilm (if available). Students then carry out a short investigation on different materials to determine whether they are conductors or insulators, and answer the questions that follow.	**Support**: Use the support sheet for a partially filled table of results. Students may need reminding how to calculate means.	**Activity**: Investigating conduction **Skill sheet**: Recording results **Skill sheet**: Calculating means

Plenary	Support/Extension	Resources
Comparing conduction (10 min) Ask students to offer the definitions of conduction and convection. Then demonstrate a short practical by placing two 30 cm rulers (one plastic and the other metal) in a beaker of hot water. Both rulers should have thermofilm attached to them, approximately 3 cm above the base (thermofilm should be above the water level at all times). The colour of the thermofilm attached to the metal ruler should change very quickly.	**Support**: Students describe observations, and explain using definitions of conduction and convection which concept the experiment shows. **Extension**: Students should offer explanations for their observations using delocalised electrons.	
Conduction versus convection (5 min) Students compare conduction and convection by listing similarities (e.g., involving particles, transferring energy down a gradient), and differences (e.g., ability for particles to move or not, currents set up or not).	**Support**: Provide a list of true/false statements on conduction and convection for students to work through.	

Homework	Support/Extension	
Students describe situations at home where energy is transferred by conduction or convection, and explain how the heat transfer is either helped (using good conductors and a large surface area) or reduced (using insulation).	**Extension**: Students research the meaning of radiation, and include sources around the home.	

2.5 Energy transfer: radiation

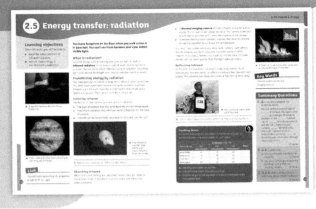

Physics NC link:

- temperature difference between two objects leading to energy transfer from the hotter to the cooler one, through radiation.

Working Scientifically NC link:

- evaluate risks.

Band	Outcome	Checkpoint	
		Question	Activity
Developing	State some sources of infrared radiation (Level 4).	A, 1	Main, Plenary 1
	State some properties of infrared radiation (Level 4).	B, 1	Main, Plenary 1
	Identify some risks in an experiment (Level 4).		Starter 1, Main
Secure	Describe some sources of infrared radiation (Level 5).	1	Main, Plenary 1
	Explain how energy is transferred by radiation (Level 6).	B, 1–3	Main, Plenary 1
	Identify risks and explain why it is important to reduce them (Level 5).		Starter 1, Main
Extending	Explain how thermal equilibrium can be established (Level 7).	3	Main
	Explain why some objects radiate more energy (Level 7).	2, 3	Main, Plenary 1
	Explain in detail how to reduce risks (Level 7).		Starter 1, Main

Maths
Students interpret a table of results in the student-book activity and use the data to calculate means.

Students use a thermometer to accurately record temperature during their experiment.

Literacy
Students use scientific terminology when explaining insulating measures around the home, for their homework.

APP
Students identify risks in their experiments and suggest ways to reduce them (AF4).

Key Words
infrared radiation, thermal imaging camera

Answers from the student book

In-text questions	**A** two from: Sun, fire, light bulb
	B It is reflected.
Activity	**Cooling down**
	a first measurement for shiny white; first measurement for shiny black
	b 14, 16, 13, 12.5
	c The ranges overlap.
Summary Questions	**1** sources, radiation, temperature, reflected, absorb, medium, vacuum (7 marks)
	2a White surfaces reflect infrared radiation so the houses will absorb less and stay cooler. (1 mark)
	b The fire emits infrared radiation so the camera cannot distinguish between the infrared radiation from the people and the infrared radiation from the fire. (2 marks)
	3 Visual summary example answers (6 marks):
	All objects emit infrared radiation. This is commonly referred to as thermal radiation or heat. Infrared is a type of wave. Can travel through a vacuum. Can be reflected. Can be absorbed. Transfers energy. Cannot be seen by eye.

Starter	Support/Extension	Resources
An alternative question-led lesson is also available. **Hot or cold?** (15 min) Set up a simple demonstration using three large beakers: one with hot water, one with cold water, and a third at room temperature. Ask a student to place one hand in the cold water and the other in the hot water for one minute, before placing both hands in the water at room temperature. What does each hand feel? A risk assessment is required for this demonstration. Invite students to suggest risks in this demonstration. **What is radiation?** (10 min) Ask students how they can tell if something is hot or cold? What do they think the word radiation means? Discuss as a class before giving the definition (energy spreading from a source), and ask for examples.	**Extension**: Students suggest ways to reduce risks involved with hot drinks. How can we find out how hot something is if we don't touch it? **Support**: Give students a list of events to classify into radiation and non-radiation (e.g., light from a bulb, sound from a speaker, a magnet attracting nearby objects, and a balloon repelling another balloon).	**Question-led lesson**: Energy transfer: radiation

Main	Support/Extension	Resources
Radiation (35 min) Explain that infrared radiation is often called 'heat', and can be detected by our skin cells. All objects emit infrared, but cooler objects emit less. Discuss the difference between absorption and emission of infrared radiation, as well as how thermal equilibrium can be established. If an infrared thermometer is available, a good demonstration compares the temperature of energy-efficient light bulbs, and incandescent light bulbs with the same light output. Incandescent light bulbs are hotter as they dissipate more energy. Students carry out a simple experiment to find a simple relationship between how hot or cold something feels, its temperature, its colour, and its texture. Students should decide what hot, warm, and cold feel like to them, before recording results. Encourage students to discuss the risks in this experiment and ways to reduce these risks during the practical. Students answer the questions that follow on their practical sheet.	**Support**: A partially filled results table is available in the corresponding support sheet. **Extension**: Students are required to explore the idea of thermal equilibrium during their experiment.	**Practical**: Radiation **Skill sheet**: Recording results

Plenary	Support/Extension	Resources
Infrared energy transfers (5 min) Students use the interactive resource to summarise some important concepts on infrared in a gap-fill activity. This resource can be used to eliminate any outstanding misconceptions from the lesson. **Keep a tin cool** (10 min) Students use ideas from the last two lessons to compare soft-drink cans and bottles using images from the Internet. They then discuss factors affecting the length of time a drink will stay cool.	**Extension**: Students give more information about each sentence by giving examples or by adding details. **Extension**: Students give the relative significance of each factor, and give simple ways to test these ideas.	**Interactive**: Infrared energy transfers

Homework	Support/Extension	
Students use their ideas from the lesson to identify ways to reduce heat losses at home. They should state what is used and describe how it works (e.g., curtains stop warm air reaching the window). An alternative WebQuest homework activity is also available on Kerboodle where students research how to reduce energy bills.	**Extension**: Students give examples involving conduction (materials), convection (air movement), and radiation (colour).	**WebQuest**: Saving on heating bills

149

Physics NC link:

- domestic fuel bills, fuel use, and costs
- fuels and energy resources.

Working Scientifically NC link:

- interpret observations and data, including identifying patterns and using observations, measurements, and data to draw conclusions.

Band	Outcome	Checkpoint	
		Questions	Activities
Developing	Name renewable and non-renewable energy resources (Level 3).	A, C, 1	Main, Plenary 1
	State one advantage and one disadvantage of fossil fuels (Level 4).	B, 1	Main, Plenary 1
	Use one source of information (Level 3).		Main
Secure	Describe the difference between a renewable and a non-renewable energy resource (Level 5).	1, 2	Main, Plenary 1
	Describe how electricity is generated in a power station (Level 6).	2	Lit, Main
	Choose an appropriate source of secondary information (Level 5).		Main
Extending	Compare the advantages and disadvantages of using renewable and non-renewable energy resources (Level 7).	3	Main, Homework
	Explain how a range of resources generate electricity, drawing on scientific concepts (Level 7).	2	Lit, Main, Homework
	Justify your choice of secondary information (Level 7).		Main

Literacy

In the student-book activity, students apply scientific knowledge and terminology to synthesise a children's story about the part of the carbon cycle relating to electricity generation.

Students collate information from a number of different sources to prepare a poster or leaflet to summarise information appropriately to their target audience.

APP

Students explain the processes involved in electricity generation (AF1), and present arguments for and against the building of different types of power stations (AF3).

Key Words

energy resource, fossil fuel, non-renewable, thermal power station, renewable, nuclear

Answers from the student book

In-text questions	**A** coal, oil, and gas
	B carbon dioxide
	C Any three from: solar, wind, wave, geothermal, hydroelectricity, tidal, or biomass.
Activity	**Chris the carbon atom**
	Story to include: tree dies, buried, over millions of years turns to coal, burnt, combines with oxygen to make carbon dioxide.

Summary Questions	
	1 non-renewable, fossil fuel, renewable, power station (4 marks)
	2 Burning coal produces steam. Steam drives a turbine. The turbine drives a generator. The generator generates electricity. (4 marks)
	3 Credit any suitable board game, for example, snakes and ladders or collecting cards/tokens relating to different types.
	Points/board relates to ways fuels are formed or ways electricity is generated.
	Point system includes ideas about climate change/pollution.
	Board game must have a suitable scoring method relating to advantages and disadvantages of each method of electricity generation. (6 marks)

kerboodle

Starter	Support/Extension	Resources
Sorting fuels (10 min) Provide samples of fuels (e.g., wood, coal, oil, ethanol, and candle) for students to put into two groups. Students should justify how they have categorised their fuels during the class discussion. Introduce the idea of energy release during combustion of fuels, and the difference between renewable and non-renewable energy resources.	**Support**: Offer suggestions on how fuels can be grouped. **Extension**: Students compare different ways of categorising fuels.	
Life without electricity (5 min) Students describe how their lives would be different without electricity, identifying activities that rely on electricity and activities that use other fuel sources.	**Support**: Students identify activities in everyday life that rely on electricity. **Extension**: Students suggest alternatives to electricity, for example, using gas stoves and oil lamps.	

Main	Support/Extension	Resources
Energy resources (40 min) Provide a range of research stations, including various levels of textbooks, information posters, and leaflets, and if possible, computers with Internet access. Students carry out research in groups or independently, using the research methods provided, in order to cover the topics posed in the research activity regarding the generation of electricity. Students must then produce a poster or leaflet to answer these questions, and if students work in small groups, they should present their findings to each other. An animation to show how electricity is generated in thermal power stations can be shown at the end of student presentations for recap. These animations are readily available on the Internet.	**Support**: A support sheet is available that gives students a much more structured approach to their research task. **Extension**: Students identify the advantages and disadvantages of using different energy resources, linking waste products from burning fossil fuels to risks.	**Activity**: Energy resources

Plenary	Support/Extension	Resources
Fossil fuels (5 min) Students complete the gaps on the interactive resource to explain the formation and uses of fossil fuels, including the advantages and disadvantages of using fossil fuels to generate electricity.	**Extension**: Students should offer a similar summary for renewable energy sources.	**Interactive**: Fossil fuels
Ranking key points (10 min) List the most important ways of electricity generation of this lesson on the board with help from students. Students should diamond rank these ways in order of importance, and justify their answers in small groups.	**Extension**: Students should rank the factors involved in electricity generation according to a given category, for example, impact on the environment.	

Homework	Support/Extension	
Students write a short newspaper article explaining the opening of a thermal power station in their neighbourhood. This should explain how the power station benefits the community, include some effects it has on local surroundings, and discuss the views of locals regarding this new power station.	**Extension**: Students should include a labelled diagram to illustrate how a power plant generates electricity.	

Physics NC link:
- comparing power ratings of appliances in watts (W, kW)
- comparing amounts of energy transferred (J, kJ, kWh)
- domestic fuel bills, fuel use, and costs.

Working Scientifically NC link:
- make predictions using scientific knowledge and understanding.

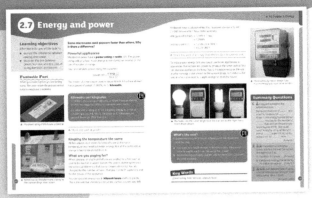

Band	Outcome	Checkpoint	
		Question	Activities
Developing	State the definitions of energy and power (Level 4).	1	Main
	State that power, fuel used, and cost are linked (Level 4).	1	Main, Plenary 1, Homework
	Predict which equipment is more powerful when given a selection of appliances (Level 4).		Starter 1, Starter 2, Main
Secure	Explain the difference between energy and power (Level 6).		Main
	Describe the link between power, fuel use, and cost of using domestic appliances (Level 6).	3	Main, Plenary 1, Homework
	Predict the power requirements of different equipment and how much it costs to use (Level 6).		Starter 2, Main, Plenary 1
Extending	Compare the power consumption of different activities (Level 7).		Starter 1, Main, Plenary 2, Homework
	Calculate and compare energy costs in different scenarios (Level 8).	3	Main, Homework
	Predict the effect on energy bills of changing the power of equipment (Level 7).		Main, Plenary 1

Maths
Students carry out simple calculations for energy, power, and energy costs.

Students also demonstrate their understanding of the number scale and an appreciation of J, kJ, W, kW, and kWh in their calculations.

Literacy
Students use scientific terminology when explaining the link between power, energy, and cost.

APP
Students apply scientific knowledge to make further predictions about the power rating of appliances (AF5).

Key Words
power rating, watt, kilowatt, kilowatt hour

Answers from the student book

In-text questions	**A** watt (W)
	B kilowatt hour (kWh)
Activity	**What's the cost?**
	a energy = 10 kW × 1 h × 7 days = 70 kWh
	b cost = 70 kWh × 10 p ÷ 100 = £7

Summary Questions	**1** joules, watts, second, kWh, lower, less (6 marks)
	2a power = potential difference × current = 3 V × 0.2 A = 0.6 W (2 marks)
	  b energy = 0.6 × 10 = 6 Ws (2 marks)
	3 QWC question (6 marks). Example answers:
	    The power rating tells you the energy that each kettle can transfer per second.
	    The higher the power, the quicker the element will transfer energy to the water.
	    The higher the power, the quicker the temperature of the water will rise.
	    A power of 1200 W is the same as 1.2 kW (or 2 kW is the same as 2000 W).
	    The 2 kW kettle will heat water faster than the 1.2 kW kettle.
	    The energy that you pay for is measured in kilowatt hours (kWh).
	    The energy that you pay for depends on the power and the time that you use it for.

kerboodle

Starter	Support/Extension	Resources
What's the power? (10 min) Show students a range of light bulbs of different power ratings (including energy-saving and incandescent light bulbs), and ask students to choose from everyday observations the bulb that will produce the brightest light, before offering the definition of power (amount of energy transferred per second).	**Extension**: Students link power to the energy transferred from a chemical store to a thermal store via electricity.	
Power appliances (10 min) Explain what is meant by power. Students list 10 appliances they used yesterday, and rank these according to power. Keep the list to reassess at the end of the lesson.	**Support**: Allow students to work in small groups. **Extension**: Students justify why they have ranked the appliances this way.	

Main	Support/Extension	Resources
Power (35 min) Introduce the difference between energy and power, and check students know the units for each. Demonstrate an energy monitor or joulemeter to show that the energy transferred depends on the power and time that the equipment is used. Compare the power of two light bulbs (an energy-saving and an incandescent light bulb), leave them on for a minute and compare their temperature. The traditional bulb is hotter and adds more to the electricity bill as it is more powerful. Students carry out the task on the activity sheet, examining different items around the home, and answer the questions that follow.	**Support**: Remind students that power is measured in watts (W) or kilowatts (kW), and that these are the only letters they should look for when reading appliance labels. **Extension**: Introduce kilowatt hours (kWh) in general terms, and allow students to read the corresponding section in the student book.	**Activity**: Power **Skill sheet:** Converting units

Plenary	Support/Extension	Resources
Reducing energy bills (10 min) Students use ideas gained from this lesson to summarise ways to reduce energy bills. They choose the correct words to complete sentences in the interactive resource. A common misconception is to confuse wasted money with wasted energy. Energy is conserved, but some of the energy we pay for is not used efficiently.	**Extension**: Students suggest the relative importance of each energy-saving measure. **Support**: Allow students to work in small groups. **Extension**: Students justify their order based on their scientific understanding.	**Interactive**: Reducing energy bills
Power appliances (revisited) (10 min) Students check their order of the 10 appliances from the start of the lesson, and decide if they still agree with their original ranking based on what they have learnt this lesson. Ask students to justify any changes made.		

Homework	Support/Extension
Students check appliances at home to find out the power rating of each. Students **must** check with their parents before unplugging or moving appliances, or else carry out this task under adult supervision. They then list these appliances in order of power, starting from the lowest power rating, and stating the relevance power rating has on an energy bill.	**Extension**: Students should provide an additional list in order of energy used (and therefore the amount of time each appliance is used per day and the cost of running each appliance).

Physics NC link:

- work done
- examples of processes that cause change with forces (work = force × distance) levers and gears reducing force by increasing distance simple machines give bigger force but at the expense of smaller movement (and vice versa): product of force and displacement unchanged.

Working Scientifically NC link:

- evaluate data, showing awareness of potential sources of random and systematic error.

Band	Outcome	Checkpoint	
		Question	Activity
Developing	State how work is calculated (Level 4).	A, 1	Main
	State machines conserve energy (Level 4).	1	Main
	State one way the experiment can be improved (Level 4).		Main
Secure	Calculate work done (Level 6).	2, 3	Main
	Apply the conservation of energy to simple machines (Level 6).	4	Starter 2, Main, Plenary 1, Plenary 2
	Evaluate results from the practical (Level 6).		Main
Extending	Compare the work done in different scenarios and by different machines (Level 7).	3, 4	Plenary 2
	Explain how conservation of energy applies in one example (Level 7).	4	Main, Plenary 1, Plenary 2
	Evaluate results (including random and systematic errors) and suggest how the experiment can be improved (Level 8).		Main

Maths
Students carry out simple calculations for work done in different scenarios, including balancing forces (moments), and use the concept of ratios in their practical activity.

Literacy
Students use scientific terminology when explaining the role of levers, pulleys, and gears in simple machines, applying their knowledge to other appliances around the home.

APP
Students evaluate the method used in their experiment and suggest possible improvements (AF5).

Key Words
work, simple machine, lever, gear

Answers from the student book

In-text questions	A work (J) = force (N) × distance (m)
	B levers, gears
Summary Questions	1 force, distance, machine, lever, force, gear, conservation, energy (8 marks)
	2 a lever (1 mark)
	b work done = force × distance = 200 N × 0.25 m = 50 J (2 marks)
	3 Climbing Mount Everest: Work done = force × distance = 600 N × 10 000 m = 6 000 000 J
	Climbing upstairs to bed: Work done = force × distance = 600 N × 2.5 m = 1500 J
	Comparing the two: 6 000 000 J ÷ 1500 J = 4000
	so climbing Mount Everest requires 4000 times the work. (4 marks)

4 QWC question (6 marks). Example answers:

A small force acting over a big distance produces a big force.

The big force cannot move a large distance because this would mean a larger output of energy than input.

Law of conservation of energy applies in gears as well.

Gears work on rotational movement.

work done = force × distance

You do work when you apply a force over a distance on the pedal.

The law of conservation of energy says that energy cannot be created, so you cannot get more energy out than you put in.

Starter	Support/Extension	Resources
What machines do you use? (5 min) Ask students to list machines they have used today. Invite some suggestions before explaining that levers, pulleys, and gears are simple machines. Give students a further minute to add some simple machines to their existing list.	**Extension**: Students should suggest why levers, pulleys, and gears are considered as simple machines.	
Can a rabbit lift an elephant? (10 min) Students may not realise how levers work at this stage. Start with a simple example that students may have experienced before, by asking them if an adult and a child can use a see-saw together. Students should realise that the adult must sit much closer to the pivot. Extend to an example using a rabbit and an elephant.	**Extension**: Introduce numerical values to the discussion, for example, a rabbit (mass 3 kg) could lift an elephant (3000 kg) if the rabbit was 1000 times further from the pivot.	

Main	Support/Extension	Resources
Work (40 min) Introduce the use of levers, pulleys, and gears as simple machines that change the size, direction, or distance a force moves. Using an example such as a screwdriver to open a paint can, introduce the terms effort, load, and pivot. Students then carry out four short experiments investigating the effect on movement of using simple machines, and answer the questions that follow on the practical sheet.	**Support**: An access sheet is available where students are given further guidance to use their results in forming a conclusion. **Extension**: Students should be encouraged to use numerical data to support their answers on the practical sheet.	**Practical:** Work

Plenary	Support/Extension	Resources
Types of machine (5 min) Students group a list of machines according to whether they use levers, pulleys, or gears using the interactive resource.	**Extension**: Students should explain the job of each type of machine in the examples given, and how energy is conserved.	**Interactive**: Types of machines
Why do we use machines? (10 min) Students use their ideas from the experiment to describe advantages of using machines (to reduce the force needed, to increase the distance an object can move, to send a force around corners, and so on).	**Extension**: Students should include examples of machines used for each advantage given, and explain how energy is conserved.	

Homework	Support/Extension	
Students describe five machines that have made their lives easier or more interesting, from transport to roller coasters. Students should give the application of each machine and state whether the machines use levers, pulleys, gears, or a mixture of these.	**Extension**: Students may choose to research exactly how one of these machines works, using a labelled diagram.	

Checkpoint lesson routes

The route through this lesson can be determined using the Checkpoint assessment. Percentage
pass marks are supplied in the Checkpoint teacher notes.

Route A (support)
Resource: P2 Chapter 2 Checkpoint: Revision

Students work through a series of tasks that allows them to
gradually revisit and consolidate their understanding of energy
resources, energy stores, and energy transfers. Students can keep
this as a summary of the topic, and use this when revising for
future assessments.

Route B (extension)
Resource: P2 Chapter 2 Checkpoint: Extension

Students act as consultants for an energy provider and prepare
reports on the most suitable energy resource to use for electricity
generation in three different areas. Students are required to
discuss common methods of electricity generation, including
advantages and disadvantages of each method.

Progression to *secure*

No.	Developing outcome	Secure outcome	Making progress
1	Identify energy values for food and fuels, describing energy requirements in different situations.	Compare the energy values of different food and fuels with the energy needed for different activities.	In Task 1 students use a table of secondary data to answer questions based on energy requirements in different situations.
2	Define the conservation of energy, and relate this to simple machines.	Describe energy before and after a change, applying the conservation of energy to simple machines.	In Task 2 students state the law of conservation of energy before describing the changes in energy when burning a coal fire and apply the conservation of energy to levers.
3	State how energy is transferred.	Explain what brings about transfers in energy.	In Task 3 students explain what brings about the energy transfer between two objects that are in contact.
4	State how energy and temperature are measured.	State the difference between energy and temperature.	In Task 3 students link the correct definition to the key words energy and temperature.
5	Describe how energy is transferred through solids, liquids, and in air.	Describe what happens when you heat up solids, liquids, and gases.	In Task 3 students complete a diagram to describe how energy is transferred during changes of state.
6	State what is meant by equilibrium.	Explain what is meant by equilibrium.	In Task 3 students explain the transfer of energy between two objects in contact with each other using the term equilibrium.
7	Describe simply what happens in conduction and convection.	Describe how energy is transferred by particles in conduction and convection.	In Task 3 students answer questions to describe how energy is transferred by conduction and convection in the context of coffee cup.
8	State that insulators reduce heat loss compared to conductors.	Describe how an insulator can reduce energy transfer.	In Task 3 students suggest the best material to manufacture coffee cups based on their knowledge of conductors and insulators.
9	State some properties and sources of infrared radiation.	Describe some sources of infrared radiation and explain how energy is transferred by radiation.	In Task 3 students describe what all sources of infrared radiation have in common and explain how energy is transferred by infrared radiation.
10	Name renewable and non-renewable resources.	Describe the difference between a renewable and a non-renewable energy resource.	In Task 4 students describe the difference between wood and coal in terms of renewable and non-renewable sources of energy.
11	State one advantage and one disadvantage of fossil fuels.	Describe how electricity is generated in a power station.	In Task 4 students fill in a table to describe the functions of different parts of the power station in sequence of how electricity is generated.

12	State the definitions of energy and power.	Explain the difference between energy and power.	In Task 5 students fills in a table to show the difference between energy and power in terms of units and whether the value changes depending on how long the circuit component is left running.
13	State that power, fuel used, and cost are linked.	Describe the link between power, fuel use, and cost of using domestic appliances.	In Task 5 students compare the cost of running two lightbulbs of different power, linking this to how much fuel is used in each case.
14	State how work is calculated.	Calculate work done.	In Task 5 students complete a calculation of work done using the equation provided.

Answers to end-of-chapter questions

1 wind, solar, geothermal (1 mark) **2a** C (1 mark) **b** kW, watts, kilowatts, W (1 mark)

3a Purple solid dissolves, the Bunsen burner heats the water around the solid, and the purple colour diffuses throughout the water in a convection current. (3 marks)

b Any three from:

Water is heated by the Bunsen burner.

The water molecules move faster.

This is replaced by cold water, forming a convection current.

The water expands/becomes less dense.

Hot water floats.

4a coal/oil/gas. (1 mark) **b** Fossil fuels are formed from the remains of plants and animals that died millions of years ago. (1 mark)

c When all fossil fuels are burnt there will not be any more as they take millions of years to form. (2 marks)

5a gravitational potential (1 mark)

b i Energy is conserved/cannot be lost. (1 mark) **ii** Some energy is transferred/dissipated to the thermal store as the ball falls through the air. (1 mark) **c** There is a force (of gravity) acting on the ball. (2 marks)

6a work done = force × distance = 500 N × 200 m = 100 000 J (2 marks) **b** work done = force × distance = 50 N × 1.5 m = 75 J (2 marks)

7a power = energy ÷ time = 6000 J ÷ 60 s = 100 W (2 marks) **b** power = current × p.d. = 0.05 A × 240 V = 12 W (2 marks)

c 12 W bulb, since kWh is lower and therefore it is cheaper to use this lightbulb. (2 marks)

8a Energy is transferred by conduction through the inner pane of glass/passed on by vibrations from the hot room. Air inside the gap heats up/conduct occurs very slowly through the air. Energy is transferred by conduction through the outer pane of glass/passed on by vibration to the cold air outside. (3 marks)

b The rate of transfer would decrease. There is no air to transfer the energy between the panes. Conduction will not occur/energy would be transferred very slowly by radiation. (3 marks)

9 This is a QWC question. Students should be marked on the use of good English, organisation of information, spelling and grammar, and correct use of specialist scientific terms. The best answers will explain in detail how insulation reduces energy bills (maximum of 6 marks). Examples of correct scientific points:

Energy is transferred from a warm house to the cold air outside.

Energy is transferred by conduction, convection, and radiation.

To keep a house at the same temperature it needs to be heated.

A lot of insulators trap air.

Air is a poor conductor.

Insulators reduce the rate of transfer of energy to the surroundings.

The rate at which you need to heat the house to maintain the temperature decreases.

A lower power heater is needed/heating is required for less time.

This reduces the number of kWh of energy used.

This will cost less money.

Answer guide for Big Write

Developing	Secure	Extending
1–2 marks	3–4 marks	5–6 marks
• Design a simple diary that students could use to log what they eat/the activities that they do.	• Describe some foods and their energy content. • Describe the energy used in some activities. • Design a diary that students could use to log what they eat/the activities that they do.	• Describe in detail foods and their energy content. • Describe the energy used in many activities. • Design a detailed diary that students could use to log what they eat/the activities that they do.

P2 Chapter 2 Checkpoint assessment (automarked)	P2 Chapter 2 Checkpoint: Extension
P2 Chapter 2 Checkpoint: Revision	P2 Chapter 2 Progress task (Handling information)

3.1 Speed

Physics NC link:

- speed and the quantitative relationship between average speed, distance, and time (speed = distance ÷ time)
- relative motion: trains and cars passing one another
- using physical processes and mechanisms, rather than energy, to explain the intermediate steps that bring about changes in systems.

Working Scientifically NC link:

- use appropriate techniques, apparatus, and materials during fieldwork and laboratory work, paying attention to health and safety.

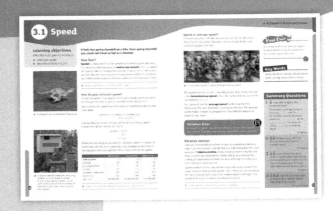

Band	Outcome	Checkpoint	
		Question	Activity
Developing	State the equation for speed (Level 4).	B	Maths, Main
	Define relative motion (Level 4).	C	Plenary 1
	Use appropriate techniques and equipment to measure times and distances (Level 4).		Main
Secure	Calculate speed using the speed equation (Level 6).	2	Maths, Starter 2, Main
	Describe relative motion (Level 5).	3	Plenary 1
	Choose equipment to make appropriate measurements for time and distance to calculate speed (Level 6).		Main
Extending	Use the speed equation to explain unfamiliar situations (Level 7).		Main, Homework
	Explain what is meant by relative motion and how it can be calculated (Level 7).	4	Plenary 1
	Choose equipment to obtain data for speed calculations, justifying their choice based on accuracy and precision (Level 7).		Main

Maths

Students carry out simple calculations to work out the average speed of objects given total distance and time taken.

Students must also use the correct units in their calculations, converting between various units of time and distance.

Literacy

Students explain the concept of speed in their practical using scientific terminology, explaining how different factors affect reaction times, and in turn suggest why motorists should slow down at different places, for their homework.

APP

Students collect data, choosing appropriate ranges of numbers and values for measurements and observations to calculate speeds of various moving objects, justifying their choice of apparatus used (AF4).

Key Words

speed, metres per second, instantaneous speed, average speed, relative motion

Answers from the student book

In-text questions	A How far something travels in a particular time. B metres per second (m/s) C The movement of a body compared to another.
Activity	**Marathon times** distance in a marathon = 42.2 km time taken to run marathon = 2.5 h average speed = distance ÷ time = 42.2 ÷ 2.5 = 16.88 km/h

Summary Questions	1 distance, time, total distance, total time, relative (5 marks)
	2 Average speed = total distance ÷ total time = 100 m ÷ 12.5 s = 8 m/s (2 marks)
	3 Their relative motion is 70 km/h either towards each other, if they haven't passed yet, or away from each other if they have already passed. (2 marks)
	4 QWC question (6 marks). Example answers: Lines are painted on the road a set distance apart. The camera takes a photograph of the car on the road. The camera takes a photograph of the car a short time later. From the position of the car the camera can work out how far the car has travelled. The camera can use the time between the photographs to find the time using the equation speed = distance ÷ time. The speed camera uses the information obtained from the two photographs to calculate the speed of the car. If the car is travelling faster than the speed limit it will travel too far in the time between the photographs.

kerboodle

Starter	Support/Extension	Resources
How fast? (10 min) Students estimate speeds in different situations, for example, walking, running, driving, flying, speed of sound, and speed of light. Use tangible examples to begin with, for example, with speed limits on roads.	**Extension**: Students discuss the importance of units when considering numerical values. Ask students how they would convert a speed from kilometres per hour (km/h) to metres per second (m/s).	
How quick was the ball? (10 min) Students measure the time taken for a ball to fall from a vertical height of one metre. This can be done as a demonstration. Discuss where the ball travelled slowest and fastest in order to introduce the difference between average and instantaneous speed. Introduce the speed equation and calculate the average speed of the ball.	**Extension**: Ask students to consider whether the average speed of the ball would change if the ball was dropped from a greater height.	

Main	Support/Extension	Resources
What's the speed? (35 min) Introduce students to the speed equation and the difference between average and instantaneous speed. Students may require practice with using the correct units in the speed equation before working independently to answer questions on the experiment. Students carry out two short experiments and answer the questions that follow. The first experiment is to obtain data to calculate the speeds of different moving objects, while the second experiment focuses on reaction times, and hence the effect of reaction times on the readings obtained in the first experiment.	**Support**: The accompanying support sheet includes a partially filled results table, with suggestions for moving objects that students can use around the classroom. **Extension**: Challenge students to record all their speeds in metres per second (m/s) in order to practise the conversion of units.	**Practical**: What's the speed? **Skill sheet:** Recording results

Plenary	Support/Extension	Resources
Talking about relative speed (10 min) Students choose the correct words on the interactive resource to summarise relative motion. This resource covers the definition, description, and an example of relative speed and motion.		**Interactive**: Talking about relative speed
What affects your reaction time? (10 min) Students discuss who had the quickest reaction time, and factors that affect it. Discuss why a quick reaction time is important for athletes and drivers. This discussion can include drink driving, use of mobile phones while driving, and reasons why motorists should take regular breaks when driving long distances.		

Homework	Support/Extension	
Produce a safety leaflet explaining when drivers should slow down (in built-up areas, during periods of poor visibility, and so on) and explain the physics behind this. An explanation of the speed equation should be included.	**Extension**: Students should be encouraged to give examples using the speed equation with numerical values.	

3.2 Motion graphs

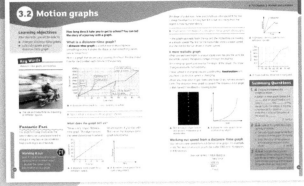

Physics NC link:
- the representation of a journey on a distance–time graph.

Working Scientifically NC link:
- present observations and data using appropriate methods, including tables and graphs.

Band	Outcome	Checkpoint	
		Question	**Activity**
Developing	Describe simply what a distance–time graph shows (Level 4).		Starter 2, Plenary 1
	Use a distance–time graph to describe a journey qualitatively (Level 4).		Starter 1, Starter 2, Main, Plenary 2
	Present data given on a distance–time graph with support (Level 4).		Main
Secure	Interpret distance–time graphs (Level 6).	A, B, 1, 2	Starter 1, Starter 2, Main, Plenary 1, Plenary 2
	Calculate speed from a distance–time graph (Level 5).	2	Maths, Main, Homework
	Plot data on a distance–time graph accurately (Level 6).		Main
Extending	Draw distance–time graphs for a range of journeys (Level 7).	3	Main, Plenary 2, Homework
	Analyse journeys using distance–time graphs (Level 7).	3	Starter 1, Starter 2, Main, Plenary 2
	Manipulate data appropriately to present in a distance–time graph (Level 7).		Main

Maths
Students interpret and manipulate data from tables in order to draw and analyse distance–time graphs.

Students calculate speeds of moving objects using distance–time graphs.

Literacy
Students describe journeys shown on distance–time graphs using scientific terminology, prepare a presentation to explain a distance–time graph they have drawn, and write a short story to accompany a new distance–time graph.

APP
Students transfer numerical data from tables and present these in distance–time graphs (AF3).

Key Words
distance–time graph, acceleration

Answers from the student book

In-text questions	A The distance that something travels in a certain time
	B The speed of an object.
Activity	**Working it out** speed = distance ÷ time = 60 ÷ 10 = 6 m/s

Summary Questions	1 distance, time, slope, stationary, changing (5 marks)
	2a distance = 3900 m − 2400 m = 1500 m
	time = 45 min − 35 min = 10 min = 10 × 60 = 600 s
	speed = distance ÷ time = 1500 m ÷ 600 s = 2.5 m/s (4 marks)
	b 0 m/s (1 mark)
	3 QWC question (6 marks). Example answers:
	Both graphs start at a distance of zero and finish at a distance of 3 km. The graph for the car reaches 3 km faster than the graph for walking. Both graphs might have horizontal sections. If the graph is horizontal the car or person has stopped. The slope of the graph for the car is much steeper. Cars travel faster than people. The car reaches school in a shorter time. The average speed of a car is much higher than that of a person. Both graphs should include curved lines. Curved lines show periods of changing speed.

kerboodle

Starter	Support/Extension	Resources
Using graphs (5 min) Sketch a distance–time graph on the board, explain what it shows, and demonstrate it to students by acting out each section of the graph. Draw a second graph for students to describe to one another in pairs.	**Support**: Label each section of the graph before acting it out. **Extension**: Students draw and interpret their own graphs.	
Comparing speeds (10 min) List typical speeds for different activities, for example, walking quickly (2 m/s) or running slowly (4 m/s). Students work out how long it will take to travel 10 m. Explain how a distance–time graph is used to compare speeds. Sketch a distance–time graph showing the three people travelling the same distance and point out the different slopes and times despite covering the same distance.	**Support**: Remind students of the speed equation. **Extension**: Students sketch and interpret their own graph.	

Main	Support/Extension	Resources
Using distance–time graphs (40 min) Introduce the idea of distance–time graphs, and explain how graphs can be used to interpret movement in detail. Demonstrate how the speed of a section of a journey can be found from the slope, and demonstrate this with two examples, in order to show that a steeper line shows the movement of a faster object. Students then interpret data on the activity sheet to plot a distance–time graph for a migrating bird, the Tour de France, or a sled dog race, and prepare a short summary of the graph they have drawn to present to the rest of the class.	**Support**: A support sheet is available where the breakdown of the times and distances during the ten-day sled dog race has been filled in for them to plot the information. **Extension**: Students carry out the extension task where they must write a short story and plot the graph of the journey described.	**Activity**: Using distance–time graphs

Plenary	Support/Extension	Resources
What can you tell from a distance–time graph? (5 min) Students match halves of sentences using the interactive resource to explain how distance–time graphs can be interpreted.	**Support**: Allow students to work in small groups.	**Interactive**: What can you tell from a distance–time graph?
Drawing distance–time graphs (10 min) Each pair of students should draw a distance–time graph on a mini-whiteboard. If a double-sided whiteboard is used, the other side can be used to write down the correct description of the sketch-graph drawn. Choose one side of the whiteboard to display, and allow students to walk around the classroom to find other whiteboards, giving descriptions of graphs shown, or imagining the shape of a graph if the description is shown.	**Support**: Choose pairs of students so that students in need of support are supported by extending students.	

Homework		
Students note down typical times and distances for their journey to or from school, a friend's house, or an after-school club. They produce a labelled distance–time graph, calculating the speed at different stages of the journey and explain what is shown on each section of the graph.		

3.3 Pressure in gases

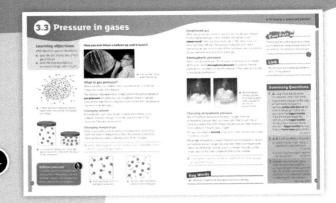

Physics NC link:

- atmospheric pressure, decreases with increase of height as weight of air above decreases with height.

Working Scientifically NC link:

- interpret observations and data, including identifying patterns and using observations, measurements, and data to draw conclusions.

Band	Outcome	Checkpoint	
		Question	Activity
Developing	State two things that can affect gas pressure (Level 4).	1	Main, Plenary 1
↓	State the cause of atmospheric pressure (Level 4).		Main
	Describe the effects of atmospheric pressure (Level 4).		Main
Secure	Describe the factors that affect gas pressure (Level 6).	1	Starter 1, Main, Plenary 2
↓	Describe how atmospheric pressure changes with height (Level 5).	B, 1, 2	Main, Plenary 2
	Interpret observations of atmospheric pressure (Level 6).		Main, Plenary 1
Extending	Explain gas pressure in different situations (Level 7).	1–3	Starter 1, Main, Homework
↓	Compare some effects of atmospheric pressure (Level 7).	2, 3	Main, Homework
	Predict the changes to the effects of atmospheric pressure at different altitudes or temperatures (Level 8).		Main

Maths
Understand and use direct proportion between pressure, volume, and temperature.

Literacy
Students explain the effect of gas pressure in different situations using scientific terminology.

Students also plan an investigation to see how the volume of a fixed amount of air changes with temperature, in the student-book activity.

APP
Students use abstract ideas and models to explain atmospheric pressure, applying these principles to different scenarios (AF1).

Key Words
gas pressure, compressed, atmospheric pressure, density

Answers from the student book

In-text questions	**A** They move more slowly.
	B Atmospheric pressure decreases.
Activity	**Balloon pressure** The plan should include: a method of changing temperature – by location or changing temperature of water, method of measuring volume – by circumference of balloon, variables to control, range of temperature, the need to repeat measurements, and a risk assessment.
Summary Questions	**1** collide with, bigger, smaller, less, fewer (4 marks) **2a** There is less oxygen as you go up a mountain because gas pressure is reduced. The density of oxygen is low. (2 marks) **b** It would take up too much space if it were not compressed. The oxygen pressure will be very high if the gas is compressed. (2 marks)

3 QWC question (6 marks). Example answers:
The temperature inside the can is much higher. The temperature of the water around the can is lower. The density of water and air molecules inside the can is much lower. The density of water outside the can is higher. The atmospheric (water) pressure outside the can is higher than the pressure inside. The atmospheric pressure from the outside pushes in on all sides of the can. The pressure on the inside of the can is less, so the can collapses.

Starter	Support/Extension	Resources
Balloons (10 min) Inflate two balloons, one fully and the other partially. Use these balloons to introduce gas pressure and explain that gas pressure is caused by particles colliding with the walls of the balloon. This means there is more pressure in the fully inflated balloon because there are more particles and more collisions. Students will have met gas pressure in C1.	**Extension**: Students should predict the effect of temperature on gas pressure, giving reasons.	
Gases under pressure (10 min) Display objects under pressure, for example, fizzy-drink bottles, aerosol cans, and bicycle tyres. Ask students to suggest what these objects have in common. Introduce the origin of gas pressure and demonstrate what happens when gas pressure is released (e.g., by unscrewing the bottle lid). Ask students to explain what is happening in terms of particles.	**Extension**: Discuss the similarities and differences between a still- and a fizzy-drink bottle in terms of gas pressure exerted by the drink, and the strength of material required in manufacturing the bottles.	

Main	Support/Extension	Resources
Investigating gas pressure (40 min) Demonstrate the collapsing bottle experiment to the class by adding a small amount of boiling water (about 15 cm^3 from the kettle) into a non-reinforced plastic bottle. Swirl the hot water around the bottle, pour the hot water out, and immediately secure the bottle lid. The bottle should collapse with a loud bang. Ask students to suggest what has happened to the bottle in terms of pressure, before offering the answer. An additional demonstration is to show the difficulty in pulling out the plunger of an empty but sealed syringe, since atmospheric pressure is pushing the syringe in, with no pressure pushing out from the inside. Students note down their observations to these two demonstrations on their activity sheets and answer the questions that follow.	**Support**: An access sheet is available with multiple-choice answers for students to choose from when explaining the scientific concept behind each demonstration. **Extension**: Students should suggest differences in observations if these demonstrations were carried out under different temperatures and pressures.	**Activity**: Investigating gas pressure

Plenary	Support/Extension	Resources
The collapsing bottle (10 min) Show a video clip from the Internet of the collapsing bottle experiment as a visual recap before asking students to reorder phrases on the interactive resource to explain what happens during this experiment.	**Support**: Allow students to refer to their access sheets during this activity.	**Interactive**: The collapsing bottle
Traffic-lighting atmospheric pressure (10 min) Summarise lesson outcomes as questions with multiple-choice answers. Students should write their choice clearly on a mini-whiteboard (1, 2, or 3; A, B, or C) to ensure whole-class participation.	**Extension**: Students can write their own questions and answers for the rest of the class to answer.	

Homework	Support/Extension	
Students research effects of atmospheric pressure and write a paragraph on 'Atmospheric pressure at work'. For example, the need for pressurised cabins on planes, why fizzy drinks aren't as fizzy in winter, or how changes in atmospheric pressure affect the weather (high pressure produces clear skies but low pressure produces unsettled weather).	**Extension**: Students should include detailed explanations of atmospheric pressure in terms of particles in their summary.	
An alternative WebQuest homework activity is also available on Kerboodle where students research atmospheric pressure and mountain climbing.		**WebQuest**: Pressure and altitude

3.4 Pressure in liquids

Physics NC link:

- pressure in liquids, increasing with depth; upthrust effects, floating and sinking.

Working Scientifically NC link:

- make predictions using scientific knowledge and understanding.

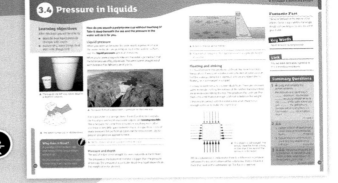

Band	Outcome	Checkpoint	
		Question	**Activity**
Developing	State simply what happens to pressure with depth (Level 4).	1	Plenary 2
	Describe characteristics of some objects that float and some that sink (Level 4).	2	Lit, Starter 1, Main 2
	Predict if water pressure will increase, decrease, or stay the same in a familiar context (Level 4).		Main 2
Secure	Describe how liquid pressure changes with depth (Level 5).	B, 1	Starter 2, Plenary 2
	Explain why some things float and some things sink, using force diagrams (Level 6).	2, 3	Lit, Main 2, Plenary 1, Homework
	Predict how water pressure changes in a familiar context, using scientific knowledge and understanding (Level 6).		Main 2
Extending	Explain why liquid pressure changes with depth (Level 7).		Main 2, Plenary 2
	Explain why an object will float or sink in terms of forces or density (Level 7).	2, 3	Lit, Starter 1, Main 2, Plenary 1, Homework
	Predict how water pressure changes in an unfamiliar context, using detailed scientific knowledge and understanding (Level 7).		Main 2

Literacy
Students use scientific terminology when explaining water pressure and floating and sinking in the main activity and in the student-book activity.

APP
Students use abstract ideas to explain water pressure (AF1), display observations appropriately in results tables (AF3), and draw conclusions based on scientific knowledge and data obtained through experiment (AF5).

Key Words
liquid pressure, incompressible

Answers from the student book

In-text questions	**A** It cannot be compressed into a smaller space. **B** It gets bigger.
Activity	**Why does it float?** The bottom of the ferry is in contact with the water. The top of the ferry is in contact with the air. The water molecules and air molecules collide with the ferry. There are more water molecules hitting the bottom of the ferry than there are air molecules hitting the top. The water pressure is higher than the air pressure. The difference in pressure between the top and the bottom produces upthrust that keeps the ferry afloat if the area is big enough. The ferry floats when upthrust is the same as the weight of the ferry.

Summary Questions	**1** all, increases, weight, bigger, upthrust (5 marks)
	2a Water pressure from the bottom creates the force upthrust. The clay boat floats because the upthrust balances out the weight of the boat. (2 marks)
	b The area is much smaller, the difference between the force pushing down and the force pushing up is not enough for the upthrust to balance the weight. (2 marks)
	3 QWC question (6 marks). Example answers:
	The ping pong ball has a small weight.
	When it is held at the bottom of the bucket there is the force of your hand pushing down.
	The force from your hand is bigger than the upthrust due to the difference in pressure.
	When you let the ball go the upthrust is bigger than its weight.
	When the ball reaches the surface it floats.
	The pressure on the bottom of the ball produces a (upthrust) force that depends on the area of the ball in contact with the water.
	The ball will sink until there is enough water in contact with the ball to produce enough upthrust.

Starter	Support/Extension	Resources
Mass versus weight (10 min) Ask if a kilogram of feathers or a kilogram of iron weighs more. Use student responses to correct student misconceptions and remind students of the difference between mass and weight. Introduce the idea of water pressure and how this relates to floating and sinking. Students predict whether a plastic bag of feathers or lead is more likely to float in water.	**Extension**: Students should apply newly-acquired knowledge of water pressure to explain their prediction.	
Water pressure (5 min) Students discuss, with reasons, how water pressure changes moving down to the bottom of a swimming pool. Many students will have experienced the increased pressure on their body at the bottom of the pool or sea.	**Extension**: Students should suggest why this is the case.	

Main	Support/Extension	Resources
Floating and sinking (15 min) Introduce the idea of water pressure. Explain how floating and sinking are related to the difference in pressure at the bottom and top of an object in a fluid (liquid or gas), causing an upthrust force. Objects float when the upthrust is the same size as weight. Students should then practise drawing force diagrams using upthrust and weight arrows to illustrate floating and sinking.	**Extension**: Students should illustrate floating and sinking using relative sizes of upthrust and weight arrows on force diagrams.	
Liquids at work (25 min) Display a range of objects for students to predict whether they will float or sink in water. Show students the drinks bottle with holes at various heights, and explain that the bottle will be filled with water to show water pressure at work. Students should fill in the prediction section of the activity sheet, watch the demonstrations, and answer the questions that follow.	**Support**: The accompanying support sheet gives students further prompts to spot patterns in their observations.	**Activity**: Liquids at work

Plenary	Support/Extension	Resources
The floating orange (10 min) Students predict if an orange floats when it is unpeeled (yes) and peeled (no). Demonstrate this experiment and ask students to explain their observations. The orange floats if upthrust equals weight. Peeling the orange reduces its weight and also its volume, but its volume decreases more than its weight. Upthrust becomes smaller than weight so the orange sinks.	**Support**: Allow students to work in small groups when explaining their observations.	
Water pressure (5 min) Students fill in the missing words on the interactive resource to explain water pressure in different scenarios.	**Support**: Allow students to look back at their activity sheets.	**Interactive**: Water pressure

Homework	Support/Extension	
Students answer simple questions about the effects of pressure in liquids, for example, why does a block of iron sink but an iron boat float? Why does some fruit float and some fruit sink? How does a life jacket keep a person from sinking? Why do air bubbles rise in water?	**Extension**: Students should be encouraged to use as many scientific terms as possible.	

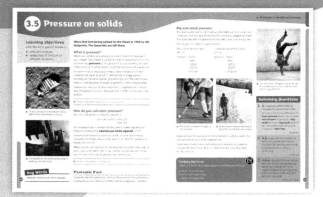

Physics NC link:

● pressure measured by ratio of force over area – acting normal to any surface.

Working Scientifically NC link:

● make predictions using scientific knowledge and understanding.

Band	Outcome	Checkpoint	
		Question	Activity
Developing	State the equation of pressure (Level 4).	1	Main
	Use ideas of pressure to describe familiar situations qualitatively (Level 4).		Starter 1, Starter 2, Plenary 1, Plenary 2
	Predict qualitatively the effect of changing area and/or force on pressure (Level 4).		Main, Plenary 2
Secure	Calculate pressure (Level 6).	2	Main, Plenary 2
	Apply ideas of pressure to different situations (Level 6).		Starter 1, Starter 2, Main, Plenary 1, Plenary 2, Homework
	Predict quantitatively the effect of changing area and/or force on pressure (Level 6).	3	Main, Plenary 2
Extending	Calculate pressure in multistep problems (Level 8).	3	Main
	Compare pressure in different situations, explaining the differences in pressure using scientific knowledge (Level 8).	3	Starter 1, Starter 2, Main, Plenary 1, Plenary 2, Homework
	Predict quantitatively the effect of changing area and/or force on pressure in a range of situations (Level 7).	3	Main, Plenary 2

Maths

Students carry out simple calculations using the pressure equation, manipulating numbers and compound units.

In the student-book activity students rearrange the pressure equation to find the correct equation to calculate force.

Literacy

Students describe the effects of pressure in different scenarios, explaining their answers using scientific terminology.

APP

Students choose appropriate range and intervals of measurements during their experiment (AF4), display observations in tables (AF3), and draw conclusions from patterns in their findings (AF5).

Key Words

pressure, newtons per metre squared

Answers from the student book

In-text questions	**A** At 90°, or normal to the surface.
	B N/m² or N/cm²
Activity	**Finding the force**
	B force = pressure × area

Summary Questions	1 force, area, big, small, N/m (5 marks)
	2 area of two hands = 150 cm² × 2 = 300 cm²
	pressure = force ÷ area = 600 N ÷ 300 cm² = 2 N/cm² (3 marks)
	3 QWC question (6 marks). Example answers:
	pressure = force ÷ area
	small area = large pressure
	The pressure of lying on one nail = 700 N ÷ 0.25 cm² = 2800 N/cm²
	A bed of nails consists of 4000 nails, so the total area is bigger.
	And the pressure is much less.
	total area = 4000 × 0.25 cm² = 1000 cm²
	The pressure of lying on a bed of nails = 700 N ÷ 1000 cm² = 0.7 N/cm²

kerboodle

Starter	Support/Extension	Resources
An alternative question-led lesson is also available.		**Question-led lesson**: Pressure on solids
Rescue! (10 min) Students suggest ways to walk through soft snow. Students discuss in pairs before offering them in a class discussion. Suggestions may include using snow shoes rather than normal shoes. Explain how these ideas reduce pressure on the snow. Introduce the idea of pressure and the pressure equation.	**Support**: Ask structured questions, for example, would you rather wear stiletto heels or snow boots when walking in snow? **Extension**: Students analyse the suggestions to synthesise the equation for pressure.	
Why is it this shape? (5 min) Students discuss why a drawing pin has a sharp point at one end and a flat head at the other. Explain the force applied is the same through the drawing pin, but the large head reduces pressure and the sharp point increases pressure.	**Support**: Prompt students by asking them to consider the effect of using the drawing pin upside-down. **Extension**: Students should be able to suggest that pressure is dependent on force and area.	

Main	Support/Extension	Resources
Investigating pressure (40 min) Introduce the pressure equation by demonstrating how changing the force or the area of an object affects the pressure. Try simple calculations on the board using this equation, and ask students to carry out calculations of their own, giving answers on mini-whiteboards. Students then carry out a short experiment to investigate pressure exerted by different masses, using different supports in a tray of sand. Students should look for patterns in their results and attempt the questions that follow.	**Support**: The support sheet includes a partially filled results table for students to fill in. **Extension**: Students should plot a graph of their results (depth of indentation versus weight ÷ surface area) if time, and evaluate their results.	**Practical**: Investigating pressure **Skill sheet**: Recording results

Plenary	Support/Extension	Resources
Useful pressure (5 min) Students categorise a list of scenarios on the interactive resource according to whether high pressure or low pressure is useful.	**Extension**: Students offer other examples of useful pressure, explaining their answer in terms of force and area.	**Interactive**: Useful pressure
Comparing tracks (10 min) Students carry out simple calculations to work out the pressure exerted by different students when wearing different types of shoes. Use the average weight of a KS3 student (500 N) for students sensitive about their weight. Answers can be shown on individual mini-whiteboards.	**Support**: Encourage students to give qualitative answers and comparisons before using a calculator for their calculations.	

Homework
Students find other examples of useful pressure in everyday life. Students should write about how pressure is created in these scenarios and how it is helpful, using the terms force and area.

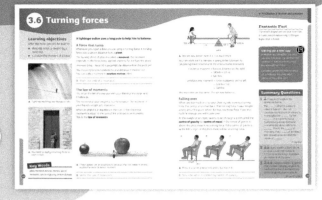

3.6 Turning forces

Physics NC link:
- moment as the turning effect of a force.

Working Scientifically NC link:
- identify further questions arising from their results.

Band	Outcome	Checkpoint	
		Question	Activity
Developing	State the law of moments (Level 4).	B	Maths, Main, Plenary 1
	State the equation to calculate a turning force (Level 4).	A, 1	Maths, Main, Plenary 2
↓	Identify questions from results with help (Level 4).		Main
Secure	Describe what is meant by a 'moments' (Level 6).	1	Main, Plenary 2
	Calculate the moment of a force (Level 5).	2	Maths, Main
↓	Independently identify scientific questions from results (Level 6).		Main
Extending	Apply the concept of moments to everyday situations (Level 7).	2	Maths, Starter 1, Starter 2, Main, Plenary 1
	Use calculations to explain situations involving moments (Level 8).	2, 3	Maths
↓	Suggest relevant, testable questions (Level 7).		Main

Maths
Students carry out simple calculations to work out forces, or distances that objects have to be away from a pivot, in order to balance. They apply the moments equation to deduce if a system is balanced.

Literacy
Students explain the applications of moments using scientific terminology.

APP
Students use models to explain the concept of moments (AF1), draw conclusions from experimental observations and data (AF5), and form further questions that can be investigated further from their results (AF3).

Key Words
pivot, moment, newton metres, law of moments, centre of gravity, centre of mass

Answers from the student book

In-text questions	**A** newton metre (Nm)
	B An object is in equilibrium if the total anticlockwise moments equals the total clockwise moments.
	C The point through which all the weight of an object seems to act.
Activity	**Sitting on a see-saw**
	If the child sits on one end she is 1 m from the pivot.
	Clockwise moment = 150 N × 1 m = 150 N m
	You need the anticlockwise moment to be the same:
	600 N × distance from the pivot = 150 N m
	Distance from the pivot = 150 N m ÷ 600 N = 0.25 m

Summary Questions	1 turning, force, distance, equilibrium, law, weight, gravity (7 marks)
	2 moment = force × distance so, 5 N × 0.75 m = 3.75 Nm
	3 QWC question (6 marks). Example answers:
	A ruler or beam that you hang things from, or something that can balance.
	A system of adding things to one side or the other.
	An explanation of what is meant by a 'moment'.
	An explanation of the law of moments.
	A scoring system that uses the law of moments, for example, predicting where you have to put something before you add it.
	An element of skill in terms of the items you can hang, or where you can put them.

kerboodle

Starter	Support/Extension	Resources
A balancing act (10 min) Set up a see-saw on the bench (using a plank and support). Students suggest how you can have two objects of unequal size and mass on either side of the see-saw. Remind students of the terms effort, lever, pivot, and load, and introduce the idea of moments.	**Extension**: Students should be able to link this idea to other objects of different masses, for example, a mouse and an elephant.	
Pivots (10 min) Pick a strong student to push a door open normally. Invite ideas from the rest of the class as to why the student's hand is placed far away from the pivot (door hinge). Then ask the same student to try pushing open the door with their hand as close to the pivot as possible. Introduce the concept of moments, and explain how a door acts as a force multiplier.	**Extension**: Students should be able to offer other examples of force multipliers and explain their choices. In doing so, they may be able to synthesise the equation for calculating moments.	

Main	Support/Extension	Resources
Just a moment! (40 min) Introduce that the moment of a force indicates its turning effect, and is calculated as force × distance from pivot. This is a difficult concept so it might be a good idea to illustrate moments using props around the classroom.	**Support**: A partially filled results table is available on the accompanying support sheet.	**Practical**: Just a moment!
Carry out simple moments calculations on the board to ensure that students are comfortable with the difference between clockwise and anticlockwise moments. Mini-whiteboards will be useful to ensure whole-class participation.	**Extension**: Students may choose to investigate moments when there is more than one force acting on the clamp stand in the same or opposite directions, if time.	**Skill sheet:** Recording results
Students then carry out a practical where they investigate the turning force required to topple a clamp stand at different heights from the base, and answer questions that follow.		

Plenary	Support/Extension	Resources
Pouring drinks (5 min) Pose the following question for students to solve: How can we pour drinks into two identical cups so that one cup has exactly twice the amount of the other without using scales or measuring the amount of liquid poured? (Using moments, place one cup twice as far away from the pivot as the other, and ensure that the cups are in equilibrium.)	**Support**: Prompt students towards what they have learnt this lesson.	
Moments (5 min) Students revise key terms used in this lesson by pairing key words to their definitions using the interactive resource.	**Extension**: Students add to the key terms listed on the resource and provide their own definitions.	**Interactive**: Moments

Homework		
Students identify five examples that use the principle of moments at home. They explain how the turning effects are balanced by comparing the distance and force either side of a pivot for each example, and research one example in detail to explain exactly how moments work in context.		

Checkpoint lesson routes

The route through this lesson can be determined using the Checkpoint assessment. Percentage pass marks are supplied in the Checkpoint teacher notes.

Route A (support)
Resource: P2 Chapter 3 Checkpoint: Revision

Students work through a series of tasks that allows them to gradually revisit and consolidate their understanding of speed, distance–time graphs, pressure, and moments. Students can keep this as a summary of the topic, and use this when revising for future assessments.

Route B (extension)
Resource: P2 Chapter 3 Checkpoint: Extension

Students investigate the changes in density when substances undergo changes of state. Students will calculate values of density using numerical data provided and will carry out research into the role of intermolecular forces in the three states of matter.

Progression to *secure*

No.	Developing outcome	Secure outcome	Making progress
1	State the equation for speed.	Calculate speed using the speed equation.	In Task 1 students calculate speeds in three different scenarios given the speed equation.
2	Define relative motion.	Describe relative motion.	In Task 1 students describe the relative motion of two students who walk in opposite directions.
3	Use a distance–time graph to describe a journey qualitatively.	Interpret distance–time graphs, including calculating speed from the gradient.	In Task 2 students carry out a calculation and describe a journey in detail given the distance–time graph.
4	State what is meant by Brownian motion.	Describe Brownian motion.	In Task 3 students label a diagram to show the direction of pollen movement to describe Brownian motion.
5	State the cause of atmospheric pressure.	Describe how atmospheric pressure changes with height.	In Task 3 students label a diagram of a mountainous area according to regions with the highest and lowest atmospheric pressure.
6	State simply what happens to pressure with depth.	Describe how liquid pressure changes with depth.	In Task 3 students label a diagram according to regions with the highest and lowest water pressure in the ocean.
7	Describe characteristics of some objects that float and some that sink.	Explain why some things float and some things sink, using force diagrams.	In Task 3 students complete a force diagram to explain how a rubber duck floats in the water, and explain in terms of forces and pressure what causes objects to float or sink.
8	State the equation of pressure.	Calculate pressure.	In Task 4 students calculate pressure exerted on the floor by a dancer when he is standing on one foot and both feet. Students are given the pressure equation as a starting point.
9	Use ideas of pressure to describe familiar situations qualitatively.	Apply ideas of pressure to different situations.	In Task 4 students apply their knowledge of pressure to explain whether women prefer to wear heels or boots in the snow.
10	State the law of moments.	Describe what is meant by a moment.	In Task 5 students describe what is meant by a moment.
11	State the equation to calculate a turning force.	Calculate the moment of a force.	In Task 5 students calculate the moment of a person on a seesaw and use the moment calculated to deduce where another person of a different weight must sit on the opposite end of the seesaw.

Answers to end-of-chapter questions

1   m/s, mph, km/s (3 marks)

2   B (1 mark)

3a B (1 mark)

 b D (1 mark)

 c C (1 mark)

4a Carrier bags have narrow handles, so the pressure on the surface of your hand is large. (2 marks)

 b A smaller pressure is required when riding over mud/fields, so tyres are wider. (2 marks)

5a 70 mph − 50 mph = 20 mph faster/in the same direction (2 marks)

 b 50 mph − 50 mph = 0 mph (1 mark)

6   Any six from:

Speed can be calculated from the slope/gradient of distance–time graphs.

Cyril started fastest, slowed down, and sped up again.

Gertie started at a steady speed, slowed down, then sped up.

Harold started slowest, sped up, stayed still, then sped up again. Harold slowed down towards the end of the race.

Cyril finished first.

Gertie came second.

Harold finished last.

Cyril's average speed was 30 cm ÷ 120 s = 0.25 cm/s

Gertie's average speed was 30 cm ÷ 160 s = 0.19 cm/s

Harold's average speed was 30 cm ÷ 200 s = 0.15 cm/s

Harold was the only snail to stop.

7a Clockwise moment = force × distance = 1.5 N × 0.3 m = 0.45 Nm (2 marks)

 b anticlockwise moment = 0.45 Nm = force (exerted by muscle) × 0.03 m

force exerted by muscle = 0.45 Nm ÷ 0.03 m = 15 N (2 marks)

 c The force is bigger because anticlockwise moment = clockwise moment (for the system to remain balanced). The distance from the pivot is much less. (2 marks)

8   This is a QWC question. Students should be marked on the use of good English, organisation of information, spelling and grammar, and correct use of specialist scientific terms. The best answers will explain in detail how a bag of crisps appears to expand at a higher altitude (maximum of 6 marks).

Examples of correct scientific points:

The bag of crisps contains air.

Air molecules collide with the inside of the bag.

Air molecules in the atmosphere collide with the outside of the bag

If the pressure is the same inside and outside the bag, the bag does not get bigger.

Atmospheric pressure decreases with height, because gravity pulls the air molecules down.

There are fewer collisions between air molecules and objects as you go higher.

The air pressure inside the plane is less than the air pressure on the ground (inside the crisp packet) so the bag gets bigger.

Answer guide for Case Study

Developing	Secure	Extending
1–2 marks	3–4 marks	5–6 marks
• Correct description of interaction of spacecraft with a gaseous atmosphere and an ocean of liquid. • Some discussion of whether the spacecraft would float or sink on an ocean.	• Discussion of change of pressure as you near the surface of the unknown planet, and at various depths in the ocean. • Explanation of what affects whether something floats or sinks in terms of liquid pressure and upthrust.	• Detailed description of how the pressure would change in a gas atmosphere, and at various depths in the ocean. • Detailed explanation of why things float or sink using the ideas of pressure differences and upthrust.

kerboodle

P2 Chapter 3 Checkpoint assessment (automarked)
P2 Chapter 3 Checkpoint: Revision
P2 Chapter 3 Checkpoint: Extension
P2 Chapter 3 Progress task (Maths)

Index

OXFORD
UNIVERSITY PRESS

Great Clarendon Street, Oxford, OX2 6DP, United Kingdom

Oxford University Press is a department of the University of Oxford.
It furthers the University's objective of excellence in research,
scholarship, and education by publishing worldwide. Oxford is a
registered trade mark of Oxford University Press in the UK and in
certain other countries

British Library Cataloguing in Publication Data
Data available

978-019-839260-6

10 9 8 7 6 5

Paper used in the production of this book is a natural, recyclable
product made from wood grown in sustainable forests.
The manufacturing process conforms to the environmental
regulations of the country of origin.

Printed in Great Britain by CPI Group (UK) Ltd., Croydon CR0 4YY

Acknowledgements
The publisher and the authors would like to thank the
following for permissions to use their photographs:

Cover image: Anekoho/Shutterstock

Although we have made every effort to trace and contact all
copyright holders before publication this has not been possible
in all cases. If notified, the publisher will rectify any errors or
omissions at the earliest opportunity.

Links to third party websites are provided by Oxford in good faith
and for information only. Oxford disclaims any responsibility for
the materials contained in any third party website referenced in
this work.